Murder on Rouse Hill

Based upon the true story of the 1915 slaying of Jasper Jacob "Jap" Francis near the tiny Ozark railroad town of Stoutland, Missouri

Murder on Rouse Hill

Based upon the true story of the 1915 slaying of Jasper Jacob "Jap" Francis near the tiny Ozark railroad town of Stoutland, Missouri

by Alan Terry Wright

Southeast Missouri State University Press
2007

Murder on Rouse Hill
by Alan Terry Wright

Copyright 2007, Southeast Missouri State University Press

ISBN: 978-0-9760413-99
Softcover, $19.00

First published in 2007 in the United States of America by
Southeast Missouri State University Press
MS 2650, One University Plaza
Cape Girardeau, MO 63701
http://www6.semo.edu/universitypress

Cover art:
Frisco Railway Depot, Stoutland, Missouri, circa 1915. Postcard collection of John F. Bradbury Jr.

"Sam," Jasper J. "Jap" Francis's Missouri Fox-trotter horse. Courtesy of Jasper J. Francis.

Portrait images of Jap Francis and Charlie Blackburn by Donna (Bloomer) Crim.

Cover design by Liz Lester.

Dedication

Ruby Georgia (Allee) Wright's personal experiences at the murder scene inspired the idea for *Murder on Rouse Hill*. Declining health prevented her from writing the story herself. With some reluctance, she passed the "baton" to me. Ruby Wright died October 16, 2004.

Without my mother's abiding interest and unfailing encouragement during the several years of researching and writing the manuscript, this project would never have been completed.

Mom, I kept my promise. I dedicate this book to you.

Notes and Acknowledgements

I never seriously thought about writing a book. I had given the idea no more thought than any one of the deluded millions who believe that between their conscious minds and the nearest keyboard dangles the next great American novel. Probably a lot less. But my mother, while in her 80s, intervened in my literary lethargy. She wanted to write *Murder on Rouse Hill* and I'm sure hers would have been a good effort. It would undoubtedly have been much shorter and included her unearthly personal experiences at the murder scene, what is known about the murder, Sam's survival, and the outcomes of the trials of Charlie Blackburn. Character development and dramatization would surely have taken a backseat to haste to the printer. When one is 84, "just the facts, ma'am" seems to suit just fine. As a dutiful son, my job was to provide research legwork and encouragement. But, as the year 2000 moved quickly into the next and beyond, the story seemed to get larger and more interesting by the day. Sadly, such exciting prospects were dampened by unmistakable signs that my mom's lease on life was waning. Slowly, as if by unspoken understanding, the book became mine.

The writing of the manuscript moved by fits and starts until the day of my mother's death, October 16, 2004. As she lay dying, I promised to finish the book—privately vowing to give it my very best efforts. Early-life accolades from teachers and later praise from employers, family, and friends of my ability to string sentences together provided a glimmer of hope. But the dark demon of self-doubt perched on my shoulder and whispered in my ear many times in the late hours of the night, when most of this book was written. Occasionally, the turning of a certain phrase pleased and amused me. My family seemed oblivious to the raucous laughter coming from my nook on the third floor of our 1906 vintage home. They probably thought some temporary madness had possessed me. Few paid calls on my nocturnal writing vigils. Innocuous insanity of a family member is a thing best left to run its course. Just roll one's eyes and move on. I must equally confess that as Sam, after being found and revived, struggled valiantly up Rouse Hill past his beloved master's body and a throng of shocked Stoutlanders, both tears and words flooded the page.

Both my wonderful publisher, Susan Swartwout of Southeast Missouri State University Press, and I puzzled about how best to characterize *Murder on Rouse Hill.* One can hardly call a book based upon a true story and possessing almost 500 documented endnotes a "novel." "Historical novel" comes closer but still misses the mark. That term seems best to describe works consisting more of fiction than fact. Historical elements may provide place, time, and perhaps even real-life characters, but great fictional leeway is given to such authors. For *Murder on Rouse Hill,* we finally settled upon "a literary docudrama with novelistic elements."

I would have preferred a book with no fictional elements at all. I wish I could say every word in this book is verifiably true. I cannot. In order to create something greater than just a journalistic rehash of a 91-year-old murder, more was needed. The real people and events of *Murder on Rouse Hill* deserved to be "brought to life" in interesting and dramatic ways. By providing conversational dialogue and recreations of events only hinted at in the records, I sought to bring emotion, dimension, and a place in time to a truly good story.

All the characters in this book are dead. It was impossible to interview them or otherwise reliably document character and dialogue of these departed souls. I had to "make it up," based upon what I knew for sure and what was strongly suggested in the years of my research. In a few cases, fanciful accounts are included that could conceivably be true but probably are not. However, only in a very few instances was the writing cut completely from "whole cloth." I urge the reader to enjoy the story and not agonize about the "complete" truth of this phrase or that paragraph. Let me just say that a paucity of endnotes may suggest portions less reliable that those more fully documented.

Since real people were involved in the story of *Murder on Rouse Hill,* some descendants will undoubtedly take issue with how their ancestors are portrayed. I can assure them that in no instance did I purposefully intend to place them in a bad light. I wrote only where my research took me and, as stated above, fictionalized some elements of the book for dramatic effect. I apologize in advance for any hurt feelings. I can only offer consolation that some characters were undoubtedly not nearly as "bad" in real life as suggested and others not nearly as "good." All are God's creatures.

I wish to first acknowledge my dear wife of 39 years, Mary DePaul (Oligschlaeger) Wright. I am not hurt by her claim to have married me for my one-syllable name. Mary has been patient, respectful of my creative space, and generous with the huge chunks of time which I have devoted to this book. She has degrees in both English and Theatre Arts, so she knows a thing or two about writing and drama. Nevertheless, she offered advice only when asked. Such advice was first-rate and very valuable. Mary, thanks for sticking with me and "letting me be me" over the years.

Our sons John, James, and Joseph Wright shouldered their way through many of their most formative years as this book was written. As a father, I hope that I did not give them short shrift. Ah, the naïveté of youth! None ever expressed a single doubt that their "old man" could write a book that someone might want to read. As this book is published, John is a graduate of Washington & Lee University and St. Louis University Law School and will soon sit for the Missouri Bar exam. James, also an alum of Washington & Lee, is a graduate of Naval Officer Candidate School, holds the rank of Ensign and is serving as a weapons officer aboard the USS *Higgins*, a destroyer on station in the Persian Gulf. Joe is a *summa cum laude* graduate of the Honors College, University of Oklahoma and will soon to be in the civilian work force. I'm so proud of you fellows.

My publisher and editor, Dr. Susan Swartwout of Southeast Missouri State University Press, certainly deserves praise. Reading between the lines of a not-so-well-crafted query letter and story synopsis, she somehow divined that my manuscript might have merit. We "hit it off" and have been of a common mind about *Murder on Rouse Hill* from the beginning. How Susan mothers all her authors, students, poets, staffers, family, and garden at the same time staggers my comprehension. She is always kind, always enthusiastic, and always has her charges' best interests in mind. Bless you, Susan.

Let me offer profuse thanks to Bob Barr of Springfield and a native of Stoutland, Missouri. Without fail, Bob provided help and insight and "eased the way" with local Stoutlanders in the writing of this book. His research alone provided the Appendix detailing old murders in the Stoutland area. These accounts support the thesis that the remoteness of Stoutland from the "long arm of the law" and a history of unpunished murders may have contributed to the killing of Jasper Francis. Bob Barr was the only person who had access to the rough-draft text of this book as it was written. He offered good suggestions and pointed out mistakes. A retired pharmaceutical sales executive, Bob is very proud of his Stoutland roots. His boyish enthusiasm for the telling of this story never waned over seven years. Bob, I tried to "do you proud."

Phillip David "Dave" Donnelly, son of former Missouri Governor Phil M. Donnelly, is a gentleman of the old school. An attorney and former circuit judge in Lebanon, Missouri, Dave responded promptly to my every inquiry about his father who, only two years out of law school, defended Charlie Blackburn and helped gain his client's freedom. In addition, Dave shared his knowledge of courtroom decorum and practices that likely prevailed in the early twentieth century. Dave Donnelly is a person who can be depended upon, and I take pride in counting him as a friend.

Mary Susan (Farris) Goodwin-Tubbesing of Ballwin, Missouri, is the daughter of Frank Hiram Farris, chief defense counsel for Charlie Blackburn. Sue does not recall her famous father, a "bigger than life" player in Missouri politics during his era. A graduate of Washington University's law school, Sue Tubbesing was only about two when her father died in 1926. Sue calls herself this author's "biggest fan" and provided invaluable files and photos of her father, mother, and herself for the writing and production of this book. Sue, you are a wonder. Thank you.

Another descendant of key attorneys in the Blackburn case is Gene Mayfield of Hilton Head Island, South Carolina. Gene promptly and cheerfully answered questions and provided a photo of his father and grandfather, Waldo and Irwin Mayfield, both of whom defended Charlie Blackburn.

Sadly, Jackson King Roach II of Addison, Texas, grandson of Sidney Crain "Sid" Roach, determined prosecutor of Charlie

Blackburn, died in 2004 of Lou Gehrig's disease. Jack Roach provided information and encouragement during the early researching of this book.

Next, let me acknowledge my "old reliables:" Jasper Jacob "Jap" Francis, great-nephew of the man of the same name who was murdered on Rouse Hill, and my dear uncle, Gene Tunney Allee, both long-time residents of Stoutland, Missouri. Jasper Francis provided copies of everything he had pertaining to the killing of his uncle, much of which was not available in public files. Family photos were also forthcoming. Uncle Tunney identified the site of the murder and the location of the tying of Sam, and provided important information about *Murder on Rouse Hill* characters known to him in his lifetime. The support, good will, and unwavering confidence provided by Jasper Francis and Tunney Allee helped sustain me and make this book a reality. Thanks, Jap and Uncle Tunney!

Financially reduced by the legal defense of their son and brother, most of the immediate family of Charlie Blackburn emigrated from their farm near Decaturville, Missouri, to Orange, Escondido, Pomona, and other California towns in the early 1920s. I "found" the Blackburns through coincidence and happenstance on the Internet. I approached them with trepidations. I simply didn't know how I might be received. I need not have been concerned. I have visited on more than once occasion in the homes of Robert L. "Bob" Blackburn and his friend Sunny DeManche of Citrus Heights, California; Bob's lovely daughter, Cindi Rich and her husband, Bill Draper of Gold River, California; and the talented and vivacious Donna (Bloomer) Crim and her husband, Jim, originally of Shingle Springs, California, and more recently, Montgomery, Indiana. I could not have been more warmly received. These members of the Blackburn family (Robert Blackburn is Charlie's nephew and Donna Crim is his great-niece) had heard only inaccurate family stories about "Uncle Charlie's" troubles in Missouri. They were eager to learn the truth about what really happened. Their curiosity was and remains as keen as my own. These Blackburns opened their files, their photos, and their hearts to this author, and I will be forever grateful. Their knowledge and perspective of Charlie Blackburn's life during and after his murder trials proved invaluable in telling the story of *Murder on Rouse Hill.*

Donna Crim was the only person in the world with the memory image of Charlie Blackburn *and* the artistic skill to accurately depict him. She wrote movingly of his acts of human kindness. Bob, Donna, and Cindi, I treasure your friendship.

In closing, I must mention others who provided invaluable help, including all my reviewers who took the time to read the manuscript and offer comments for the book's cover. They are listed there and I thank them for their efforts. Others include:

- Ken Winn and his able assistant, Laura Jolley, at the Missouri State Archives. Without preservation of the Blackburn Supreme Court case file at the Archives, this book could not have been written. Ken offered valuable suggestions concerning historical content and accuracy of the manuscript.
- John F. Bradbury Jr. of the Western Historical Manuscript Collection, University of Missouri—Rolla. John provided the front cover photo for the book and first acquainted me with Senator Frank Farris's early connection with the "Boodle Scandals."
- Blackburn family genealogists Ben Blackburn, Earnestine Chapman, and Wanda Kovazovich whose accumulated research was most helpful.
- Veterinarian Marc Markway who provided professional suggestions about why Sam survived his ordeal and how he may have been revived and rehabilitated.
- Judy and Don Varner, Camden County genealogists and historians, who worked "hands on" with me early on, sifting through long-forgotten public documents.
- The Reverend Dan Sample of High Point Baptist Church, who organized a corps of teenaged "forensic archaeologists" that filtered through the mud of Charlie Blackburn's well.
- Lucille (Alexander) Gregory, whose father was a close friend of the murdered Jasper Francis, provided photos and continuing interest and encouragement.

- A legion of courteous and helpful historians, librarians, museum curators, and state and local government officials. A few must be mentioned:

Donna Reed of the Rolla Public Library; Noel Holobeck of the St. Louis Public Library; Nancy Ogg of the Missouri Supreme Court Library; Suzanne Burris, Burlington Northern & Santa Fe Railroad Museum; Daphne Jeffries, Camden County Museum and Archives; Frances Shepherd Metzger, Stoutland historian; Judy Armstrong, Museum of Western Colorado; Ramona Tomka, Missouri Division of Finance; John C. Konzal, Western Historical Manuscript Collection, University of Missouri, Columbia; Tommy Sallee, Missouri Agricultural Statistics Services; Nancy Webster and Terri Katron, Webster County Circuit Clerk's office; and Marilyn Moulder, Camden County Circuit Clerk's office.

Many others must go unnamed. My thanks go to all.

Introduction

A Brief History of Stoutland, Missouri

The tiny Missouri town of Stoutland, population 177, is located in the south-central part of the state, a scant 5 miles north of Interstate 44 and what remains of the celebrated U.S. Route 66. The nation's "Mother Road," completed and certified in 1926, began in Chicago's Grant Park on Lake Michigan and ended at the ocean front in Santa Monica, California. This wisp of two-lane highway crossed Illinois, Missouri, Oklahoma, Texas, New Mexico, Arizona, and California along the way. The famous road carried the hopes, dreams, and adventures of millions of restless Americans, a people always on the move and constantly looking for something better.

From the end of the "Roaring 20s" and through the depths of the Great Depression, desperate families like the Joads, immortalized in John Steinbeck's *Grapes of Wrath*, packed their families, along with their pitiful possessions, and headed west on Route 66. During the war years, Greyhound buses plied the highway, full of soldiers traveling off to war. Or, too often, returning with crutches and purple hearts. Through the prosperous and peaceful 50s, when even Democrats admitted they "Liked Ike," the top speed of many a brand-new Ford or Chevy was tested by teenagers on 66's straight ribbon of concrete—often with tragic consequences.

For generations, Stoutlanders have used "Ole 66," now I-44, as their way of getting to and from work at the "Fort" (Fort Leonard Wood, a sprawling U.S. Army reservation some 20 miles east), going to the doctor, buying groceries in the nearby city of Lebanon, or otherwise just "gettin' around." But little of the commerce of this great highway has ever filtered its way into Stoutland. The town is a bit too far off its beaten path. No, Stoutland is, or more properly, *was*, a railroad town. Today, the main line of the Burlington Northern and Santa Fe Railroad slices the town in half, but no trains have stopped to pick up passengers or unload freight in nearly 40 years. Its railway station, telegraph office, and stockyards have long since been dismantled. No traces remain of the town's railroad roots except the air horns of fast-moving freights, the rattle of windowpanes and the forlorn jangle of the town's single crossing gate. After passage, the roar and screech of wheel against rail swiftly mutes—swallowed into the black hole of an earlier time.

It would be an exaggeration to say that Stoutland lived and died with the railroad, but as a commercial center, it is on life support. Main Street consists of mostly vacant or underused storefronts and miscellaneous buildings dating to the early 1900s or even earlier. Photos taken then and now reveal few differences in the building line, and progress is marked by little more than the street's conversion from dirt to asphalt. A few businesses remain, including a café, small grocery, gas station, library, video arcade, and those true essentials, funeral and beauty parlors. The post office, Stoutland R-II school, several lovely churches, and a mayor determined to complete the town's sewer system and build a public park lend hope for the future.[1]

Stoutland is a bedroom town of old resident retirees and a smattering of their children and grandchildren who chose not to seek their fortunes in the "big city." Preferring the known to the unknown, they enjoy the relaxed pace of small-town life, support the school's baseball and basketball teams, go to PTO meetings, and attend church on Sunday. Connection with the big world is made through ubiquitous satellite dishes.

In recent years, new residents seeking cheap housing have moved into town. They are looked upon with disdain by those who keep up their properties and manage without food stamps. Suspicion of drug activity lends a whiff of moral decay to the civic stew.

No, Stoutland is not what it once was. It began in 1869 when William Wair built an 18' x 24' store building where the newly laid tracks of the Atlantic and Pacific Railroad crossed a well-traveled wagon road. The road led northerly to the Camden County seat at Linn Creek, a steamboat freight landing on the Osage River. In a southerly direction, it connected with a state road leading from Rolla to Springfield that would eventually become U.S. 66. Wair's store was quickly joined by another, and the building boom was on. By 1874, eighteen families, four general merchandise and grocery stores, a drug store, a land agency, and a newspaper composed the town.[2]

Prominent and prolific early Stoutland families, some of whom have present-day descendants in the area, include the Hillhouse, Fulbright, Evans, Pritchett, Calkin, Craddock, Bohannon, DeBerry, Hammer, Marshall, Alexander, Begley, Carlton, and Rowden families.[3] Other arrivals before and after the turn of the century were the Barr, Blackburn, Francis, and Allee families.

The town was named after Captain Stout, a director of the Southwest Pacific Railroad, a name later changed to the Atlantic and Pacific Railroad.[4] Regularly scheduled passenger, freight, and mail service to Stoutland was likely begun in the 1870s, and the town began using its official railroad name shortly thereafter. Until then, it was known only as the "switch."[5]

By the turn of the century, Stoutland had become a thriving farm-trade and shipping center. As the only railroad town in Camden County and straddling the Laclede County line, it became a busy shipping point for farmers selling livestock, poultry, milk, and eggs to St. Louis and other markets. A substantial wagon freight business had developed for manufactured goods and commodity staples from Stoutland to towns as far north as Linn Creek, some 20 miles away.

All this meant prosperity and growth in Stoutland. With several general merchandise and specialty stores, a bank, newspaper, livery stable, blacksmith shop, restaurant, hotel, three churches, shoe shop, two physicians, and both an elementary and high school, by 1915, Stoutland had become a "going concern." Since most accounts of Stoutland's history were written by proper church ladies, no mention was made of saloons or pool halls, but it is doubtful that a town catering to stockmen, wagon freighters, railroad crews, section hands, and factory workers lacked at least one such establishment.

The Atlantic and Pacific Railroad later became a part of the more modestly named St. Louis & San Francisco Railroad.[6] Even this name proved too ambitious, since the lines owned by the "Frisco" traveled southwest from St. Louis through Oklahoma, only to just beyond Dallas, Texas. The Frisco had recognized the importance of Stoutland as a shipping point by constructing a goodly sized station with ticket and telegraph office, a seated waiting area, and an ample freight room and dock. On the south side of the tracks, a large stockyard had been built with its own siding where numerous pens and ramps speeded the loading of cattle, hogs, and sheep on railroad cars for shipment to slaughterhouses in St. Louis. "Ship it on the Frisco" would become the slogan of a railroad with an established reputation for well maintained trackage, fast, coal-burning trains, and on time service. The raising, trading, and speculation in livestock had become big business in the Stoutland area. All made possible by instant telegraph communications and efficient rail shipping.

Stoutland—A Climate For Murder

In November of 1915, all seemed well in this not so unusual little Missouri railroad town, except for one disturbing thing. The Stoutland area had developed a reputation for something other than commercial success. Something much less desirable. Something little discussed by civic and church leaders. Something that, from time to time, raised its ugly head and made the God-fearing folks of the town shudder and shake their collective heads. It seems that murder had become an uninvited but frequent visitor to the area. Most of the killings were the result of longstanding disputes or family feuds. Some were fueled by romantic jealousy or revenge. Many were assisted by a plentiful supply of locally distilled spirits. All resulted in a singular lack of punishment for the killers. The appendix of this book recounts a few of these slayings.

Some have speculated that such little concern for the law was the result of not much presence of the Law. Located on the extreme southeastern edge of Camden County, Stoutland could not have been located farther from the Sheriff's office at Linn Creek and still remain in the county. By the time a sheriff or deputy was summoned, strapped on his trusty firearm, saddled his horse, and rode the 25 miles of difficult road to Stoutland, the gunfire was silent and the knives had long since been put away. Before a telephone line from Stoutland to Linn Creek was completed and Model-T Fords were used to transport law officers, this whole process took about six hours. Even those modernisms left Stoutland isolated. Phone connections were unreliable and the roads so rough that the good lawmen might have to stop and patch inner tubes several times along the way. By the time they arrived, it was "all over but the shouting." With nothing but a stiffened body and a trampled crime scene, little remained to be done except to interview witnesses and track down perpetrators.

At various times, Stoutland was served by untrained and poorly paid constables and a few town marshals. These gentlemen's principal job was the restraint of drunken young rogues, whipping their horses up and down Main Street in the wee hours of the morning. Such horseplay was often accompanied by gunplay and blood curdling screams akin to the rebel yells last heard by the town's aging Civil War veterans. Mercifully, most were deaf.

Before dawn, Wednesday, November 10, a murder unlike any that had preceded it took place just outside Stoutland. Its motive was dark and sinister. The murderer's coolness of plan and audacity made prior killings in the area seem merely the work of hot-blooded amateurs. The savagery inflicted upon the victim, one of the area's leading citizens, was shocking. Even the town's two physicians winced when they examined the body. Obstruction of justice by Stoutland's leading citizens in the investigation and prosecution of the accused killer set new standards for cowardice and self-interest. The case helped launch the political careers of a two-termed governor of Missouri and a U.S. Congressman. The most powerful member of the Missouri Legislature, a colorful character whose oratory was compared with William Jennings Bryan,[7] acted as the defendant's lead attorney. Six years later, at least a dozen lawyers, four doctors, one hundred witnesses, forty-eight jurors, four trials, a Missouri Supreme Court decision and the only eye witness, a Missouri fox-trotter horse named "Sam," had not resolved the puzzling case. After 92 years, truth and justice still elude those who have sought them in the murder of Jasper Jacob "Jap" Francis.

This is the story.

Prelude

Late July, 1928

It was sometime before noon on the Fulbright Road just outside the small railroad town of Stoutland, Missouri. Ruby and Mildred Allee, ages 12 and 14, chattered busily with each other as they walked the three-quarters of a mile from their farm to the family's mailbox at the gravel lane's intersection with the more heavily traveled Linn Creek Road. The battered metal container, nailed securely to a white oak post, stood in a rank with three or four others. It had been inherited from the prior occupant of the "old Gallagher place" when the Allees had moved into the community a year earlier. With green hand-painted letters, it now boldly read "H.G. Allee."

The Allee girls' father had been named Horace Greeley by his Union-leaning father. His "secesh" mother, having no love for the famous newspaper editor and abolitionist, insisted on calling her youngest son "El," probably short for Elbert. The latter name stuck, and for the rest of his life Mr. Allee was simply known as "El Allee."

This hot and sticky morning, Ruby moved determinedly along, with Mildred a couple of paces behind. Less interested in their destination than her sister, Mildred was hoping for excitement that might appear any moment in the form of neighborhood boys riding on horseback or perhaps driving a sputtering motor car. If the girls were lucky, Bernie Hammer might pass in his fancy Maxwell car and honk. In the best of all girlhood fantasies, he would stop and give them a ride. Bernie was sort of a backwoods "Fonzie" and the town's scalawag. His entire family, except him and his baby sister, had been killed in a Frisco train wreck.[1] His reckless ways were tolerated by the good matrons of Stoutland who clucked, "Bernie's really a good boy at heart—he's just a little wild."

Today, neither Bernie Hammer nor anyone else appeared. As the grade up Rouse Hill steepened, Mildred, disappointed and bored, began uttering audible sighs. The excited gabfest, filled with speculation about which friends they might see at the upcoming

Stoutland Picnic and what the pair might wear to the grand event, had noticeably lagged.

Two years separated the Allee sisters, but Ruby's recent growth spurt had made them about the same height. Although having similar facial features, their coloration and dispositions were markedly different. Mildred, with arresting dark hair and eyes, a confident manner and a level gaze, was already turning young men's heads and was considered one of the prettiest young girls around Stoutland. Mildred's approach to life was purely practical and no-nonsense, with little time for books or the stretching of her imagination.

Ruby, on the other hand, was a blonde with dreamy gray/green eyes that mirrored a personality full of wonderment and curiosity. It had only been a few childhood years since she had been dubbed "cotton top" by her beloved Grandpa Duncan. She was at that awkward age where legs and arms can find no place to be at ease.

Hard work for everyone, including children, was considered the utmost virtue in the Allee household. To her parents' consternation, Ruby was often found curled up with any book she could find or borrow. Whereas Mildred was only an average student, Ruby excelled in every subject and was the "teacher's pet" of Mr. Merlin Carlton, who taught all eight grades at the one-room Craddock School.

The continuous high-pitched hum of the cicadas disturbed an unnatural quiet that had settled over Rouse Hill. This was a year that these strange insects appear and shed their outer shells, leaving exact lifeless and hollow facsimiles of themselves firmly attached to the bark of trees. Only the cicadas and the fading caws of a couple of crows, flapping their way from the heat of Rouse Hill to the cool shade of nearby Stoutland Creek, could be heard as the girls reached their destination.

Ruby eagerly unlatched the mailbox and grabbed a small bundle of mail, including the anxiously awaited *Capper's Weekly* that was serializing Zane Grey's romantic potboiler of the old west, *Riders of the Purple Sage*. She was handing the "box holder" junk mail to Mildred for her disinterested inspection when both girls heard something they would never forget. A man's voice, groaning loudly in what seemed an attempt to command attention or summon help, came from across the main road and toward the top of Rouse Hill.

"Oh—Ruby, what was that?" uttered Mildred through clenched teeth. All thoughts of Lassiter, Jane Withersteen, and the sweet smell of desert sage flew out of Ruby's mind as another agonized, wordless moan shattered the morning calm. The cicadas paused, as if wondering what nature's next act might be.

Drawing near to Mildred and clutching her hand, Ruby whispered, "Do you think it's someone trying to scare us?"

"I don't know what it is," replied practical Mildred, "but let's run home and tell Mom and Dad." As if discerning the girls' wavering intent, a louder groan came forth, deep from the diaphragm, after a long, wheezing gasp for air. This chilling sound was followed by a strange liquid gurgling.

Human survival instincts, bred into the genes for millenniums, permit recognition of certain sounds. Although Ruby and Mildred had never heard the sound of a mortally injured man, they unmistakably recognized it when they heard it. Nature told them that danger was near and they should flee. And flee they did, as fast as their road-toughened feet could take them. Mildred, the better athlete, glanced furtively over her shoulder, hoping that Ruby's visage had not been replaced by a bloody apparition, bony arms clutching for her. For a daydreaming bookworm, Ruby wasn't doing so badly, legs pumping furiously with precious store-bought sandals in one hand and *Cappers* in the other.

As they ran up the wooden steps and rushed into the house, they let the screen door slam with a bang and burst into the kitchen. Cora Duncan Allee, a calm and sensible woman, recognized in an instant that her out-of-breath and overheated girls were nearly scared to death. A sense of dread overcame her as she quickly wiped the flour off her hands, reached for them, and said, "Sisters! What in the world is the matter?" Before the girls could speak, El stepped onto the back porch after plowing with team and horses all morning. The three turned and rushed to him.

Ruby stammered out, "Some—somebody is d-d-dying over on Rouse Hill—we ran all the way home!"

Mildred chimed in, "We heard somebody groanin', makin' terrible sounds up the road from the mailbox. Daddy, you gotta get somebody and go up there. It sounds like he's hurt bad!"

Cora said, "Now, you girls settle down; it was probably just some teenaged boys from town trying to scare you."

With a worried look, El said, "Corrie, maybe I ought to walk over there and look—something sure 'nough scared these girls."

"Now El, that's a long ways over there and you know you're tired out—you need to eat your dinner and get some rest. Why, even if someone did need help, surely somebody has come by there by now on the main road—you'll just be wasting your time.

Resignedly El answered, "Corrie, I guess you're right; if it was somebody hurt they've probably got him to Doc Carlton by now—I reckon we'll hear about it if there really was anything."

Reluctantly accepting their parents' decision, the girls headed for the porch. The company of family and their mother's fried chicken and milk gravy, string beans with new potatoes, along with baking powder biscuits would soon soothe their childhood fright.

As soon as they were alone, El looked meaningfully at his wife and in a low voice, said, "You know, Old Man Winfrey in town told me that a fella by the name of Francis was shot and beat to death up there on Rouse Hill a few years ago. Do you think maybe . . . ?"

As her husband's voice trailed off, Cora impatiently waved her hand and interjected, "Now El, you know I don't believe in ghosts or any other such a thing like that, and don't you be telling the girls and scaring them more than they're scared already." El bit his lower lip and shook his head.

The Allees never heard a report of anyone hurt on Rouse Hill. Ruby and Mildred summoned the courage to return to the mailbox many times in the years they lived on the Gallagher farm. But they never went alone and they never loitered. Yet on that day, Ruby and Mildred's lives were somehow changed forever. Their youthful innocence had been bruised by a frightening experience never explained but vividly remembered after 70 years. The menacing presence lurking on Rouse Hill that hot summer morning in 1928 still seemed near and immediate. Shortly before Mildred's death in 1998, the sisters discussed it together one last time.[2] The elderly ladies could speak of it only with hushed voices while tightly pressing each other's hands.

Chapter 1

Friday, October 29, 1915

A cry of "Halloh! Halloh! Jap, are yuh at home?" startled Jasper Jacob "Jap" Francis awake at about two o'clock in the afternoon. It was Friday, and Jap was looking forward to finishing his afternoon chores and getting to bed early. He intended to go to Stoutland the next day and do a little trading for groceries and sundries. Jap had earlier finished a simple bachelor dinner of cold cornbread, butter and molasses, fresh milk, and a couple of fried eggs, and had then settled into a rocking chair to read the *Capper's Weekly*. Anxious to catch up on the latest war news from Europe and check recent cattle prices, he had dozed off after peeling and munching a fresh Winesap apple, his favorite. His younger brother, Simpson "Simp" Francis, who lived nearby, had brought a bushel basket of the fruit over the day before. The sweet aroma had spread from the kitchen throughout the house.

Jap Francis lived quietly in the old log house that his family occupied when they first moved to Camden County some 20 years earlier. Seeking inexpensive land and escape from factory drudgery, the Francis family had migrated to Missouri from the smoky industrial city of Wheeling, West Virginia, in the 1880s. Their first home was near the small hamlet of Bear Thicket in adjoining Laclede County. The whole family, including Jap's parents, Bill and Lucy Francis, along with his brothers and sister—Ben, Simpson, and Murtie—had moved to the Camden County farm in 1894. They had never regretted it.[1]

The Francis family had prospered on the "Barr" place, located about 8 miles north and west of the busy railroad town of Stoutland. The farm consisted of 460 acres of gently rolling land on both sides of a road giving them ready access to Stoutland and the larger town of Lebanon, as well as the small villages of Decaturville, Montreal, and Wet Glaize. Both parcels of land sloped down to small streams lined with willows and sycamores. It was considered a good farm by their neighbors. The Francises had labored hard to make it better by clearing out scrub oaks and cedars on the higher pastures and felling large sycamores, walnuts, and hickories in order to cultivate more of the rich bottomland. Keeping these pastures from returning to their natural woodland state required backbreaking hours of cutting sprouts, but it had all proved worthwhile. Most of the open ground was sown in grass to feed increasingly larger herds of cattle. Narrow bottomfields were dedicated to row crops, mainly corn, with some wheat. Grain not used to feed livestock was sold or ground into flour or meal at Stoutland to feed the family. The ability to easily ship fattened cattle to the St. Louis markets on the Frisco railroad added to the value of their enterprise.

Upon reaching manhood, Simp and Ben had "sparked" local girls, gotten married, and moved out of the house. Jap had remained a bachelor and stayed. It wasn't because the young ladies had not been interested. In his younger years, Jap had been considered quite a catch when he showed up occasionally at school pie-suppers and revival meetings at the Liberty Christian Church. Heavily chaperoned "play parties" were lively events within the neighborhood. Only the "nicer" young men and women were invited. Jap was always on the A-list but rarely attended. He just "had too much work to do."

After the marriage of his older brother Ben, Jap assumed responsibility for running the farm and tending his chronically ill mother and aging father. Little time was left for romance. Besides, Jap was decidedly shy with members of the opposite sex. In his early years, a couple of "flames" had flickered but gone out. Leaving his parents had always been out of the question, and potential brides despaired of starting married life sharing his large responsibilities and the modestly small Francis home.

Sadness struck the family shortly after 1900, with the death from tuberculosis of Murtie Francis in her early twenties. Murtie, a lovely girl, was briefly married to one Lilburn DeBerry in 1896, at the age of 16.[2] The marriage was either annulled or ended in divorce shortly thereafter. A few years later she entered a state sanitarium and apparently died there.

Some said that Lucy Francis died of a broken heart over the death of her beloved daughter. She died of heart trouble in 1905 despite the best efforts of young Doctors Pool and Carlton in Stoutland and various heart specialists in the distant city of Springfield. Bill Francis died suddenly of a massive stroke in the summer of 1906.

Jap had never gotten over the death of his sister and the passing, in quick succession, of both parents. Only today, he had suddenly choked up, tears brimming in his eyes, when he had looked at his mother's old woodburning cookstove. The smell of the apples had brought back memories of countless apple pies and cobblers that Lucy had baked for the family. That was before taking permanently to her bed, too short of breath to get up. Jap had seen to it that a lovely heart-shaped stone monument marked his parents' graves at the Old Liberty cemetery. "Death is another life" was inscribed upon it, providing his only consolation in these lonely, sad moments.

At the age of 45, Jap Francis remained a fine-looking man, about 5'6", 150 pounds, and sturdily built. He had a broad, chiseled face, a firm jaw, and clear gray-blue eyes that twinkled when he was amused. His full head of dark hair had become "pepper and salt" in recent years, with his neatly trimmed mustache and sideburns almost completely gray.[3] With reluctance and some embarrassment, he had recently bought a pair of wire-rimmed "spectacles" necessary to read fine newspaper print and do the chores in the dim light of the barn.

Hearing another "Halloh!" coming from the front gate by the road, Jap arose, laid his glasses on a nearby table and peered through the parlor window. Seeing a familiar figure, he thought to himself, "I wonder what Charlie Blackburn is doing over this way?" He opened the door and stepped onto the front porch.

"Howdy, Jap, I didn't know if you wuz at home or not," called out Charles "Charlie" Blackburn, sitting astride a tall but somewhat thin chestnut-colored horse. Jap's keen eye for horseflesh determined the animal to be a plow horse saddled by Charlie for the 5 mile ride from the Blackburn farm.

"Hello, right back at you!" cheerily spoke Jap as he walked toward the gate. "Tie that horse up and come on in, Charlie—I haven't seen you in quite a while."

"Well, Jap, I wouldn't want to impose on yuh—it's just that I heard you had some stock you wuz a-fix'un to sell, and I've been lookin' to do a little dealin'." Without dismounting, he continued, "Yuh know, I sold all my stock back in September when prices wuz good, but with the weather bein' as warm as it has been, I've still got pretty good grass to graze a few head for a while."

"Well, I'm always willin' to talk a trade," responded Jap, "but I wish you would come in and sit a spell. Y'know, I don't get too many visitors out this a-way."

Shaking his head, Charlie responded, "Naw, Jap, I'd be pleased to if I had more time—but with it gettin' dark s'early, I reckon I'd better not."

Like many of the Ozarkian school, Jap was reluctant to launch so quickly into business, preferring to "chew the fat" awhile before getting down to serious matters. But he knew Charlie Blackburn as a rather sour man, not big on chitchat, so he decided to accommodate him. The truth was that Jap had mentioned to a few people at Stoutland that he was thinking about shipping his remaining cattle soon because he did not want to feed them through the winter. The herd consisted of 27 head of crossbred steers, 4 cull heifers, and an aged bull. After inquiring about the health of Charlie's family, including "Miz Craddock" (Charlie's mother-in-law and matriarch of an old-line Stoutland family), Jap invited Charlie to look over his herd.

"Well, Charlie, I'm runnin' the cattle over on the back eighty. You know, I'd only be interested in sellin' them all together, but if you want to see'm, let me saddle up Sam and I'll go with you." Sam was Jap's fine Missouri fox-trotter horse.

"Noooh, Jap, there ain't no need for that. I've got my horse right here, and I'll just ride over there and look 'em over—if I can't find 'em all, I'd trust you for what you'd tell me they are."

Shrugging his shoulders, Jap replied, "Whatever suits you." He then directed Charlie through the front gate, down an old road behind the house leading to a creek, and up a hill to the south pasture. As he watched Charlie depart, Jap thought to himself, "Charlie Blackburn seems awful anxious to buy some cattle—I wonder if he knows somethin' that I don't?" Mulling this thought for a moment, he surmised, "Aah, he's probably lookin' to buy 'em real cheap, and I'm not sellin 'em that way—I wouldn't take less than 37 or 38 dollars a head for the steers and a little less for the small heifers and the old bull."

Ten minutes later, Jap was surprised to hear the clattering hooves of Charlie's horse as he urged the nag up the steep wagon road toward the house. "Shoot, he's hardly had time to even find 'em, let alone look 'em all over," thought Jap, with hope fading for selling the cattle at a reasonable price. Avoiding the need to drive the cattle to Stoutland and paying for a railroad car and a commission to a St. Louis cattle broker had been an appealing thought. "Charlie Blackburn's prob'ly just talkin' through his hat—thinkin' he can buy 'em for nuthin'," muttered Jap as he walked back to the house and seated himself on the front porch.

"Them steers look a little thin, but they're toler'bly good," said Charlie after dismounting and tying his horse to the gate post. Charlie was a lean, wiry man, weighing only about 155 pounds and at 5'9", three inches taller than Jap. Charlie emphasized his height, already above average for men in 1915, by wearing two-inch-heeled western-style boots and a broad-brimmed, high-crowned Stetson hat. It was a hat that he rarely removed because his sandy brown hair had thinned to the point of almost complete baldness. Charlie was sensitive about that. His hawkish face included high cheekbones, a long and thin hooked nose, deeply set eyes, and a small, rather prim mouth resting above a weak jaw with a cleft chin. But it was Charlie's eyes that left an impression. They were pale blue, cold, and expressionless.[4] In both appearance and demeanor, Charlie Blackburn was not someone that you wanted to chum up with.

Stepping up on the porch and leaning against the railing, Charlie continued, "I couldn't find 'em all, Jap. Some of 'em musta been down in the woods—yuh say you got thirty-two head altogether?"

"Yep, thirty-two, that's right," responded Jap, helpfully, "and they've gained real nice and 'pear to me to be right near ready to go to market." Jap sat lazily, leg crossed over knee, on an old wicker settee. Pulling a small Barlow pocketknife from his pocket, he cut off a chew of tobacco from a fresh plug. His relaxed body language was that of a man unanxious to sell but willing to listen. Placing the chew in his cheek, Jap continued.

"I bought most of 'em as calves way back in the spring from Rube Winfrey when he sold his place. They've had plenty of grass, and me and Simp have been givin' them a lot of corn here lately. I'd say the steers average about nine-hundred pounds and the heifers some less. I don't know about our old bull, but I'd be surprised if he was less than fourteen-hundred pounds."

Determined to see how serious Charlie was, Jap glanced directly at him and asked, "Charlie, what do you think you would want to give for 'em?"

Tilting his head back and forth, averting his eyes downward and dragging his toe in an arc on the wooden porch floor for a few seconds, Charlie replied, "Aw, I don't know, I guess I kind of had in mind about $38 a head for 'em if you wuz a wishin' to let 'em go."

Jap was surprised and pleased, but a good cattle trader keeps a poker face and never accepts the first offer—it's just the rules of the road. It seemed a little odd that Charlie hadn't first inquired how much he wanted for the cattle before making an offer. "Well, I don't know, Charlie, the market has held up pretty good here lately—I think I can prob'ly do a little better in St. Louis. Maybe I'll just hang on to 'em awhile longer." It was a ploy to see if the offer would be increased.

Charlie bit. "Jap, I don't think I could go any more cash money for them cows, but I'll tell you what—if you could use a little span of mules, I'd be willin' to throw 'em in as a bonus—they're not real big, but they're worth a hunnert dollars each, easy. They're only about six or seven years old, and they got a lotta work left in 'em."

"Those mules are probably not worth a dang," thought Jap to himself, "but if they're of any account at all, I'll be way ahead because I've already got a good price for the cattle, 'specially since Charlie's payin' too much for the heifers and the bull." Shaking his head with feigned reluctance, Jap replied quietly, almost sadly, "Well, if you say those mules are alright, I guess I'd go along with it." More cheerfully, and without giving Charlie a chance to change his mind, he added, "If you need some help drivin' 'em over to your place, I'll shore do it—just whenever you wanta take 'em."

"I'd 'preciate it if you would, that'd sure 'nough help me out," replied Charlie. "Listen, Jap, I know yore good at figgerin', bein' a dy-rector of the bank and all—how much exackly is that gonna be, altogether, on the cattle?"

"Let me get my little book and a pencil," quickly replied Jap as he lurched to his feet and stepped through the front door into the house.

The deal was done. With the mules valued at $100 each, the total came to $1,416 or just over $44 per head for the cattle. In a generous mood, Jap said, "Charlie, why don't we just call it an even $1,400 and taking into account a hundred each for the mules, you'll just be owin' me the balance of $1,200."[5]

"Well now, I 'preciate that, Jap—that's right nice a' you," replied Charlie. After agreeing to settle up after the livestock were moved, Charlie promised to bring the mules over to Jap's place the next afternoon, Saturday, October 30. "We prob'ly won't be able to get the cattle b'fore Sunday afternoon, if yore expectin' to be at home. I'll get my boy and Skip [Charlie's hired hand, Harrison F. "Skip" Archer] to give us some help."[6]

The two then shook hands before Charlie mounted his horse and headed east on the road toward home. As horse and rider receded into the distance, Jap sat down again on the old wicker settee that his mother had brought from West Virginia many years before. He crossed his arms on his chest and chewed his tobacco thoughtfully. "It 'pears like I may have skinned him a little—I wonder if ole Charlie Blackburn knows just what he's a-doin'?"

Chapter 2

Jap Francis had been acquainted with Charlie Blackburn ever since Charlie had married a local girl, Miss Minnie Craddock, in 1897. The couple had moved in with Minnie's widowed mother, Miz Mary Craddock, and Jim, her unmarried son. Jim had married and moved out in 1904, and Miz Craddock had sold the farm to Charlie and Minnie. Jap had little more than a nodding and speaking acquaintance with Charlie, and had never had any business dealings with him. He believed Charlie to be more of a speculator than a serious farmer, paying a hired hand to do most of the heavy work. Charlie's wife, Minnie, lived in Stoutland[1] and in today's vernacular was "high maintenance."

Sometime after 1910, Minnie and Charlie had separated. No one knew exactly why. Minnie claimed it necessary to move into town so that their son, Robert Ray Blackburn, could finish grade school at the Stoutland School. Minnie deemed the school superior to the nearby one-room Craddock School, named after her parents. They had donated the land for its founding in the 1870s. In the fall of 1915, young Ray Blackburn had begun high school at Stoutland, the only such school within 15 miles. Few bought Minnie's excuses for living apart from her husband and the expensive upkeep of two residences. After all, the Blackburn farm was only 2½ miles away from Stoutland, an easy commute for a young man on a horse. Most felt that the couple simply could not get along under the same roof.

Minnie's haughty ways and expensive tastes were a constant source of conflict. It was said that Minnie rarely missed an opportunity to remind Charlie that he was working her "daddy's" farm, with her inheritance being the couple's only equity in the property. Legally, the farm remained in Minnie's name.[2] Charlie seemed to get along better with Minnie's mother than he did Minnie. He was always civil, even deferential, to "Miz Mary." The need to borrow substantial amounts of money from the old lady may have helped keep Charlie's prickly disposition in check. Money was needed to keep Minnie and Ray dressed in the best that money could buy and pay Ray's high-school tuition. Charlie's uncommon courtesies to Miz Mary would not go unrewarded. There would come a day when Miz Mary's good will would come in very handy.

Attractive and well-preserved at the age of 40, Minnie deigned no appearance in Stoutland when not "dressed to the top," literally. Her fashionable satin dresses with bustles emphasizing the derriere, buttoned soft kid-leather shoes with matching gloves, all topped with the latest millinery creations, never failed to cause a sensation when she appeared on the town's sidewalks.

Minnie had a lust for the flower- and feather-bedecked hat monstrosities of the WWI era. They were purchased during frequent shopping expeditions to nearby Lebanon. Catering to the "finer ladies" of that fair city, the proprietors' exploitation of feminine vanity would put the coiffed and condescending clerks of Saks and Neiman to shame.

Minnie's cologne-laden morning departures from the Stoutland depot, on the Frisco's "Southwest Special," were sights to behold. Not even the smoke-belching, steam-hissing, brake-screeching Baldwin locomotives pulling the "Special" could drown out the wolf whistles. Minnie tossed her head, primped her mouth, elevated her nose, and pretended to ignore the unwashed and uncouth louts loafing on the streets. Her late-afternoon returns, laden with packages and a hatbox or two, caused tongues to wag. "My word! Just how *does* a married woman, traveling alone, fritter away the entire day in the big city?" clucked the town's modest matrons. No one knew for sure.

Charlie and Minnie had borrowed the money to buy a small white cottage on the eastern edge of town. Visits paid by Charlie to his wife and son's town home were well monitored by nosey neighbors who kept track of whether he stayed overnight or not. Unstated was the burning question of whether such visits were conjugal. Most thought not.

In Minnie's defense, her early married life had been saddened with the death in infancy of her two firstborn children. Clyde, born in the same year of their marriage, was stillborn. Floyd, born March 6, 1900, had lived only 3 months.[3] Robert Ray Blackburn, known only as "Ray," had been born in 1903, and Minnie was determined that nothing bad would ever happen to him. She constantly fussed over his health and spoiled the child. When Ray was dressed in store-bought polished shoes, knickers, woolen suits, starched collars, and bow ties, his plain-living Blackburn relatives compared him to "Little Lord Fauntleroy."[4]

As Jap Francis quietly chewed and spat, reviewing the day's events, he wondered about the easy sale of his cattle to Charlie Blackburn at what seemed an above-market price. Jap kept up with the cattle markets, buying an occasional copy of the *St. Louis Globe-Democrat*, a bundle of which was thrown off the Meteor, the Frisco's express passenger train that sped westward through Stoutland early every morning. Jap was vaguely troubled. "I just don't see how Charlie Blackburn can come out ahead on this trade," he said to himself as his mind wandered to what he knew about Charlie's mother-in-law and the Craddock family. He was comforted by the fine reputation of the Craddocks. "I just don't believe that Miz Mary Craddock would let Charlie beat me out of anything."

The Blackburn farmhouse stood close to the road on the way to Stoutland, and Jap would occasionally stop and chat with Charlie, Miz Mary, or their hired hand, Skip Archer. Charlie had little to say and the conversations began and ended with the weather and crop conditions. Skip liked to talk, but was usually busy watering, feeding, gathering corn, or fixing fence. He was being paid to work, and Charlie cast disapproving glares if Skip loitered too long. Miz Mary Craddock was a woman who would talk your arm off if given half a chance. Although Jap liked the old lady, he usually tipped his hat and called, "Afternoon Miz Craddock," while at the same time gently spurring Sam to a quicker trot. Mary Craddock never failed to give a friendly wave and a "Howdy, Jap!" as he sped by.

With her sunbonnet, Miz Mary Craddock, an energetic 77-year-old, was often seen on her knees working in the lovely flower beds adorning the single-storied concrete house with white wooden gables and a tin roof. In about 1880, the "new" house had replaced the family's log cabin at the bottom of the hill near a small stream. Mary's late husband, Richard "Dick" Craddock, had hewed the logs and built the dwelling when the couple was first married.

Having patented the 160 acres of land from the U.S. Government just after the Civil War, Dick and Mary Craddock were truly "old settlers" of the Stoutland area. The "old" house was now used as a corn crib and a nearby stone-lined well that Dick had dug by hand was used to water the cattle during hot summers when the nearby spring went dry.

His mind returning to Charlie, Jap knew that the Blackburn family hailed from the little town of Decaturville some 14 miles away. Jap knew several of the Blackburns, including Charlie's uncle, Smith Blackburn, who lived in Stoutland and his brother, Bob, who lived near Buckner. Smith's son, Carl, was a good friend. As a teenager, Carl had worked for Jap when he operated a furniture store in Stoutland for a few years. After his brothers left home, Jap had sold the furniture business to devote full time to the farm. As far as he knew, Charlie's father, McGary "Mack" Blackburn and his mother, "Dolly" (Hogue) Blackburn, were honest and hardworking folk who enjoyed good reputations around Decaturville.

Mack Blackburn's father, Isaac, had been ambushed and killed in the Civil War on the same day he first put on a uniform and joined the Union militia.[5] Sturdy sorts, the Blackburns had survived and prospered. The family was closely knit—some would say clannish. The men were known to have hot tempers, and Jap had heard a rumor that as a young man, Charlie had hurt somebody pretty badly in a fight—but that was all long in the past.

The more he thought about it, the more puzzling it seemed that Charlie Blackburn would appear out of the blue after all these years and offer Jap such a good deal on a herd of cattle—seemingly on the spur of the moment. At a time when a good farm with a house and barn in the Stoutland area could be bought for $7,000 or $8,000, a $1,400 cattle deal wasn't small potatoes.

"Well, I know what I've got in those cattle and $1,200 and a couple of mules will make a nice profit," thought Jap to himself. "Charlie will just have to work out his own salvation on this deal—I sure didn't make him buy 'em from me."

Jap went in the house, grabbed a couple of winesaps out of the basket in the kitchen, and walked out to the corral fence by the barn. He called, "Yo, Sam! Here, Sam!" Sam, his fine saddlehorse, came trotting up from the bottom of the field, displaying the smooth, high-stepping gait characteristic of Missouri fox trotters.

Eighty-five years later, the Missouri's Legislature would dub Sam's breed the official "State Horse." With head held high, the big bald-faced sorrel gelding swept around the barn and slid to a stop in front of Jap. Sam knew the drill. He nodded his head and nickered expectantly. Jap threw him an apple which Sam caught in midair and crunched delightedly. After the process was repeated, Jap rubbed Sam's nose, scratched his ears, and spoke softly to him. More than 16 hands high at the withers, Sam was the best horse Jap had ever had, and he had owned more than a few. Sam was a Lincoln Continental of horseflesh. His brisk, fluid gait gave his rider an easy, velvety ride.

With a couple of water stops and a few munches of grass, Sam could easily cover 50 miles in a day without tiring. Jap had given some thought to buying a newfangled automobile—he could easily afford a Model T Ford or an even finer Maxwell, Dorris, or Hupmobile. But the roads around Stoutland were a quagmire in wet weather and filled with tire-piercing flint rocks in summer. Jap often passed broken-down "Tin Lizzies," their owners covered with dust, patching inner tubes or filling boiling radiators with creek water. He was tempted to yell, "Get a horse!" as he swept by on Sam.

Sam dutifully followed Jap into the barn where he was led to his large stall for the night. It was clouding up and Sam was not a horse one left out in the weather. After currying him and checking his shoes, Jap brought him a five-gallon bucket of water and began the feeding ritual. He measured out a peck of oats mixed with a scoop of milled grains, a splash of cod-liver oil, and a couple spoonfuls of molasses. A large pitchfork of clover hay was tossed to the side to finish the feast. The bond between man and horse can be very strong. Only death would separate Jap Francis and his beloved Sam.

Jap patted Sam's face and then walked down and across the creek to the south pasture. He needed to pitch some hay and throw out some corn for the cattle. He felt relieved that after Monday this chore would be over. He spat a little tobacco, sighed, and went to work. His two Jersey cows still had to be milked and turned in with their calves, and the hogs needed feeding. The last rays of sunshine were disappearing through the wood line in the west, and the evening gloom would soon descend over the farm. As November neared, the daylight hours were getting progressively shorter. Jap Francis could not have imagined that his days had suddenly become numbered.

Chapter 3

Saturday, October 30, 1915

As promised, Charlie Blackburn delivered the span of mules bright and early Saturday morning. Jap didn't expect much and didn't get much. The mules were undersized and poorly matched. An examination of their teeth showed them to be considerably older than advertised. They also displayed a balky disposition and a willingness to kick at the slightest provocation. Jap unhooked a fence gate, shooed the critters into the pasture by clapping his hands and said nothing. As long as the animals were breathing and could walk, the deal would stand. Jap vowed to sell the sorry creatures at the earliest opportunity.

Charlie told Jap that he, along with his son Ray and Skip Archer, would return Sunday afternoon to drive the cattle along the 5 miles to the Blackburn farm. Jap reaffirmed his willingness to saddle Sam and help with the move. Charlie remounted his horse, yelled, "See yuh tomorrow!" and rode quickly away.

"I'm about half afraid of those durned Charlie Blackburn mules," exclaimed Jap to his brother, Simp, that evening over supper. Simp and his wife, Ida, lived across the road and down a lane on 220 acres of the original Francis farm. Jap often took dinner or supper with the couple. Ida was an excellent cook. Jap wasn't. His specialties extended no farther than fried potatoes, fried meat, fried eggs, fried apples, soda bread, corn bread, corn meal "johnny cakes," and red-eye gravy—all cooked in a skillet on top of the stove.

Simp and Ida had long since given up hope of having children. They enjoyed Jap's company, and Simp's older brother was always dropping off a little something special from the grocery store in Stoutland, as well as sharing the best cuts of beef, pork, and lamb at butchering time. The couple used the old family garden spot behind Jap's house. Jap constantly improved the already rich loam soil by tilling it up and adding a little dry horse manure in the fall. In the summer, Simp and Ida planted and raised a plenitude of fresh vegetables for the table and canning. In the fall, Simp would dig enough white potatoes and sweet potatoes to last them all through the hard Missouri winters, and sell several wagonloads besides. Ida kept a flock of chickens and supplied Jap with fresh eggs. It was a cozy, cooperative relationship.

"Jap, you'd best be careful with them wild mules," exclaimed Simp. "Lord only knows where Charlie Blackburn got those creatures. He's always tradin' for somethin'. He undoubtedly got 'em in on a deal somewhere—I'll bet he hasn't had 'em two weeks."

Jap explained the rest of his cattle trade with Charlie. "I sure hope you get your money," commented Simp, a little worried. "As far as I know, Charlie pays his debts, but I've heard he's got a lot of 'em, and he may be robbin' Peter to pay Paul."

"Yep, I know that the bank is holdin' quite a bit of Charlie's paper, but I don't know exactly how much," responded Jap. "I guess I should a' checked at the bank."

Ida chimed in, "With Minnie spending money like there's no tomorrow—I'm surprised they've got anything!"

"I reckon you're right, but you know something? I just can't imagine Miz Craddock allowin' Charlie and Minnie to let a debt go bad. Why, I've heard that old Dick Craddock was as honest as the day is long—and Miz Mary, too," was Jap's hopeful reply.

Simp shrugged his shoulders, and Jap turned his attention to the large slice of raisin pie and a steaming cup of coffee, mellowed with fresh cream, that Ida had set before him. It was Jap's favorite. "You know something, Ida, when I get to heaven, I just hope they've laid in a good supply of your raisin pies! If they haven't, I reckon I won't be stayin' very long."

Beaming at the compliment, Ida modestly replied that she imagined that the angels could come up with something "a blame sight better than this lumpy old thing."

In good spirits, Jap took his leave shortly after supper and surprised the two by announcing that he would probably see them at church in the morning. At best, Jap Francis was an irregular churchgoer. Simp and Ida never missed a Sunday at the nearby Liberty Christian Church.

"Maybe my brother is finally gonna start takin' his religion seriously," remarked Simp to his wife, as Sam's hoofbeats receded over the hill.

Sunday, October 31, 1915

True to his word, Jap Francis rode Sam the 3 miles to the Old Liberty Christian Church Sunday morning for the 10:00 services. Simp observed his arrival just after the opening hymn, "Shall We Gather at the River." Jap nodded to several acquaintances and seated himself beside his brother in the fourth pew on the left, next to the aisle.

It was customary among some Christian Churches (Disciples of Christ) and their stricter brethren in the Church of Christ for the women, girls, and small boys to sit on the right side of the church with the men and older boys seated on the left. No one knew the origin of this practice. Perhaps it was a holdover from the Puritans, reducing opportunities for lustful thoughts and temptations among God's children. More likely, it allowed the men to doze while the preachers droned on about Paul's letters to the Ephesians and Galatians and Thessalonians and other ancient peoples known only to Bible scholars and archaeologists. Occasional sharp glances from ever-vigilant wives, safely distanced on the other side of the church, were much preferred to pokes in the ribs, up close and personal. Church decorum seems to always have a higher priority among women than men.

Jap had recently ridden to the Stoutland Baptist Church to hear an itinerant negro evangelist, William "Brother Billy" Driver, preach. Driver was mid-Missouri's black Billy Sunday of his day. A small, impeccably dressed man, Driver "brought the message" with a magnetism and eloquence that kept his audience spellbound. Racial intolerance was alive then and now, but Brother Billy was unusual. His brilliant oratory and sheer force of personality gave him welcome in both black and white churches. Driver's fame sometimes required venues larger than country churches. The *Linn Creek Reveille* of April 20, 1917, reported that Driver, "something of a celebrity, would preach at the courthouse tonight." An audience of hundreds overflowed the steps and grounds to "receive the word."

No one nodded off the day Driver preached in Stoutland. Brother Billy didn't believe in confining himself to the pulpit. Offering an open Bible to heaven with one hand while gesturing dramatically with the other, his sermons were delivered with full bass volume, up and down the aisle, front to back. His truths were so profound and his rhetorical skills so forceful that even the staid white farmers of Stoutland were inspired to stand and shout, "Amen, Brother." The church was filled not only with Baptists, but a sprinkling of Methodists, Presbyterians, "Campbellites," and probably a closet atheist or two. William Driver was a happening that no one wanted to miss. When he was finished, everyone knew about heaven and hell, how to get there, and the relative merits of both destinations.

This day, Jap could not help but compare Driver's style with the measured, calm presence of Brother Frank Moneymaker, who divided his time between the Stoutland Christian Church and the Liberty Church. As Moneymaker pleaded for the souls of the lost and implored sinners to "confess, repent, and be baptized," the service ended with "Softly and Tenderly," a song of invitation. The words ". . . earnestly, tenderly, Jesus is calling, calling for you and for me" would be the last hymn that Jap Francis would hear on this earth.

As the crowd left the church house after the closing prayer, Ida urged Jap to "take dinner" with them, but he declined. "No, I'd sure like to, but I've got to make sure those cattle are ready to go when Charlie Blackburn and Skip Archer come by this afternoon." Jap mounted Sam and left at a quick trot. Simp and Ida lingered for a while, socializing with the brothers and sisters, before returning home in their one-horse buggy.

Arriving home just after the noon hour, Jap changed into work clothes and built a little fire in the cookstove. He baked some cornbread in a small iron skillet and then crumbled it, while still warm, into a large glass of sweet milk. The milk was stored in an ironstone jug in the well just outside the back porch. Lowered and retrieved by a pulley and rope, the cold foaming milk, with a layer of cream on top, is a luxury almost unknown in the twenty-first century. Mixed and consumed with a spoon, cornbread and milk was a bachelor's quick and nourishing meal. Jap's praise for Ida's raisin pie the evening prior had produced the desired results. Covered with a clean dishtowel, the pie pan, with about half of its contents, had been pressed into Jap's hands. His feeble protests had been ignored. A generous slice of pie, combined with a steaming cup of coffee brewed in his mother's blue graniteware pot, finished off this quick and tasty meal. Grabbing a couple of ripe Bartlett pears from an ancient wooden bowl, Jap headed outside.

Jap had left Sam saddled and tied, loose-reined, to a fence post at the side of the yard. Upon hearing the screen door slam, Sam paused from munching grass, jerked his head up, and neighed gently. Sam was not picky when it came to fruit treats. He liked them all. "One for you and one for me, partner," spoke Jap to his favorite horse as he tossed him a pear. Sloppily consuming the ripe and juicy fruit, Sam was ready to go.

Riding to the feedlot in the south pasture, Jap spent the next half hour throwing out corn and hay for the cattle. Hearing Jap's call, the cattle, grazing near a tree line some distance away, seemed confused at such an early feeding. But led by a bull, "Old Domino," the steers and heifers soon assembled, and Jap carefully counted them and checked their condition while slowly circling on Sam to keep them from straying. Jap hated to see Domino shipped off for slaughter. The animal came by his name naturally. Domino was partly Black Angus, but with a white curly face and a few white spots, he was sometimes mistaken for a Holstein. A huge animal, Domino was legendary in the neighborhood for producing prodigiously large and healthy offspring. Having grown old, Domino's paternal efforts had become unsatisfactory. It had come time for him to become part of the food chain.

Domino was as gentle as he was big. Jap shook his head sadly when he recalled how his nephews, Ray and Ward, loved to ride the massive creature. The amiable beast not only tolerated this insult to his dignity but seemed to enjoy it. The mischievous boys were the sons of Jap's older brother, Ben, and his wife, Lucy. Jap had sorely missed them all when Ben and his family had moved to South Dakota a few years earlier. Now living in California, Ben had recently sold his small ranch. He and the family were expected to return to Missouri within the next week or two.[1] Thankfully, the boys' pet would be out of sight and out of mind by then.

Deep in thought and pondering Domino's fate, Jap heard a distant call coming from near the house and moved to where he could see several riders assembled by the road. Yelling and waving for them to come ahead, he was soon joined by Charlie Blackburn, Skip Archer, and Charlie's boy, Ray. Skip was riding a nondescript horse that looked to be a match for Charlie's horse that Jap had pegged two days earlier as a common workhorse. Jap thought about asking what had happened to the latest of several fine saddlehorses sported by Charlie in recent years, but thought better of it. Ray Blackburn was riding a sturdy pony that Jap recognized as the horse that Minnie Blackburn was occasionally seen riding to and from the Blackburn farm. For all her pretenses of modesty, Minnie routinely broke convention by using a man's saddle.[2] Few mature women of the era would be caught dead in the act of mounting and straddling a horse. The risk of exposing an ankle, or even more, to leering mankind was unthinkable.

Ray Blackburn was a pale, pudgy boy of 13 years. He appeared distinctly uncomfortable and bored with the job at hand. Dressed in his Sunday suit with a tight, starched collar and bow tie, Ray met all the qualifications of a "momma's boy." Determined that her son not become a common farmer, Minnie had high aspirations for Ray. She had enrolled him two months earlier at the Stoutland High School, expecting that Ray would someday be a doctor, lawyer, or businessman. Ray's grades in elementary school had been mediocre, and his high-school prospects seemed equally dismal. But needing all the paying customers he could get, Professor D.H. Clark had admitted young Blackburn to the freshman class.

In 1910, several local grade schools had been consolidated to form the Stoutland free elementary school. The high school, with only ten or twelve pupils[3], required tuition and was beyond the reach of many Stoutland-area families. Minnie and Charlie were happy to pay Ray's tab, believing it would set their only child on a path to success. Besides, having her son at the high school reflected a certain affluency that Minnie felt was her proper station in life. It was a thought that Charlie readily shared. The Blackburn clan was a proud lot in its own right.

Some thought that Charlie Blackburn had married Minnie Craddock for her money and had become a "big feeler." People who had known Charlie as a child and as a young unmarried man knew that he had always had a high opinion of himself. "He thinks he's a lot smarter than anybody else," opined some.

One wag suggested, "If you could buy Charlie Blackburn for what he's worth and sell him for what he thinks he's worth, you'd be a millionaire."

Charlie's father had once cautioned Charlie, "Boy, I hope you make a lot of money, because with your expensive ways, you're shore 'nough gonna need it." But when it came to haughtiness, Charlie was hardly in a class with Minnie. Charlie often groused that she was "givin' that boy too many airs." Only the day before, he had insisted that Minnie send Ray out to the farm on Sunday to help with the cattle move. Minnie protested that Ray would miss a music recital. But after mother and son had attended Sunday school at the Stoutland Baptist Church, Ray sullenly saddled his mother's pony and headed over Rouse Hill to the farm.

Skip Archer was an amiable fellow, of only average intellect, renowned for his hard work and exceptional skill with a chopping axe. Each year, Skip routinely claimed the $5 prize and a blue ribbon for winning the wood-chopping contest at the Stoutland Picnic.

Watching Skip chop wood was like watching a buzz saw, the blade of the axe seemingly moving faster than the eye could follow. Woe to the person who stood too close to the flying chips. A slip of the axe many years earlier had severed a tendon in his ankle, causing a pronounced limp. Determined to move at a speed that could "outwork any man," Skip sped about with a gait not quite a walk and not quite a run—hence his nickname. Skip's gnarly hands, slender build, and stooped back told a tale of hard labor from childhood. His toothy grin, cheery greetings, and ready willingness to help any and all at the drop of a hat made him a favorite around Stoutland. "Why, you can't help but like old Skip Archee!" was the oft repeated phrase.

In rural Missouri, surnames are routinely mispronounced. Around Stoutland, "Archer" had become "Archee," just as "Cochran" had become "Co-horn" and "Rausch" had become "Rouse."

Held in late summer, the annual Stoutland Picnic was the community's biggest social event, drawing hundreds of people from miles around, with more than a few arriving by train. Many families came by team and wagon with food packed in baskets and camped on the grounds. "Merry-go-rounds" with steam calliopes thrilled the children. Carnival barkers lured the men into sideshows exhibiting the macabre and salacious. The grand opportunity to dress up, visit endlessly, and "see and be seen" satisfied the ladies' needs. Feats of strength, games of skill, and endless strings of electric lights created an atmosphere as irresistible to the hard-working folk of Stoutland as a black light to a moth. For many children, their first taste of iced lemonade and watermelon came on their daddy's knee at the "Picnic." Newfangled "hot dogs" and "iced cream cones," that wonderful confection invented for popular consumption at the St. Louis World's Fair, completed this all-too-fleeting taste of heaven.

Many Stoutlanders held fond memories of saving a little extra money in the summer of '04 and loading the family onto one of the Frisco's special "Fair" trains for the three-hour ride into St. Louis's Union Station to attend this impossibly modern event. The Station itself, a cavernous marble, brass, and stained-glass monument to the age of steam, was well worth the trip. However, much greater marvels awaited.

An electric-trolley ride to the fairgrounds brought visitors to a place imagined only in their dreams. By day, the fair was a gleaming city of monumental beaux-arts buildings, stuffed with the wonders of science and progress of the industrial age. Every state of the Union and nearly every nation in the world had put on display the best they had to offer. None skimped. By night, the first World's Fair lit entirely by electricity, switched on a half-million incandescent bulbs, creating a bejeweled fairyland of light and color.[4] The glow in the night sky could be seen for 50 miles, far outshining Halley's Comet which would come and go in 1910.

As intended by the city fathers, "The Fair" put St. Louis on the world's map. Later, little Judy Garland's "Meet me in Saint Looey, Looey, meet me at the Fair," a catchy tune from a movie inspired by the Fair, would put "Saint Looey" and the "Hoochie Coochie" on the lips of the nation. One hundred years after the Fair, New York cab drivers still call the city "Saint Looey." The blue-blooded descendants of the City's co-founders, Pierre Laclede and Auguste Choteau, along with a few determined Francophiles, insist that

"Sauhn loo-wee" is the *de riguere* pronunciation for the old French fur-trading post. Most just call it "Sant Lew'is."

Jap and his brothers, Simp and Ben, along with their wives and children, had gone to "The Fair" and would never forget it. Today, Jap had a cattle trade to finish.

Chapter 4

Exchanging greetings, the cattle crew quickly got organized. The men decided that after permitting the herd to drink at the stream below the hill, the cattle would be driven onto the main road. Domino would lead, and the steers and heifers would naturally follow. Ray would ride ahead and warn approaching traffic. Charlie and Skip would ride on the outsides, discouraging the beeves from straying onto unfenced land along the way. Jap would bring up the rear, rounding up stragglers.

All went well. The drive met a few folks on Sunday outings in buggies, hacks, and on horseback. All pulled off the road and permitted the cattle to proceed. One automobile, a sputtering and backfiring open touring car driven by Harry Taylor, caused some unrest and bawling among the herd, but Domino was old and in no mood for leading a stampede. Harry and several others of the younger set, dressed in dusters, goggles, touring caps, and scarves, shouted cheery greetings as the herd and its "cowboys" passed. The merrymakers were enjoying the warm Indian summer weather with a jaunt to the Wet Glaize spring for a picnic.

Two hours later, the herd arrived at the Blackburn farm. Ray and Charlie opened a barbed wire and stake gate, and shooed the cattle into a field. They ran at a trot to the bottom of the hill where a small stream widened into a clear hole of water just below the old Craddock log house and dug well. Thirsted by the two-hour drive, the cattle stood shoulder to shoulder, knee deep in the cold water, and refreshed themselves. The riders returned to the house, tied their horses and stepped on the porch to finish the business.

"Daddy, you said you wuz gonna pay me," whined Ray. Charlie glared at his son, reached slowly into his pocket, withdrew a silver dollar and flipped it with thumb off forefinger toward his son. Ray leaped for it and missed. Jap caught it in midair and handed it to Ray.

"Looks like the pay is pretty good around here," remarked Jap with a faint grin. At a time when fully grown men worked for only a dollar or two a day, it was obvious that Ray was being overpaid and indulged. Jap noticed the grimace on Skip's face as he shook his head with resignation and headed to the kitchen to get a drink of water. Skip was paid by the week and was getting nothing extra for working Sunday afternoon.

"Well, look who's here!" spoke Miz Mary Craddock as the white-haired old lady, wiping her hands on a blue gingham apron, stepped sprightly from the front parlor onto the porch. "Jap Francis, now you're going to have to stay for supper; I know that you're tired and famished."

"Naw, Miz Craddock, I can't stay long. I've got to get back and milk my cows and turn their calves in with 'em," protested Jap.

"Well, you come inside and sit a spell. I just made some lemonade—I'll pour you a big glass—you must catch me up on how everybody is over your way—how are Simp and Ida getting along? I hear that Ben and Lucy are coming back to Stoutland! Now you just sit right here in the big chair and tell me everything you know."

Physically tugged into the parlor, Jap grinned sheepishly and decided there was no sense in swimming against the onrushing tide of feminine curiosity. Besides, fresh lemonade was a luxury not passed up lightly. Settling himself in an overstuffed parlor chair, he heard Ray decline any refreshments and, with the silver dollar burning holes in his pocket, shout, "I gotta go—Ma's expectin' me!" and he was gone.

Reluctant to leave, Charlie eyed Jap and Miz Craddock nervously. Mumbling something about being "back in few minutes," he headed to the barn to help Skip. Some 20 minutes later, Charlie returned to the house and found Jap putting on his hat and backing out the front door under a fusillade of friendly protests from Miz Mary. Apologizing for not being able to stay longer, Jap insisted, "I surely do appreciate that lemonade, Miz Craddock, but I need to settle up with Charlie and get on home."

"You stop and see us—anytime you come by," implored Miz Mary. "I canned a lot of gooseberries this summer, and most folks like my gooseberry pie—you come and get some, you hear!"

"Yes ma'am, I sure will," was Jap's earnest reply as he turned and met Charlie near where Sam was tied at a hitch rail and watering trough.

"I'll tell you, Miz Craddock can sure talk a mile a minute," grinned Jap. "I swear, I thought she said that you and Minnie were a-plannin' on selling your farm to me. Shoot, I've got all the farm I can handle right now—another farm is the last thing I need."

Giving Jap a sharp look, Charlie lowered his voice and said, "Aw, Miz Craddock's got to where she gets all confused, and she don't hear too good neither."

"She sounded awful sure of herself to me; why, she was a worryin' about having to move off this place after all these years," responded Jap. "I feel kinda sorry for her—you ought to speak to the poor old lady and kinda set her straight—maybe it'll ease her mind."

"Well, Jap, I may have mentioned wantin' to buy yore place sometime, and she just got it all turned around. Anyhow, Jap, that's what I wuz wantin' to talk to yuh about. I'm on a deal with Joe Givens over by Decaturville to sell this place to him. He's s'posed to be over here Tuesday mornin' to get me the cash part, and I wuz a-wunderin' if you wouldn't mind waitin' for your money a couple of days? What I'd do is—as soon as I get his money, I'll come on over and write you yore check on the cattle. How's that sound to yuh?"

Warning bells were ringing in Jap's mind, but he was a naturally trusting person who believed that a "man's word is his bond." He felt a little queasy about this turn of events, but there wasn't much that he could do about it. The cattle were in Charlie Blackburn's field—he could hardly turn around and drive them home himself. Besides, Jap was in no hurry for his money—he had nearly $1,500 in the bank. In fact, his deposits had been so large in the recently defunct Bank of Stoutland that Marvin Calkin, president of the competing People's Bank, had lured Jap and his money to that bank a year earlier. Promised a seat on the People's board of director's, Jap had accepted, knowing very well that it was a thinly veiled ploy to build the People's Bank's assets—and help put the upstart Bank of Stoutland out of business.

Cocking his head to one side, Jap replied, "Well, Charlie, I kinda wish you'd a told me a little more about this before we drove these cattle all the way over here to your place—but I reckon it'll be alright." With a little impatience in his voice, Jap continued, "That is, as long as you keep 'em right here, and you and Joe Givens are gonna finish up your deal pretty quick like."

"Oh yeah, old Joe is mighty anxious to buy this place—I'll plan on ridin' over to your house Tuesday afternoon and write you a check," spoke Charlie reassuringly. "By the way, Jap, if you ever do take a notion to sell your place, I'd sure 'nough be interested."

Puzzled and a little amused by a man who in the same breath could delay payment on a fairly agreed-upon cattle trade while offering to buy his farm,[1] Jap replied, "No, no Charlie, it's not for sale—I'm real comfortable where I am, and you know that Mom and Dad bought it and both of 'em died there. Why, I'd never let that old place go—when I do, I reckon they'll be carrying me away in a pine box," chuckled Jap. Charlie wasn't laughing. His expressionless blue eyes looked intently at Jap for a moment and then glanced away.

Jap mounted Sam, turned his head toward home, tipped his hat to Charlie, and called, "I'll be lookin' for you on Tuesday!"

"Yeah, I expect about one or two o'clock!" yelled Charlie as Jap and Sam sped away.

Almost a quarter of a mile away, where the road turns abruptly near the Craddock School, Jap had the weird sensation of being watched. It's that shiver in the spine. The hair on the neck rising to attention. Slowing Sam to a walk, Jap turned in the saddle and peered back toward the Blackburn house. Charlie was standing just where Jap had left him. Arms across his chest, he stared intently at horse and rider. The motionless figure quickly turned and disappeared.

What Jap Francis did not know would hurt him. Charlie Blackburn was a man with a negative net worth and getting worse. Charlie was full of pride and full of himself. He was as bad a cattle trader as he was poker player. He had never seen an inside straight to which he wouldn't draw. He and Minnie had borrowed heavily against the farm and had borrowed most of the money that Miz Craddock had. Charlie had tried to borrow money from his father, his brothers, and his uncle, Smith Blackburn. All had politely turned him down. "I would, Charlie, but I just don't have it," was the diplomatic reply. They knew Charlie's situation too well.

Paying for Minnie's extravagances, losses on deal after cattle deal, and an unwillingness to put in the sweat equity to make the farm pay had pushed Charlie Blackburn to the edge. Maintaining an image of prosperity equal to their egos had placed the Blackburns near bankruptcy. High-school tuition for Ray, the luxury of a hired hand to do most of the farm work, and Minnie's highfalutin' ways had put them in a financial squeeze from which there seemed no escape.

Charlie had recently sold Max, his fine saddlehorse and a match for Sam, to make an overdue mortgage payment on the farm. He had taken Max by train as "baggage" in a freight car to a horse auction in Marshfield, some 40 miles away. While there, he had sold his hand-tooled saddle to a tack shop. He then dejectedly took the train back to Stoutland and walked home. He hadn't been able to bear the thought of seeing the prize animal ridden around Stoutland by someone else.

Charlie Blackburn was staring public humiliation in the face, and he didn't like what he saw. In Charlie's eyes, Charlie could do no wrong—it was always the other guy's fault. "They" had gotten him into this mess, and he had no doubts that "they" would get him out—one way or another. Charlie Blackburn was a man on the brink.

Chapter 5

Tuesday, November 2, 1915

Charlie Blackburn arrived at Jasper Francis's house early, a little after the noon hour. Jap had spent the morning helping Simp mend fences and had just returned. The brothers had trimmed, sawed, and put in a couple of new Ozark cedar corner posts and some new white-oak line posts. Allergic to cedar sap, Jap was on the back porch washing his hands with strong Castile soap and water when he heard the horse and rider halt at the front gate. As he reached for a towel, there was a sharp rap on the front door.

Charlie's greeting was a curt, "Hello, Jap."

Jap invited Charlie in and asked him to take a seat at the kitchen table. "Just give me a minute, Charlie; I've been trying to get this sticky old cedar sap off my hands and arms. This durned stuff just eats me up."

Charlie sat quietly at the table, nervously lacing and unlacing his fingers, twiddling his thumbs and rubbing his palms together as if he were cold. It wasn't cold. It was already 75 degrees, with the temperature headed to 85.[1] November of 1915 was one of the warmest on record in Missouri.

Stepping back into the kitchen, Jap said, "It sure is a warm one for November—my daddy always said that you didn't get real Indian summer until it gets warm like this after all the leaves are down."

"Yeah, I guess that's about the size of it," responded Charlie glumly.

Sensing Charlie's nervousness and discomfort, Jap pulled up a chair and got right to the point, "Did you and Joe Givens get your deal done this mornin' alright, like you said?"

Glancing sideways at Jap, Charlie shook his head and spoke apologetically, "Well, Jap, ya know, Joe sent me word that he won't be able to get over here 'til next Saturday. I don't know what's a-holdin' him up, but I reckon we'll just have to wait a few days."

The word "we'll" brought redness into Jap's face. Jap was a mild-mannered man, but finding that payment for his cattle had become hostage to Charlie's real-estate deal had him nettled.

"Charlie, are you sure that you and Joe Givens have got a solid deal on your farm? I don't know Joe real well, but I'm kind of surprised that he'd want to move all the way from the other side of Decaturville."

"Nooo, Jap—he don't plan on movin', he's just gonna rent it out for shares. He's a givin' me a real good price and tuh tell you the truth, I'm kinda hopin' that Miz Craddock will decide to go live with her son Jim and Jennie. Me and Minnie are a-thinkin' about sellin' the house in town, too. I reckon I might buy another farm, but I've been studyin' on movin' to Oklahoma—maybe get in the oil business down that a-way."

Although Charlie's scheme sounded a little "windy," it seemed believable. Like a banker with a non-producing loan, Jap resigned himself to giving his creditor a little more time. Besides, he had no interest in reclaiming the cattle and shipping them himself—he liked Charlie's price better than the latest St. Louis cattle prices printed in the *Globe-Democrat*. The cattle market had been poor that fall. Speculation about the war in Europe had sent prices skyrocketing in 1914, but 1915 would end on the downside, with losses concentrated late in the year.[2] As usual, Charlie Blackburn had bought into a poor market. As usual, Charlie was a man with a plan.

"I'll tell you what, Jap, if you've got a checkbook handy, I'd be pleased to go ahead and write you yore check for $1,200 on the Bank of Stoutland. If you could date it for next Saturday, I expect that Joe'll have me my money by then, and there'll be plenty of money to make that check good! Why, if you want to, you could go ahead and leave it at the bank so they can put the money right in yore account as soon as Joe's money gets in. How's that sound to yuh, Jap?"

Wanting something in writing from Charlie, Jap readily agreed. "I think that sounds alright," replied Jap as he arose, went through the parlor into the bedroom and grabbed a small self-closing leather valise from the top of his mother's old marble-topped dresser.

Made in Cincinnati just after the Civil War, the dresser had been a wedding present to Lucy from her parents. Inside a rotating "wishbone" frame, an oval mirror was centered above a slab of fine white marble. Two small, raised, side drawers above and three large drawers below gave plenty of storage space for a bachelor. The lovely piece, veneered with the finest figured mahogany wood, was Jap's most prized possession, next to Sam.

Returning to the kitchen, Jap dropped the valise on the table and said, "Let me get my fountain pen—I expect that I left it in my coat." Jap had recently bought a newfangled Schaefer fountain pen, "The Pen That Will Not Leak," at Greenstreet's jewelry store in Lebanon.

While searching the pockets of a dress coat hung in an old walnut shifferobe, Jap's eye caught a slight movement in the mirror of his mother's dresser. Charlie had arisen from the table, and with his back turned, appeared to be fumbling with the valise. Mildly peeved by such liberties, Jap signaled his return to the room by clearing his throat and announcing that he had found the pen. Noticing Charlie startle and replace the valise on the table, Jap observed, "Charlie, you ought to get yourself one of them—they come in real handy."

"Yore right, Jap, that's a right nice little leather case—I was just lookin' at it. I reckon I could use one a' them."

Jap quickly wrote out the $1,200 check, dating it November 6, 1915, and Charlie signed it with a distinctive, shaky, and irregular scrawl. While Jasper was blowing on the wet ink to speed its drying, Charlie took a new tack, "Jap, yuh know I was a thinkin' that maybe you could help me and Joe Givens out a little bit. With you bein' a dy-rector of the bank and all, maybe you could write me up a check and a note so that all Joe has to do is sign 'em, and I can take 'em to the bank and get ever'thing took care of there. Then all me and him would have to do is meet at Linn Creek and file the deed."

A little flattered by Charlie's deference to his business knowledge, Jap agreed. Helping facilitate a farm sale that would assure his own cattle payment was not a hard decision. Besides, Jap had some curiosity about the price that Joe Givens was willing to pay for the Craddock place.

"What me and Joe has agreed on," continued Charlie, "is a price of $7,500 for the whole place—lock, stock, and barrel."

When Jap heard the figure, he inhaled deeply, pursed his lips and whistled. "Charlie, you were right, that is a real good price—farms must be gettin' awful scarce around here. If a man can get that kind of money, I'd sure take it."

Charlie then outlined the "partiklars" of his sale to Givens and sought Jap's help.

"Joe is gonna give me a check for $1,500 and a $3,000 note due in a month that'll all go to my account. He'll take out a $3,000 mortgage on the farm at his bank and that'll pay off my mortgage. So, if you wouldn't mind writin' that check and that note up for him to sign, it'd save us some trouble. I don't know much about writin' up notes, and I wanta be sure everthing is done just the way the bank wants it."

Shrugging his shoulders, Jap pulled out a blank check and standard promissory note form from the valise and began to write. It was agreed that the $3,000 note and the $1,500 check would be dated back to Saturday, the 30th of October, since that was the date that Joe Givens had agreed to finalize the deal. "Since they know him, I reckon the Stoutland Bank will take Joe's note, but Charlie, you know, they'll discount it a little to you so the bank can get some interest for their trouble."

"Yeah, I reckon."

Noticing Charlie's indifference, Jap thought to himself, "If I was gettin' that kind of price for that old farm in the shape it's in, I wouldn't be worried about a little discount either." Aloud he said, "Just have Joe sign these and you can take 'em to the bank, and as soon as Joe's bank pays off your mortgage, you should be home free."

As quickly as the papers were filled out, Charlie Blackburn mounted his sway-backed steed and took his leave. Watching him depart, Jap had a disquieting feeling in the pit of his stomach. "I've lived here for nearly 20 years and had no dealings with Charlie Blackburn," he thought. "I'll be durned if I ever do it again."

As Charlie disappeared into the distance, Jap was unaware that Charlie owed $3,311 in personal notes at the People's Bank of Stoutland. His 265-acre farm was mortgaged for $4,000, plus several hundred dollars in back interest. The farm and the house in

Stoutland also secured a loan for $2,223.60 in principal and unpaid interest from Judge W.I. Wallace of Lebanon, Missouri. Not taking into account money owed Miz Craddock, Charlie and Minnie Blackburn owed close to $10,000.[3] With a farm worth only $6,000 or $7,000, and a small house and 2 acres on the edge of Stoutland worth no more than $1,000, the couple owed considerably more than they owned. With only a few dollars in the bank, Charlie and Minnie Blackburn were broke.

Seventy-five-year-old Judge Washington Irving Wallace had been retired from the bench since 1892.[4] He now juggled a leisurely law practice with a booming, private lending business. As a "lender of last resort," W.I. Wallace specialized in high-risk, high-interest-rate loans.[5] Unkind observers called Wallace a loan shark. Defenders said that by satisfying a demand for such loans, he was doing a favor for "common folks" who couldn't get credit anywhere else. It was a time of tight money, and banks required plenty of collateral for their loans.

Whatever Judge Wallace was doing, it made him rich. When he died in 1923, his estate was reputed to have liquid assets of more than $1,000,000, making Wallace the first known millionaire in Laclede County.[6] When she died in 1929, Wallace's widow, Louise G. Wallace, bequeathed $20,000 to be used for the construction of Lebanon's first hospital. Some five years later, with an additional $30,000 endowment from the Wallace estate, the "Louise G. Wallace Hospital," a 24-bed facility, opened on the site of the couple's lovely old Victorian home.[7] Usurious or not, loans to debtors like Charlie and Minnie Blackburn eventually found a virtuous public purpose.

Wallace Hospital retained the name until 1979 when it was renamed "Breech Medical Center" after receiving some $2,300,000 in donations from Ernest Robert Breech and his wife, Thelma Rowden Breech.[8] Thelma was a lovely Stoutland girl who married "Ernie" Breech, a Lebanon blacksmith's son. Young Breech would parlay a keen mind, charismatic personality, and a degree from tiny Drury College into the chairmanship of Ford Motor Company. Ernie Breech would serve as mentor to the young and fabulously wealthy Henry Ford II. The two would save the post-WWII Ford

Motor Company with better cost accounting and the introduction of the beautifully styled and hot-selling 1949 Ford.[9]

Civic fame is both fleeting and fickle. In 1999, a new hospital named "St. John's Hospital—Lebanon" was constructed. The site of the old hospital was turned into the "Louise G. Wallace Park and Community Center." Ernie Breech's name is nowhere to be found.

Fascinatingly, Charlie Blackburn's sister, Imogene ("Aunt Jean") claimed to have known Ernie Breech during their teen years. When asked if she regretted not dating (and perhaps even marrying) the future multimillionaire, she is reputed to have said, "Heavens no!" while referring to Breech, a diminutive man, as "Poor little Ernie." The Blackburns are a very proud clan indeed.[10]

Collection letters from Judge W.I. Wallace were rarely ignored. Many borrowers, juggling lenders, chose to pay off "Old Judge Wallace" first. Charlie and Minnie's latest letter from Wallace had prominently mentioned the word "eviction." Charlie needed to get current with Judge Wallace, or his entire world, full of pride, pretense, a spoiled son, and Minnie's airs, would come crashing down. Charlie Blackburn was a desperate man. W.I. Wallace's need to be repaid and Jasper Jacob Francis's life were on a fateful collision course.

Chapter 6

Thursday Morning, November 4, 1915

Rolla "Rollie" Smith, the assistant cashier of the People's Bank of Stoutland, had finished filling the cash drawer in the barred teller's cage with $200, consisting of $20, $10, and $5 gold coins, $1 greenbacks and some silver and copper coinage. He had just closed the safe and spun the dial when the jangling of a bell announced the day's first customer. Rollie's job was to open the bank promptly at 8:00 A.M. each day. Virgil Evans, the cashier and principal administrative officer, had not yet arrived. Virgil divided his time between the bank, a general store, and other of his enterprises throughout the town. The bank's president, Marvin Calkin, had ridden out early that morning to appraise a farm for a prospective loan.

The People's Bank of Stoutland had been chartered by the State of Missouri in 1905 to serve the increasing depository and loan needs of the community. An outgrowth of the much larger Pulaski County Bank of nearby Richland, the People's Bank was opened with $12,500 in capital. Numerous Stoutland residents, including Smith Blackburn and his nephew, Charlie, had purchased one or two $100 shares. Marvin Calkin, L.F. Fulbright, and Corbett Evans had bought five shares each. Only 20 years old at the time, Virgil Evans (not related to Corbett) was not an original investor. As a handy alternative to the banks in Richland or Lebanon, the People's Bank prospered.[1]

The People's Bank was housed in a single-storied red brick building on the north side of Main Street. With tenants sharing a common roof and dividing walls, the building was the equivalent of today's "strip" shopping center. Lest anyone wonder about the building's ownership, "Calkin & Evans" had been carved in stone and mortared into the top of the building's façade. Prosperously chic in 1915, the bank sported a lovely green and white striped canvas awning. Dutifully lowered and raised each day by Rollie, the scalloped canvas provided refuge for the bank's customers when it rained and shade from Missouri's blazing summer sun. The entryway consisted of a sturdy oak door centered between two large plate-glass windows. Inside, lovely lead-glass skylights provided additional light on gloomy winter days. A cozy boardroom with a green tiled fireplace occupied the rear of the bank.

Some 90 years later, the stony presence of "Calkin & Evans" still presides atop the rundown building. The sad remnant of Stoutland's one and only financial empire peers gloomily southward toward the town's cemetery. The deeply carved tombstone of the baron of that empire, Mr. Virgil Evans, stares somberly back. The People's Bank is now Stoutland's town hall. Its large safe is empty except for a few old, yellowed records. Hardly a center of commerce, it now hosts lively discussions about how the weeds will be cut and the dire need for a sewer system. If those walls could only talk.

By 1915, country banks were relaxed and friendly places with rarely more than one or two bank officers on duty. Few were armed. Forty years earlier, Jesse and Frank James had put Missouri forever in the annals of crime by relieving many such lax institutions of their depositor's hard-earned cash. Along with their cousins, the Younger brothers, they also relieved a few bankers of their lives. While decrying such brazen and lawless behavior, Missourians still take a measure of pride in the daring exploits of the James boys. A lovely and informative display in the Missouri State Capitol at Jefferson City commemorates the James Gang's contributions to Missouri's history. As pioneers of daylight armed bank robberies in peacetime, their accomplishments go uncontested.[2] They also had a knack for robbing trains. The James's followers in crime, John Dillinger, Pretty Boy Floyd, Bonnie and Clyde, and a slew of modern miscreants are considered cheap imitators by truly patriotic Missourians. A few old timers of the "Show Me State," when they believe themselves alone, can still be heard singing the ditty:

> *That dirty little coward*
> *that shot our Mr. Howard* [Jesse's alias],
> *Has laid poor old Jesse*
> *in his grave.*[3]

From just after the Civil War, until his death in 1882 at the hand of the traitorous Bob Ford, many a dozing bank cashier was awakened to the alarming view of a handkerchief-masked face and the business end of Jesse James's Smith & Wesson Schofield 45. Rollie Smith would face no such terror as he looked up to greet one of the bank's directors, Jap Francis.

"Why, howdy doo, Jap!" exclaimed Rollie as he quickly stepped from the teller's cage, circled cashier Virgil Evans's large oak desk and, nearly tripping, hurried to the counter to greet one of the bank's best customers. "I ain't seen you in quite a spell, Jap; it's mighty good to see you!" declared Rollie in a high-pitched whiney drawl. Rollie's fawning was accompanied by a fully extended high-pumping handshake that threatened Jap's wrist with a sprain.

Extricating his hand and coolly responding, "Oh, I'm doin' alright, Rollie," Jap inquired, "Is Virgil or Marvin in this mornin'?"

"Naw, they ain't, Jap. Mr. Calkin's out looking over some property, but I expect that Virgil'll be in here after awhile." Sensing serious banking business afoot, Rollie, whose reach always seemed to exceed his grasp, volunteered, "Jap, is there anything I can do for yuh?"

Pursing his lips and gazing intently at Rollie for a moment, Jap responded, "Well, Rollie, I expect that you can—let's sit down a minute."

Delighted with the opportunity to represent the bank in a conference with one of its directors, Rollie was as nervous and anxious to impress as Barney Fife in the presence of J. Edgar Hoover. Quickly raising a hinged section of the gray Carthage marble counter to permit Jap to enter the office area, Rollie pulled up a side chair beside Virgil Evans's desk. Then, waiter-like, he stood with both hands on its back until Jap had seated himself. He then offered a cup of hot coffee, freshly brewed in the back over a pot-bellied stove. Jap politely declined. Seating himself in Virgil Evan's oak swivel chair, Rollie crossed his legs and casually tilted the chair backward to a comfortable position. Clasping his hands before him while clearing his throat, he then inquired in a voice lowered a full octave, "Now then, Jap, what can the bank do for you?"

Quietly, but with some urgency, Jap began, "Listen, Rollie, I sold thirty-two head of cattle to Charlie Blackburn last week, and I mailed in his check for $1,200. You keep that handy and pay it just as quick as he gets the money in here. Now then, just how much do Charlie and Minnie owe the bank, anyhow?"

Reckoning that Jap's status as a director trumped the privacy of the bank's customers, Rollie uncoiled from his chair and said, "Wait just a minute, Jap, and I'll take a look." Stepping into Marvin Calkin's large office in the back, Rollie withdrew a thick green alphabetized ledger from the bank president's desk. Flipping to the "B's", Rollie glanced nervously at the Blackburn account and with the help of a little whispered "figurin'" to himself, hustled out of the office. Even presumptuous Rollie Smith, who often occupied and spun Virgil Evans's chair, didn't wish to loiter in Calkin's space.

"Jap, it looks like Charlie and Minnie owes us exactly $3,311.[4] It's all unsecured paper—you know we sold their $4,000 mortgage on the farm to the State Savings Bank a' Springfield a while back. I understand that they've got a second with Judge Wallace on the farm and on the house here in town, too."

Arising and tapping his forefinger on Rollie Smith's shoulder for emphasis, Jap spoke earnestly, "Now listen to me, Rollie; you be sure and tell Virgil and Marv that Charlie Blackburn has sold his farm to Joe Givens and has got the papers, and you boys want to get your money![5] He don't want anything said about it until the deed is drawn and recorded, but I know he's done it because I wrote up the note for him and a check a few days ago."

Jap briefly sketched the deal that Charlie had related to him. After receiving Rollie's assurance that he would inform the other bank officers to be alert to get the bank's loan and his own check paid, Jap Francis bade farewell. Stepping outside, he mounted Sam and rode briskly home. Passing the Blackburn house, he saw nothing of Charlie.

Friday Afternoon, November 5, 1915

Thirty-eight-year-old John Frey had been assigned as the Frisco Railroad's station agent at Stoutland about 1910. John, his wife

Hettie, and their children had settled in and made the town their home—becoming active in church and community. Frey was fiercely loyal to his employer and scrupulously followed all the railroad's rules and regulations.

In Harold Bell Wright's classic novel, *The Shepherd of the Hills*, postmaster Uncle Ike Morrill "reigned supreme" as the official "gov'ment" representative in the four square feet of U.S. property inside his log cabin home at "The Forks."[6] Not unlike wizened and irascible Uncle Ike, John Frey reigned supreme over railroad matters in Stoutland. Whether it was scheduling train crews, assigning "section gang" work orders, signaling, passenger ticketing, telegraphy, or freight handling, John Frey was "the railroad man" in a railroad town. It was an important job with big responsibilities. John had a businesslike manner about him. He, like his Frisco trains, ran on time and delivered the goods.

When he retired in 1940, John Frey received a gold Elgin pocket watch commemorating more than 30 years of service to the railroad. Trained as a telegrapher at the Frisco's headquarters in St. Louis, John could "press a key" with the best of them.

During America's brief but decisive foray into WWI, Frey had the unpleasant duty of delivering telegrams from the War Department to parents of Stoutland-area doughboys fighting "Over There." "Wounded in action," "missing in action," or "killed in action" were the only reasons for these sad, impersonal messages. From April 5, 1917, when President Woodrow Wilson asked congress to declare war on Germany, until an armistice ended the war November 11, 1918, nobody wanted to see portly and balding John Frey headed toward their house. John had a nervous habit of whistling while he walked, making his approach all the more ominous.[7] The only source of sympathy and consolation when the messages were read, John, a kindly Christian man, did the best he could. He hated the task. Retired by the beginning of WWII, John avoided the torrent of such messages that followed.

The Frisco's Stoutland station was well kept and freshly painted a light gray with dark gray trim. "Stoutland Missouri" was neatly lettered in black on both ends of the building near cupolas created by the building's wide eaves and roof bracing. A bay window gave the station agent an unobstructed view of the tracks in both directions while sitting in his office. Signal post levers were accessible through a port in the wall, permitting the agent to change signals from his office in any weather. The east side of the building included a small, passenger ticketing and waiting lounge with a dozen or so laminated wooden flip-up seats mounted on decorative iron legs screwed to the painted wooden floor. The west side housed a secure freight room with a sliding door leading to a covered dock. Incoming freight was offloaded onto a large, high-wheeled freight wagon and then pulled by the station agent to the dock for storage until delivery. It was not work for the feeble or lazy. In later years John Frey employed local boys to help him when the freight trains came in, scrupulously requiring them to sign cash vouchers acknowledging receipt of as little as 10 or 15 cents.[8]

Frey was unloading several parcels onto the dock that had just arrived on the eastbound afternoon freight, when Charlie Blackburn walked up. "Hello, Charlie, what can the best of the St. Louis and San Francisco Railroad do for you this hot day?" was John's jovial greeting. The month of November continued unseasonably warm with the afternoon temperature holding at 82 degrees.[9]

Ignoring Frey's attempt at humor, Charlie's response was terse: "John, I need to get some cattle to St. Louis pretty quick. How soon do you think you can get me a car?"

"Well—Charlie, if I wire my Springfield dispatcher right away this afternoon, we can have it here by Sunday morning. I reckon you could load 'em out before noon and they'll be in the St. Louis yards Sunday evening—is that soon enough for you?"

"The sooner the better," curtly replied Charlie, adding, "I got thirty-two head. Can you get 'em all on one car?—I'm not wantin' to pay any extry charges."

"Well, Charlie, I think you can—as long as they're not too big you should be able to get 'em on one of our new double deckers. I didn't know you were running any stock, Charlie; how long have you had 'em?" inquired a mildly curious Frey.

"Not long. I been speculatin' a little bit," replied Charlie without providing details.

Schooled in minding his own business, Frey shrugged, "Unless you want to go with 'em, you'll need to wire a broker to feed and water 'em when they get there."

"Naw, I don't wanna go with 'em—me and my boy will load 'em up. I figger to use Clay & Robinson—they got me a good price before and I'll just use 'em a'gin."[10]

Agreeing to meet Frey at the station Sunday morning to load the cattle and make final arrangements, Charlie turned abruptly and walked down the well-worn gravel path behind the station, and disappeared into an alley leading to Main Street.

"That Charlie Blackburn is sure 'nough a cold fish if I ever met one," fumed Frey to himself. "He acts like he's a little better than anybody else—I don't know which is the worst, him or Minnie. Here I'm gonna have to miss church to get his cattle to St. Louis market Monday morning and he doesn't even give me a fare-thee-well!" Still wondering where Charlie had obtained such a large herd and why he was in such a hurry to ship them, Frey wiped his brow with his handkerchief, shook his head, and finished unloading the freight wagon.

Saturday, November 6, 1915

It would be another "warm one" in Stoutland. By the middle of the afternoon, the government weather observer at Lebanon would record 86 degrees, a record for the date.[11] Old residents shook their heads in wonderment and apprehension. "Danged if we might have us a 'tornadee' when she finally cools off," observed 79-year-old George Turner. Sporting a long white beard and a hickory cane, Turner was both a veteran of the Civil War and the "whittlin' and spittin' bench" in front of Mooney's livery stable.

Jap Francis had arisen early, and after completing the few farm chores, changed into clean clothes and rode into Stoutland. Tying Sam to a hitchrail in the shade, Jap headed to the little barbershop on the south side of Main Street. Seeking a shave and a haircut, Jap stepped through the door adorned with the traditional red and white striped pole. Inside, he was warmly greeted by an assortment of Stoutland's manhood. Barbershops are enclaves where men are able to talk "man talk," mainly jokes shading from mildly vulgar to crudely dirty. Uncomfortable with such talk, Jap passed off even the best knee-slappers with a faint grin and a resigned shake of his head.

The younger lads pretended to ignore all of the ribald remarks and lewd advice while listening raptly lest any piece of the great birds-and-bees puzzle escape their inquiring minds. If questioned about their personal knowledge of the subject, the callow youths ducked, blushed, and writhed in agony until their torturers diverted their attentions to other deserving adolescents. Male rites of passage are uncomfortable and memorable in equal portions.

The comparative "looks" and reputations of Stoutland's young women were always fair game at the barbershop—although never in the presence of fathers or brothers. The ears of even the purest and primmest of Stoutland's stock of future wives and mothers burned inexplicably on Saturdays when the barbershop was full.

Some women walked to the other side of the street to avoid passing the barbershop, knowing that their beauty and morals would become the immediate subject of animated debate. A few, with inhibitions and good judgment overwhelmed by the alluring aromas of witch hazel and bay rum, found reason to stroll and swish back and forth in front of the entrance. With wandering eyes, fluttering lashes, and spinning parasols, they seemed irresistibly drawn to the mysteries that lay within. After several passes, the boldest of these young things, intoxicated by the reservoirs of testosterone inside, would stand adventurously near the entrance and banter with the occupants. Reputations teetered precariously at the door's threshold. After all, no "decent woman" would dare step foot inside this all-male redoubt.

When not talking about women, war is an irresistible subject for the male gender, full of fascination and imagined heroism. With "Kaiser Bill's" U-boats running amuck in the Atlantic, the subject was more than theoretical in November of 1915. Arguments raged over whether America should be drawn into the European war.

"We'll show them Brits and Froggies how to fight!" exclaimed one hot-blooded Spanish-American War veteran who had steamed with Admiral Dewey into Manila Bay.

"Our Marines'll give them damned Huns the what-for—that's for shore!" exclaimed another.

"T'aint none of our danged business—I don't want no son o' mine a-fightin' in them damned trenches and bein' mowed down by machine guns," hotly responded another.

When passions run high, barbers are the best of peacemakers, spreading oil on troubled waters as delicately as vaseline on freshly cut hair. The subject was diplomatically changed. But peacemakers and diplomacy failed to keep America's doughboys out of WWI, the most senseless of wars. By 1918, thousands had fallen in the fields of Château-Thierry, Belleau Wood, and the region of Meuse-Argonne. A few from Camden County. A couple from Stoutland. John Frey would know.

At the store, Jap bought some canned Alberta peaches and jack mackerel, hard crackers, a plug of Horseshoe tobacco, and a small sack of horehound candy. Placing his purchases in a rucksack, he tied them securely to Sam's saddle and cantered out of town. On his way, he intended to stop at the Blackburn house and inquire how the farm sale was progressing. Charlie's unpaid check for $1,200 resided at the People's Bank, and Jap was getting a little anxious about it.

As he arrived, Jap noticed Skip Archer and another man in the lower field near the old Craddock log cabin, now used as a corn crib. Jap's cattle grazed lazily in the high grass on both sides of the stream near the spring. As he got closer, he recognized Fred Jacobs, a young hardware and farm implement salesman. Jap greeted the two and learned that Charlie had gone to Stoutland.

"Why, Skip, I just came from town, and I didn't see a thing of him."

"I guess you shore missed him—maybe he wuz over at Minnie's," replied Skip.

"You haven't seen anything of Joe Givens today have you, Skip?" prodded Jap.

"Naw, I ain't seen Joe Givens in years—what makes you think he'd be in these parts?"

Recognizing that Skip was unaware of Charlie's plans to sell the farm, Jap passed the matter off with, "Oh, somebody told me that Joe was lookin' to buy a farm over this a-way—but there's probably nothin' to it." Never had Jap Francis been so right.

After some idle talk, Jacobs asked Jap if he intended to go to Bob Peters's sale at Toronto on Monday. Toronto was a tiny town consisting of little more than a store, blacksmith shop, and a few houses next to a large spring flowing from under a limestone bluff.

"I was kind of thinkin' about it," replied Jap. "It's a long ride over there, but if the stock goes pretty cheap, I might buy a few head."

"Well, old Bob's sellin' more than the livestock; I hear he's puttin' up the farm, the furniture—the whole works to pay off the bank. They've been threatenin' to foreclose. I expect Virgil Evans'll be there watchin' like a hawk to see what things bring and make sure the bank gets paid. If they don't, he'll just take 'er over." Fred continued with some bitterness, "These danged banks get people in over their heads in debt and then don't think a thing about puttin' 'em right down the road."

As a director of the bank, Jap saw things a little differently but chose not to argue the point. Turning Sam's head toward the road, he good-naturedly suggested, "I've got to get on home—you boys watch your hindparts now." Never had Jap Francis needed more to follow his own advice.

After urging Sam up the wagon trail leading to the road, Jap stopped Sam at some distance, turned in the saddle, and shouted, "Skip, when Charlie gets back, you tell him I wanted to know if everything's alright—he'll know what I mean."[12]

Cupping his ear, Skip asked Jap to repeat the message, and then nodded and shouted back, "Sure will, Jap, sure will!"

Jap had left a veiled message reminding Charlie that he was more than curious about how and when the $1,200 check at the bank would be paid.

"I wonder how I missed Charlie in town—maybe he's just tryin' to avoid me," spoke Jap softly to himself as he turned Sam westward toward home.

Chapter 7

Jap Francis had not seen Charlie in Stoutland because Charlie was arranging to ship Jap's cattle to St. Louis as fast as their hooves and an eastbound Frisco freight train could take them. Charlie had been at Minnie's house demanding that Ray come to the farm that evening and be ready to help drive the herd to town early Sunday morning. The Stoutland stockyard was directly across the tracks from the Blackburn cottage. From there, Charlie could make certain that the afternoon Frisco freight delivered the promised cattle car.

John Frey was a man of his word. What John commanded, the Frisco delivered. Precisely on time, the eastbound freight, black smoke boiling from the Alco (Schenectady) locomotive's smokestack, "blew" for the Stoutland crossing and then slowed as it approached the switch on the east edge of town. Slowly screeching to a halt, the brakeman broke the train at the desired car to be dropped. The engineer moved the train forward past the switch and then reversed the huge drive wheels. Amid hisses of steam and a cacophony created by empty cars banging together as the slack was taken up, the train was backed into the sidetrack serving the stockyard. The brakeman unhooked the wooden slatted cattle car by the loading ramp. On signal from the conductor, the engineer then moved the train forward and then back to pick up its loose appendage. Grasping a swing bar with one hand and leaning precariously from the caboose footstep, the conductor signaled the "all clear" to the engineer who acknowledged with a brief, mournful toot on his steam whistle.

The train then chugged rapidly out of town for points east, "highballing" through places like Richland, Swedeborg, Crocker, and Newburg, some 130 miles to the blue-collar St. Louis "burbs" of Catawissa, Crescent, and Valley Park. Stops like "Garnsay," "St. John," and "Templar Park"[1] have been lost to history—their presence marked only by farm crossings and green algae-covered ponds. Once used to feed the hissing goliaths' unquenchable thirst for water, these shallow reservoirs now provide refuge for frogs, snapping turtles, and large serpents. Nearby, like children's pick-up sticks, twisted rails, long since dismembered from their rotten "sleepers," protrude from the high weeds. Rusty remnants of humanity's march, they lie strangely overlapped and askew as straws tossed about by the wind—or as burdensome baggage tossed aside by restless spirits moving ever westward.

Minnie groused about her delicate child having to miss Sunday school at the Stoutland Baptist Church. "Just how is it going to look," bawled Minnie, "if the brothers and sisters of the church, intent upon God's work, see two-thirds of the Blackburn family keeping the Sabbath holy by driving a herd of bellowing beef through the middle of town?"

"Don't you worry," spoke Charlie coldly. "We're not gettin' anywhere's near them Sunday-go-to-meetin' hypocrites—me and Ray are gonna drive 'em up the Stoutland Creek and bring 'em up the back way." Charlie Blackburn had a lot of things on his mind. Christian sensibilities were not among them.

Sunday Morning, November 7, 1915

Just after dawn, Charlie Blackburn rousted Ray out of bed. Walking through the kitchen to the back porch, he passed Miz Mary Craddock clad in an old blue print dress and a yellow apron. Charlie respectfully stepped around her while glumly greeting her with, "Mornin' Miz Craddock."

Ever cheerful, Mary responded with, "Good morning, Charlie; how did you rest?"

"Well enough, I reckon," muttered Charlie as he pumped some water from the cistern into a white enameled pan and washed up for breakfast. From long habit, Mary had arisen early and had bacon, eggs, and hot biscuits nearly ready to serve. It would be plenty to sustain her grumpy son-in-law and coddled grandson.

Wordlessly, Ray soon joined Charlie at the table, only grunting as his grandmother hovered over him. She served the beloved boy generous portions before placing the platter of easy-over eggs and salted slab bacon on the table for Charlie to help himself. In Ray's honor, Miz Mary had retrieved a small jar of wild red-plum preserves from the cellar. Skip Archer had found and picked the plums into his hat earlier in the summer. He brought them to Miz Mary, who removed the seeds and cooked the sour fruit down with lots of sugar. Using bottle-green canning jars, she had "put up" two pints of this fragrant Ozark delicacy. One went to Skip's aging parents, Marian and Mattie Archer. The other was saved for a special occasion. This was it.

The sight of the red preserves improved Ray's appetite and disposition as he used a tablespoon to slather several biscuits and greedily stuffed them into his mouth. A rare reprieve from the anguish of donning his Sunday suit and slouching by his mother's side to the Stoutland Baptist Church had turned Ray nearly civil. The expectation of soon getting another silver dollar for his cowboy efforts had perked him up so remarkably that he actually spoke aloud. "I sure wish Mom could make biscuits like this," he complained between huge bites.

Mary made no effort to defend her daughter's cooking, since Minnie's reputation for ineptness in the kitchen was well known and well earned. Walking over and patting Ray's shoulder, she replied, "Honey, you come out to Grandma's house any old time and you'll get all the biscuits you can hold."

Then, in an act without precedent or antecedent, Ray Blackburn cleared his dishes from the table and placed them in the big dishpan on the counter of the kitchen safe. Lest his sullen image be too much improved, without further courtesies he strode outside to saddle his pony.

"How come Skip's not helping you today?" inquired Mary. The absence of dutiful Skip when a major work effort was required was an oddity that had not escaped the observant old lady.

"He said he had to take his mother to church and had work to do over there this afternoon. Maybe he's gotten wind that I was thinkin' about sellin' this place and is out a lookin' for another job, for all I know," replied the always suspicious Charlie.

"Are you sure that just the two of you can handle it?"

"Oh yeah, me and Ray won't have no trouble—besides, John Frey'll meet us at the yard to help load 'em out." Charlie licked his fingers and left the house to join Ray.

Sitting down to eat something herself, Miz Mary Craddock's thoughts turned to her life spent on the farm.

"I don't know whether I can stand to leave this old place—why, Dick and me were not much more than kids when we came here with nothing but a team and wagon—and we put our whole lives into it," she thought sadly to herself. "He sawed and notched the logs for the cabin, and I mixed the lime mortar and helped him chink the cracks—the snow still blowed in through the eaves and we 'bout froze to death that first winter—that seems so long ago."

Her reminiscence continued:

"I remember the spring going dry the second summer we were here in '65. The old timers told us it was the first time in mem'ry that it had been that hot and with no rain. Dick worked so hard to dig a water well. Why, it must have taken him a month, working with nothing but a pick and shovel. He couldn't get anybody to help him—most of the men were still off in the war. I'll never forget how hot it was way up in July when he come running into the house a-yelling, 'Mary, Mary, we've got water! It's a-startin' tuh come in.' I was heavy with Nancy at the time, but I ran down there to look. We both laughed and cried too—we were never so happy and relieved."

As if to confirm it was still there, she looked out the back-porch window and could faintly see the concrete wall surrounding the old well far down in the pasture near the creek. It had stood as sturdily against the ravages of time as Mary herself. The onrushing memories of her beloved husband's labors to create house and home suddenly brought Mary to tears. She bent over, placed her face in her hands and sobbed in despair.

"Dick, Dick, they just might as well kill me as take me away from here," she moaned to her long-dead husband. After a while, Mary felt better and a little embarrassed. "Why, I haven't cried like that in years; I've got to get a hold of myself—Dick would be ashamed of me." Recovering her pioneer spunk, she arose, squared her shoulders, and set about washing the dishes. Consoling herself, the 77-year-old spoke aloud, "What's going to be is what's going to be—I'll just worry about all that later."

Miz Mary Craddock had no idea how much worrying she still had to do.

It was no mean task to get 32 head of cattle rounded up and moving in the same direction, but with the help of docile Old Domino (who understood his role as leader of the herd but not the fate awaiting him and his fellow beasts), Charlie and Ray got the drive started. By 8:00 A.M. they had moved over Rouse Hill to the north edge of Stoutland, well ahead of Minnie's churchgoers. Here, in the bottomland, the cattle were permitted to rest and munch the plentiful grass along Stoutland Creek. After an hour or so, Charlie and Ray began pushing the herd up the hill on the back side of Stoutland. As they neared the summit, 67-year-old Ruben "Rube" Winfrey suddenly appeared out of the trees and hailed Charlie. He was the last person Charlie wanted to see.

Rube lived in a house on Main Street as it descended toward Stoutland Creek and became the Linn Creek Road. A cattleman for many years, Rube and his 42-year-old wife, Mary, had sold their farm and livestock in the spring and moved to town. With time on his hands, Rube spent most of it loitering uptown, learning everybody's business. He was an old friend of Jap Francis and had been well acquainted with Jap's parents.

"Well, I'll swear, Charlie, some of them steers are the ones I sold to Jap Francis back in the Spring—did you get 'em from him?"

Startled and irritated, Charlie pulled up his horse and replied, "Yeah, Rube, I bought 'em from Jap awhile back."

"Are yuh takin' 'em to the yard to ship 'um?"

"Naw, me and Ray are just movin 'em over on Bear Creek to let 'em fatten on some of that good grass for a while."[2] Charlie then spurred his horse away and up the hill.

Winfrey shrugged his shoulders and trudged back toward town. But Charlie Blackburn wasn't about to take the cattle all the way to Bear Creek, some two miles distant, for further fattening. Charlie's convenient lie would have a shelf life of less than an hour.

Loading cattle onto a railcar is difficult and dangerous. It requires seasoned veterans with a knack for it. Neither Charlie nor Ray met that standard, and without Skip Archer, by 11:30 A.M. they were getting nowhere fast. When John Frey arrived at the depot to pick up a standard shipper's contract for Charlie to sign, he could tell from the angry shouts, combined with the bawling and milling of the herd, that things were not going well. Father and son were at loggerheads about what to do and who was to blame. Charlie had shown his ugly temper, and Ray, thoroughly cowed, was sniveling and threatening to go home to his mother.

John Frey quickly sized up the situation. Cattle shippers assumed responsibility for loading their animals, but John's determination to provide service to Frisco customers overcame his dislike for Charlie. Shaking his head reprovingly, John spoke first, "Charlie it looks like you and that boy need a little help."

Full of Blackburn pride, Charlie declined, "No, not a-tall John, we'll be alright—we're just gonna need us a little more time here."

John was having none of it. "At the rate you two are going, you're gonna miss my afternoon freight—you know it runs early on Sunday. She'll be here at 12:30, and this car needs to be locked down and ready to go with all the papers."

About that time, a new voice was heard. Continuing his Sunday morning constitutional, Rube Winfrey had walked uptown, but finding no one with whom to jaw, was returning home when he heard the commotion. Ambling down the railroad tracks, Rube found Charlie and his cattle nowhere near Bear Creek.

"Charlie, I thought you was headed to Bear Creek with them steers?" questioned the great inquisitor.

Charlie was abrupt, "Well, Rube, I changed my mind. We ain't got time to take them all the way down there and back."

Rube climbed over the wooden fence and, without invitation or hesitation, took charge. "Let's get 'em loaded up," he resolutely declared.

Grabbing a hickory stick left by others for the purpose, Rube began aggressively cutting shying animals from the herd which had crowded defensively in the corner of the corral. Shooing them up the entry ramp, Rube quickly produced a steady stream of animals following the leader. With Frey helping and Charlie working the car, the job was finished in short order.

After the slatted doors were closed and locked, Frey produced the shipper's contract and filled it out, including the name and address of the shipper, the broker (Clay & Robinson Commission Company of St. Louis, Missouri) and instructions where the auction proceeds were to be sent. Charlie ordered the "returns" sent by wire draft to The State Bank of Lebanon for deposit in his name. Surprised, Frey glanced quickly at Charlie and opened his mouth as if to question the destination. Thinking better of it, he repeated, "The State Bank of Lebanon," and filled in the appropriate blank. Charlie signed the form, and Frey handed him a carbon copy. The original was then placed in a waterproof, locked box on the car.

Ever prideful, Charlie barely mumbled an "appreciate it" to Rube and John while complaining, "If my hired hand had been on the job—the way he's supposed to, we wouldn't a-needed any help."

Charlie flipped a silver dollar to Ray, who skedaddled with his pony toward Minnie's house. Charlie then mounted his horse and rode away.

"That Charlie Blackburn'll never change," volunteered Rube. "He's always been a big feeler and figures he's the cock of the walk—he just couldn't hardly stand it that he had to get a little help from somebody."

"Well, Rube," responded John wearily, "I guess you've got him pegged just about right." He then shook Rube's hand and headed back to the depot to finish more paperwork before meeting the afternoon freight. Sunday dinner would be cold by the time he got home.

Jap Francis's herd of cattle was now the property of the Frisco Railroad and Clay & Robinson. The proceeds of the sale weren't going to the People's Bank of Stoutland to pay Charlie Blackburn's bogus check to Jap Francis. Inexplicably, the money had been directed to a bank in Lebanon where Charlie did not even have an account.[3] Something wasn't right.

Chapter 8

Tuesday, November 9, 1915
7:30 A.M.

By habit, Jap Francis had arisen at 5:00 A.M., fixed a modest breakfast for himself, and as daylight was beginning to break, attended to the few remaining farm chores. With the harvest in and having disposed of his herd, Jap's immediate concern was getting in enough wood to feed the heating and kitchen stoves during the long winter months ahead. As soon as the "sap was down" he and Simp would grab the business ends of a two-man crosscut saw and go to work. Wood cut too early was hard to split and created smoky, slow-burning fires with lots of ashes.

As always, Sam was first on Jap's list, getting a big bucket of fresh water and a generous portion of grain and hay. Instead of turning him out to graze, Jap patted the big horse's head, scratched his ears, and left him in his stall. Today, this limousine of horseflesh had a long road ahead of him.

After partially milking his cows, Jap turned the brindle colored Jerseys and their calves into the pasture together and briefly watched as the little creatures guzzled greedily and noisily while periodically butting their mothers' udders with impatience. He then poured several quarts of "shorts" (a by-product of the milling of wheat) into the pig trough, added some water, and called the hogs by beating on the feeding trough with a stick while yelling "soo-eee—soo-eee." While the half-dozen hogs quickly occupied themselves at the trough, Jap threw out a couple armloads of corn to supplement their "finishing" diet. As soon as Missouri's weather turned cold, it would become hog-butchering time. He and Simp and a couple of neighbors would turn these fattened porkers into hams, loins, ribs, bacon, and sausage for the breakfast and dinner tables. Helpers were paid with a portion of the meat. The more generous the reputation of a neighbor, the more willing the help. Some of the chilled fresh meat would quickly be consumed, with the remainder salted and cured in the smokehouse away from varmints.

Returning to the house and lowering the fresh milk into the well to cool, Jap washed up and donned a clean set of summer drawers and an undershirt. He then set about removing three days of beard stubble. A handsome man who always liked to look his best, Jap had some "gussying up" to do before starting the hour-and-a-half ride to the Peters sale at Toronto.

A little hot water from the tea kettle into the shaving cup and a vigorous stir with a horsehair brush produced a rich soap lather spread generously and uniformly on his face. After stropping his dad's old ivory-handled straight razor, he carefully shaved, using short scraping strokes, while frequently rinsing the razor in a pan of hot water. The contortions men use to stretch and flatten the irregular terrain of their faces for shaving are the subject of rapt female curiosity and the wonderment of little boys. The latter often mimic their male mentors in the very mirror being used for the purpose. Such distractions have caused more than one wounded face, the urgent application of astringents and the spouting of un-Christian-like words.

Jap had neither observers nor imitators. When finished trimming his short mustache, he carried the wash pan to the back porch, threw the contents out the door, and then doused his face with cold well-water. A splash of Lilac Vegetal cologne, a little alum on some minor scrapes, a dab of Brilliantine hair oil, and the vigorous use of a good hairbrush finished off the manly regimen. He then donned blue pinstriped trousers with suspenders, a clean white shirt, a wine-red knotted necktie, and a buttoned waistcoat. A gray vest had pockets for a watch and a pearl-handled penknife connected with a hanging gold chain. Polished black boots finished off the snappy attire. Jap's warm Prince Albert double-breasted overcoat with an inlaid black velvet collar was left in the shifferobe. Although a chilly 40 degrees, the sun was shining and the early morning fog had lifted. Sixty-two degrees by mid afternoon, it was a nice day for a sale.[1]

Jap had saddled Sam and was leading him from the barn to the house when he nearly bumped into Charlie Blackburn sitting on his horse holding a 12-gauge single-barreled shotgun. Both Sam and Jap startled.

"Why, Charlie! I didn't know anybody was on the place!" exclaimed Jap in surprise.

Nervously flinching one shoulder, Charlie spoke with a touch of derision: "Why, I didn't mean to skeer you, Jap—just thought I'd come by."

Speaking quietly to calm Sam, Jap regained his composure. "Charlie, I was just gettin' ready to head over to Toronto to Bob Peters' sale—I sure didn't hear you ride up." A little irritated, Jap had only one thing that he wanted to discuss with Charlie Blackburn. "Say, Charlie, I was by your place on Saturday—I was lookin' for you and Joe Givens. Skip said you had gone to town—did you and Joe get your business taken care of the way you said?"

Charlie's mouth tightened as he reached for the brim of his hat and shoved it back slightly on his head. He then flipped the reins around the saddle horn and moved the shotgun to port arms, with his right hand cradling the gun, left finger on the trigger guard and the muzzle pointed skyward just over Jap's head. "Well, sir, you know he didn't show up—but I got a letter from 'im and that's why I come over—I wanted to tell you what he's a-sayin'."[2]

"What'd he tell you, Charlie? You know I need to get my money pretty quick; this is takin' a lot longer than I expected."

Unconsciously, Charlie gripped the shotgun tighter, and his finger moved imperceptibly to the trigger. "Oh, he just said that he wuz gonna send the money straight to the People's Bank in my name, but it shore never got there—he must've sent it to the wrong place."[3]

It was a lame explanation, and Jap knew it.

Watching Jap intently, Charlie continued, "I'm a-ridin' over to Decaturville to his place jist this mornin' to find out about it."[4]

Increasingly skeptical, Jap looked Charlie in the eye and spoke as sharply as the soft-spoken man could muster, "Charlie, it seems a mighty funny thing to me that Joe Givens doesn't seem to know where Stoutland is!"[5]

Charlie's left hand fingered the shotgun's trigger. A little angry and frustrated with a situation that he could not resolve, and anxious to be on his way, Jap suddenly changed the subject, "Whattaya doin' with that old gun, Charlie?"

Surprised by the abrupt and unexpected question, Charlie glanced nervously down at the weapon and shifted his weight in the saddle, causing the confused horse to turn sideways to Francis. "Oh, you mean this old thing?" replied Charlie, lowering the muzzle of it to Jap's midsection.

Jap knew a little about guns and recognized it as a very old Stevens breech-loading, hammer-fired model. "Charlie, you be careful where you're a-pointin' that thing! What in the world do you expect to do with that old blunderbuss? You know, you could hurt yourself real easy with something like that."

Squinting into the morning sun and aiming it at an imaginary point in the sky, Charlie pulled the hammer back, cocking the weapon, and replied slowly and ominously, "Jap, you just never know when you might need to protect yoreself from somebody in these parts. Besides, if I see me a fat rabbit along the way, I wanna be ready."

"Shoot, if you shot a rabbit with that piece of artillery, there wouldn't be enough left to put in a skillet," replied Jap dismissively. He then turned his back to Charlie, putting his foot in Sam's stirrup to mount. The muzzle of the ancient Stevens moved back toward Jap.

At that moment, the sound of a team and wagon was heard. Simp Francis, coming up the private road leading to his house, was making the first of several runs to the large potato patch that he and Ida had planted in the spring. Because of the unusually warm weather, harvesting had been delayed. Worried about a possible frost, Simp had decided to dig the "spuds" and lay them out in the barn to dry.[6]

Concluding that his business "lay rolling," Charlie shifted the shotgun back to his right hand and, with his favored left, loosened the reins from the saddle horn and wheeled the horse around. Riding through the yard gate, Charlie turned and shouted, "I'll let you know what Joe says—you should know somethin' by tomorrow!"

"Don't bother to close the gate, but if I was you, I'd uncock that old gun—it's liable to go off and kill somebody," replied Jap helpfully. For once, Charlie accepted advice. Pulling his horse to a stop, he carefully uncocked the lethal firearm and, resting it across the saddle, set out at a slow trot toward Decaturville, in the opposite direction of his farm.

Not waiting to greet his brother, Jap headed Sam toward Toronto. The sale would start promptly at 10:00 and Jap did not want to be late. Thinking he might overtake Charlie's slower-moving horse before the road forked, Jap was surprised to see nothing of horse and rider. Charlie Blackburn had disappeared into thin air. Jap thought no more about it. He had grown weary of worrying about Charlie Blackburn.

***10:00* A.M.**

The urgent chant of the auctioneer had just begun when Jap and Sam arrived at the Peters farm a mile or so from Toronto. Using a handheld megaphone to amplify and direct his voice, Jack Starmer could sell with the style and speed of the best tobacco auctioneers in the drying barns of Virginia and North Carolina. With a signature bowler hat and a brass-headed walking stick, Starmer was renowned as the best auctioneer in Pulaski and Camden Counties. Once he described the lot, touted it for its quality, and sought an opening bid, interested parties had best pay attention. "Colonel Jack" waited for no laggards. From long experience he realized that moving at an urgent pace kept bidding lively and also made for a shorter day.

"Look at the fine old coal-oil lamp, extra fancy [true], made before the Civil War [maybe]—they say it came from Ulysses Grant's house in Saint Looey [a patent lie]. Think about takin' that home to your blushing bride—why it's even full of oil, you won't need to fill it 'til next spring." The lamp was sold in less than 20 seconds:

"All right now, and what am I bid? How about a half a dollar? Got a haffa dollar! Now six bits, six bits, six bits, got six bits!, Now a dolla, now a dolla, now a dolla—it's a goin' cheap, got a dollar!, Now a quarter, now a quarter, now a quarter, got a quarter! Now a half, now a half, now a half—the man says *Noo!* Are we all done now? Can't wait—can't wait. We all done? [Hesitation.] Sold! To the lovely lady [homely as a mud fence] in the blue flower hat for a dollar and a quarter!"

And so it went.

Learning that the livestock would sell last, Jap looked over the beef cattle, sheep, and hogs, made some notes in his little red notebook, and began circulating in the crowd. Spotting a few acquaintances, he greeted and bantered with them in the lively carnival atmosphere. Around noon, he ran into Charlie Winfrey, a close neighbor and old friend. Charlie was a cousin of retiree Rube Winfrey, fast becoming the Stoutland clearinghouse for all information, both large and petty.

In 1898, Jap and Charlie had volunteered together for an American army to fight the Spanish after the mysterious sinking in Havana Harbor of the battleship *Maine*. William Randolph Hearst's "yellow journalists" used the incident to fan the flames of war white-hot. Young Americans burned to give the cruel Spanish a whipping and bring relief to the oppressed Cubans and their revolutionary leader, General Calixto Garcia.

Sadly, newly commissioned Colonel Teddy Roosevelt, in a uniform tailored at Brooks Brothers and sporting full trappings and regalia, beat the Camden County boys to the action. With saber drawn and pince-nez secured, Teddy led a small regiment of sweaty and malaria-fevered volunteers up San Juan Hill, yelling, "Remember the *Maine*!" as they charged. Mouths agape at the sight, the Spanish defenders were routed long before the aspiring Missouri warriors got within a thousand miles of the fight. Heroic ambitions dashed by Admiral Dewey's capture of the entire Spanish fleet in Manila Bay, Jap and Charlie were mustered out and returned to the hum-drum of their Missouri farms.

At noon, Charlie and Jap each bought a ham sandwich and a quarter of a cherry pie for 25 cents and a nickel cup of coffee (all you can drink) from the ladies of the nearby Baptist Church. The Baptists met at a lovely new church building called "Twelve Corners," improbably shared with a tiny congregation of Mormons led by a family named Willoughby.[7] Mercifully, the services were held at times that did not overlap. These Mormons were refugees from a colony at Independence, Missouri. Tired of persecution for their beliefs, they adopted monogamy and assimilated nicely into the Toronto/Wet Glaize community. Determined to add an elegant touch to their new church, the ladies were raising funds to buy "factory made" carpets. Civic contribution complete, Charlie and Jap ate their dinner outside, making use of the Peters' furniture scattered forlornly on the lawn.

Arising to take their china and tableware back to the good ladies of the church, Jap and Charlie observed an automobile winding its way up the hill toward the house. The Model-T Ford "Tin Lizzie" jerked and backfired to a halt by a huge lilac bush. Out stepped Virgil Evans, cashier of the People's Bank of Stoutland. Virgil grabbed a leather businessman's briefcase and headed for the auction clerk's table set up in the shade of the front porch. Virgil's officious swagger suggested his presence lent consequence to an otherwise mundane gathering. In a way, he was right. The Bank owned pretty much everything in sight, and Virgil, like a military loan shark at the end of the enlisted men's pay line, was there to make sure the bank got its money. The deal wasn't done until Virgil Evans said it was done.

A pudgy 29-year-old with a mop of well-oiled dark hair atop a moon face, Virgil could not be considered handsome. His full, rather effeminate mouth was usually turned down at the corners unless there was word of a profit to be made. He then easily morphed into a lively charmer and "hail fellow, well met." Virgil believed himself a friend of all and enemy of none. To meet Virgil was to observe that awkward but ambitious young fellow with the bow tie, hand perpetually extended, always running for class president.

America's Progressive Era instilled the hope, if not expectation, that "any man" could succeed with his wits, a little business initiative, and a lot of hard work. Virgil Evans had read Horatio Alger's dime pulp stories of the rise of street urchins from rags to riches. Virgil was well on his way to realizing that dream, although his start was hardly that lowly. Born of prosperous Stoutland farmers W.H. "Bill" and Nancy Evans, Virgil had married Miss May Shubert, daughter of H.C. Shubert, a Richland printing company owner, and his wife, Anna.[8] By Stoutland standards, the Shuberts were a fairly well-to-do family. Bankrolled by his relatives and ambitious to a fault, Virgil now owned a dry-goods store, a furniture and undertaking establishment, and a growing interest in the People's Bank of Stoutland. He was a young man on the move.

Businesses would come and go (mainly go) in Stoutland over the next 49 years, but Virgil Evans's slice of the diminishing pie would grow ever larger. Evans's rule over dollars flowing in and out of Stoutland was meekly conceded by most—as if by "divine right." The only threat to Virgil's reign as Stoutland's financial tycoon came some 40 years later when a band of citizens accused him and a couple of lackeys of miscounting the election ballots in order to ensure his reelection to the Stoutland school board. Virgil had served on the board for as long as anyone could remember and was routinely awarded contracts to supply most everything the school needed. That is, until wary guardians of the public purse concluded that Virgil's prices were more than a tad high.[9]

On election night, Virgil was predictably declared the victor by the "official" counters. The "Jimmy Stewarts" of Stoutland, representing "everything that's good and right in America," demanded to recount the ballots. While the dispute raged with more than 100 angry citizens at the door of the polling place, a shadowy figure was seen running out the back door with the ballot box. It seems those pesky pieces of paper quickly became fuel for a fire found burning behind the First National Bank of Stoutland (the old People's Bank building).[10]

Undeterred, the reformers obtained sworn affidavits from voters as to how they had cast their ballots. The results proved that Virgil could not possibly have won. He promptly resigned from the board.[11]

In his last years, Virgil Evans managed his diversified commercial empire from his general merchandise and grocery store. The pungent smell of aged cabbages and grapefruit signified an establishment that would surely flunk modern health inspections. Virgil was a casket salesman and funeral director, used furniture peddler, amateur lawyer and notary, and the principal buyer of eggs, chickens, cream, turkeys, rabbits, and hides in Stoutland. His real-estate holdings were numerous—mostly small farms he had foreclosed upon after making loans that small farmers could not repay during the Depression.[12]

Stingy with his accumulated wealth, Virgil led a Spartan lifestyle, holed up in a small, untidy room in the back of his store. It is said that the old man could be observed late at night hunched over a desk counting his cash, promissory notes, and the deeds to his many properties. Too stingy to turn on the naked electric bulb above his bed, he performed his nocturnal ritual by candlelight. Silas Marner was reincarnated right on Stoutland's Main Street.[13]

But that was all in the future. Today, Virgil busied himself with helping total the tally sheets and counting the checks and cash. Those tasks completed, he surveyed the crowd and spotted Jap and Charlie. Bouncing quickly down the limestone steps, Virgil approached the two older men and blurted, "Hey, Charlie, how's your wife and my kids?"

Good natured Charlie Winfrey grinned, spat, and fired back, "Now that you mention it, Virgil, a couple of 'em are turnin' out downright homely—I was thinkin' about sendin' 'em home to their daddy!" Well used to Virgil's impertinence, Charlie moved away to get closer to the action of the auctioneer.

Virgil then homed in on Jap. In the spirit of those who truly enjoy delivering alarming news, Virgil exclaimed, "Say, Mister Jasper Francis, I was a-lookin' for you! I run into Rube Winfrey yesterday and he was tellin' me that him and John Frey helped Charlie Blackburn load out a car of cattle Sunday morning." Giving his head a slightly worried cant while scrutinizing Jap's face, Virgil continued, "Rube was a-thinkin' that some of them stock were the ones he sold you last spring."[14]

Pursing his lips and raising his eyebrows, Jap looked like a man whose wife had just confessed infidelity. "Well, I sure did buy some calves from Rube, and they're the same ones I sold to Charlie no more than a week ago," replied Jap indignantly. Turning this bit of news over in his head and pondering its meaning, Jap continued:

"Why, Charlie was just by my place this mornin'. He didn't say a word about shippin' the cattle—he just said that Joe Givens had sent some of the money for his farm, but it had gone to the wrong place. He said he was on his way to Decaturville to see Joe and get it all straightened out.[15]

"Virgil, you know you've got my check from Charlie up there in the bank waitin' to be paid on the cattle I sold him.[16] He's supposed to be payin' me from the money for his farm. He had no business shippin' those cattle until I got paid. Have you got any returns in yet from St. Louis into Charlie's account?"

"Noo, Jap, not that I know of,"[17] happily replied Virgil, "but I didn't go by the bank before I left this morning."

Rubbing his temple with his forefinger, Jap Francis was grappling with things that didn't add up. "A man's word is his bond" is the credo of honorable men doing business with one another. Even in Jap's patient and trusting world, that bond was stretching thin. Maybe it had already snapped. Vague and elusive, honor had disappeared as a thief into the night.

With resignation, Jap finally spoke, "Virgil, I think maybe I'd better come on up to the bank this evenin'. I want to know if any money has come in, and if it hasn't, I want to talk to John Frey to see what he knows."[18]

"Why shore, Jap, me and Rollie will be in the bank 'til six o'clock—shoot, we'll get to the bottom of it—everything is prob'ly alright—no sense worryin' about it," replied Virgil, more flippant than consoling.

Jap looked intently at Virgil and then shook his head slowly in puzzlement. Everything wasn't alright. Everything appeared wrong. Anger and foreboding wrestled to a draw in Jap's mind. Jap Francis was in a contest that he didn't want to play, didn't know the rules, and couldn't fathom the end game.

Chapter 9

Jap stayed at the sale to see the livestock sell, but his heart was no longer in it. In a way, he was pleased that sale prices were high. He had always liked Bob Peters and knew that he would need every dollar to pay his debts and make a fresh start in Oklahoma. Tickets for himself and his growing family on the Frisco's crack passenger train, the "Oklahoman," would not be cheap. Like the "Sooners" and "Boomers" before him, Bob would discover that the red soil of Oklahoma was not especially fertile, much of it drying up and blowing away during the great droughts of 1934 and 1936. The sweet promised land of California would beckon to many. Bob Peters and his family would be among them.

By 3:00, the sale was winding down, and Jap had about three hours of daylight in which to get to Stoutland and take care of business. Charlie Winfrey decided to ride along. Grateful for the company, Jap was anxious to share the twists and turns of his dealings with Charlie Blackburn. Winfrey had a level head and Jap needed advice. Letting their horses drink deeply in the little stream below the Peters house, the two proceeded at a slow trot southwest toward Montreal. Jap repeated a litany that would be consistent through its telling to Winfrey and four others before the day was out:

"Charlie Blackburn has shipped those cattle, and I didn't know anything about it until I got down here to the sale. Virgil Evans told me. Why, he [Blackburn] was at my house just this morning and never said a word. He just said he was going over to see Joe Givens about the money that Joe had sent to the wrong place; it is a danged funny thing to me that that Joe don't know where Stoutland is at!"

In disgust, Jap finished the woeful tale with, "I'll tell you one thing, my friend, this will be my first and last deal with Charlie Blackburn!"

Shaking his head sympathetically, Charlie removed a large plug of tobacco from his cheek and spat it to the wayside. "Jap, I ain't a bit suh'prized. I shore wisht you would a' talked to me before you made any deals with Charlie Blackburn. What he's a-tryin' to do to you, why, that ain't even the half of it."

Charlie Winfrey then related what he knew about some of Blackburn's recent business doings. What exactly he told Jap has been lost to history. Rules of hearsay evidence never permitted its utterance before judge and jury.[1] Whatever it was, it crystallized in Jap's mind the plain truth that Charlie Blackburn likely had no intention of ever paying him for the cattle.

"I didn't know anything about that! If I had, I would never have traded with him," replied Jap. "I'll tell you one thing for sure—after we stop at your place, I'm goin' on into town and see if that draft has come in, and if it hasn't, I'm stoppin' by Charlie's place this very evenin' and tell him what's what!"[2] Jap was on a roll. "There is no way that I'm goin' to lose my money on them cattle. All I've got to show for my herd is a $1,200 bad check and two scrawny little mules—and mean ones at that."[3] Jap's high dudgeon ended with:

"Charlie Blackburn has got the nerve of a brass monkey—can you believe that he was actually talkin' about buyin' my place? Why, he can't pay for what he's got, let alone buy anything else. I've put up with all of it I'm goin' to. If I don't get my money real quick, I'll garnishee everything that Charlie Blackburn has got before tomorrow night!"[4]

Little else was said during the nearly 13-mile ride. As a long time friend, Charlie understood that Jap was in no mood for further talk. "A friend in need is a friend indeed" was Charlie's motto, and he recognized Jap's need to be left alone with his thoughts.

When the two reached the lane leading down to the old Winfrey homestead, Charlie shook Jap's hand and offered to help: "If there is a single thing that I can do, you let me know—you know I'd do anything in the world for yuh!"

"Naah, Charlie, I don't expect that I'll need any help—maybe I won't even need to go by there [Charlie Blackburn's] this evenin'."

Winfrey persisted, "If you need a little support, I'd be happy to go over there with yuh. To tell yuh the truth, I don't like hit one bit how you and some others has been treated. That Charlie Blackburn's gonna have to be reined in by somebody—what he's a-doin' to you just ain't right! That ain't how we do things here in Camden County."

"Don't you worry a thing about it," replied Jap confidently. "I'll be able to take care of it alright."

In their youth, when Jap Francis and Charlie Winfrey had ridden off to Linn Creek to volunteer for the Army, they had vowed to look after each other no matter what the danger. A worried look crossed Charlie's face as he considered his friend's predicament, but he knew there was no need to argue the matter further. A friend respects the opinions of a friend and Charlie deferred to Jap's judgment. "Whatever you think, Jap—whatever you think." He then bid Jap farewell and rode down the hill toward home. Every man must make his own decisions, and Jap had made his.

Charlie Winfrey would never see his friend again.

About 4:15 P.M.

Charlie Blackburn left the field where he and Skip Archer were gathering corn with a wagon and team of horses. Minnie had called around noon, summoning him to Stoutland to read a telegram. John Frey had paid a boy a nickel to deliver the message to Minnie's house. Miz Craddock had relayed the message when the workmen had come in for dinner, but Charlie had chosen not to go to Stoutland until the late afternoon.[5] On foot, Charlie took a path overland and covered the 2 miles in about 30 minutes. Entering Stoutland unobserved, Charlie arrived at Minnie's house at about 4:45 P.M.

Charlie had not been to Decaturville and had not talked with Joe Givens that morning. His trip in that direction had ended in a thicket of cedars on the edge of the Francis farm. From there he silently watched Jap ride past on his way to the sale. He then quickly spurred his horse back into the road for the ride home.

What so urgently required Charlie's presence in Stoutland? He could not have relished the 4-mile roundtrip walk. Why did he have to read the telegram from the Clay & Robinson Commission Company in person? What was so hush-hush that could not pass Minnie's lips over the telephone and save her husband's aching bunions and calluses? The answer lies in the "party line" telephones of the era.

Although each phone customer had his unique "ring" consisting of a certain number of longs and shorts, every user heard every "ring up." By lifting the receiver, curious souls could listen in at their leisure. As long as one didn't clear one's throat, cough, or swear at dog or spouse, it was possible to remain anonymous while learning the delicious details of a neighbor's business. Party lines were as informative as a tap on the phones of Walter Winchell and Hedda Hopper three decades later.

Charlie did not want his business known to sundry and all, especially his creditors. Minnie had her marching orders to never discuss such matters over the phone. This particular piece of business had special reasons for confidentiality. Charlie had sold a herd that did not "officially" belong to him. In addition, he had ordered the proceeds to go to a bank where he did not "officially" have an account. Meanwhile, Charlie's $1,200 check to Jasper Francis, humiliated by a large red ink stamp proclaiming "Insufficient Funds," remained in the custody of Rollie Smith at the People's Bank.

Minnie Blackburn would later testify that the telegram from Clay & Robinson did not specify how much that the cattle had brought but merely related that 27 head had sold in one lot and 5 in another. It stated that "later news" about the sale would be sent to Charlie by mail.[6] A 4-mile walk to learn such spare and unrevealing details? It seems that Charlie wished to keep interested parties, especially Jasper Francis, in the dark about his designs as long as possible. The revealing of even these innocuous details would not be prudent. Especially on a party line shared with Simp and Ida Francis.

Jap Francis considered Mr. Bell's newfangled gadget an unnecessary nuisance, and although the wire was strung right by his house, he declined the service. Not so for his sister in law, Ida, who considered the wooden box on the wall indispensable for modern life. The contraption, consisting of a fixed mouthpiece, an earphone hung on a cradle, a ringer crank, and a large set of bells, held an irresistible fascination for her. It got awful lonely out there on the farm, some 8 miles from Stoutland. The phone seldom rang when Ida didn't "pick up"— just to make sure that there wasn't an "emergency" that needed her attentions. It seemed only the neighborly thing to do.

It was a long trudge for Charlie into Stoutland, but the arrival of the unexpected telegram had made him uneasy. Charlie was full of apprehension and nervous energy. He would be a very busy man in the next 24 hours and he was just getting warmed up.

About 4:45 P.M.

A thoughtful and deliberate man, Jap wanted more facts before confronting Charlie and decided not to stop at the Blackburn farmstead on his way to Stoutland. Sam, the big sorrel gelding with a white star on his forehead, was proving his breeding. He had carried his master 47 miles since early that morning, and the journey's end was not in sight. As Jap neared the Blackburn house, he urged Sam from his "foxtrot" into a canter. For Sam, this was the equivalent of a car's passing gear. The "rack" was his top speed, but Jap held the eager animal back and quickly returned him to a slow trot after passing the house. As the horse and rider swept by, Jap distinguished Skip Archer working alone in the late afternoon shadows.

Arriving in Stoutland just after 5:00, Jap rode immediately to the People's Bank. Virgil Evan's dust-covered Model T was parked in front with steam still rising from its radiator. Jap dismounted and entered the bank, vigorously ringing the little doorbell. Virgil Evans was sitting at his desk totaling the checks and cash proceeds from the Peters sale. Rising, Virgil answered his visitor's unspoken question:

"Jap, there hasn't been a penny of returns come in for Charlie's account—I wish I had better news. I'd go see John Frey about it and see if he can tell you anything.[7] I just don't understand it. Charlie has always used Clay & Robinson, and they always send the money right here—it just seems odd!"

"You're right, Virgil, it is odd; this whole deal is odd," replied Jap quietly, "I'll walk over and see John; maybe we can still send a wire up to St. Louis and find out somethin'. I'll stop by and let you know."

Jap strode out of the bank, crossed Main Street, and climbed the chat-covered incline up to the Frisco depot where he was warmly greeted by John Frey. Jap explained his problem as judiciously as one can when hinting that a mutual acquaintance might be a liar and a thief. Frey confirmed that Blackburn had indeed shipped 32 head of cattle the prior Sunday to the Clay & Robinson Commission Company.[8] Beyond that, Frey volunteered little. John Frey had contracted a serious case of ethics.

As a Frisco employee, Frey was concerned with the privacy of the railroad's customers. Each shipment was a contract with the shipper, the details of which were not deemed public knowledge. Frey chose not to disclose to Jap that a telegram had arrived that morning respecting the cattle sale and had been delivered to Minnie Blackburn. Frey also knew exactly where the returns from the sale were to be sent. He had filled out the shipper's contract ordering that the proceeds, after commission and expenses, be sent to The State Bank of Lebanon in the name of Charlie Blackburn. If anyone was going to tell Jap where the money trail led, it would be Clay & Robinson and not John Frey. Frey's silence may have cost Jap Francis his life.

"John, I want to send a telegram to Clay & Robinson and find out where the returns are. Those cattle are mine. All I've got is a bad check from Charlie Blackburn and a couple of mules that are just about as useless."[9]

Frey balked at the idea. "Jap, it's late, and everybody up there has long since gone home. We can send it now, but you won't get an answer until tomorrow morning, which means you'll have to come back anyhow. Why don't you just come by first thing in the morning? We'll send 'er up there and see what they say."[10]

A trusting man, Frey hoped Charlie's reasons for sending the proceeds to Lebanon were on the "up and up."

Accepting Frey's advice, Jap prepared to leave the depot. In departing, he repeated to Frey the same plan of action he had related to Charlie Winfrey: "I didn't mind the cattle runnin' on Charlie's land as long as he needed to get the money to pay for 'em but since he's shipped 'em, I'm gonna have to do somethin' about it!"[11]

Warming to the subject, Jap continued, "You know John, I've never had any dealings with Charlie Blackburn, and I've told you a lot about what's been going on and I can tell you a whole lot more; why, Charlie Winfrey told me . . ."[12]

Winfrey's bombshell about Charlie Blackburn's character again went forever unreported. No judge would allow it.

Promising to return in the morning, Jap walked back to the People's Bank and found Virgil Evans and Rollie Smith locking the front door. While standing on the sidewalk in front of Burhams Drug Store, Jap was nothing if not consistent. He told the two: "If that money isn't here by tomorrow—I'm gonna garnishee everything that Charlie Blackburn has got[13]—I'm gonna stop and see Charlie on the way home and tell him that somethin' is gonna have to be done."[14]

Virgil gave Jap a quizzical glance, puckered his mouth, shook his head, and counseled otherwise:

"Jap, I don't know whether I'd do that or not. You know Charlie and Minnie are mortgaged to the hilt, including a loan to old Judge Wallace. At his rates, there's no tellin' how much they owe him. On top of that, they owe the Bank more than $3,300, unsecured. Now then, if you go down there tonight and push old Charlie too hard and threaten him, he just might cut and run.[15] Heck, everybody knows him and Minnie don't get along—he just might leave tonight, and the Bank never will get all its money back. Shoot—your little cattle deal is standing last in line anyhow, and a court order could muddy things all up. I'd leave him alone for now—he's worth a blame sight more to us here than gone!"

"Little," thought Jap to himself. "Twelve-hundred dollars is not little in my book." Francis was nettled by Virgil's concern for the bank's claims and lack of sympathy with his own predicament. Charlie Blackburn might be deeply in debt, but passing bad checks was still a crime in Jap's book, and he was determined to get satisfaction. The chips would have to fall where they may. Pursuing the discussion no further, Jap replied, "Virgil, maybe you're right—maybe I'll just take the other road and not even let him know I was in town this evenin'."[16]

"That's the smart thing to do, Jap—yep, that's sure the smart thing to do!"

Rollie and Virgil watched Jap untie Sam and lead the big animal east on Main Street.

Chapter 10

Approximately 5:30 P.M.

Retired and with time on his hands, Rube Winfrey was rapidly becoming the biggest busybody in Stoutland. Like most small towns, it was a title sought by several well-known contestants. Too much underfoot of his wife, Rube spent most of his days "up town" meeting, greeting, and interrogating one and all. No detail was too small for Rube's attentions and, like a magpie, he allowed no tidbit to go unrepeated for more than five minutes.

Spying Jap Francis on the sidewalk in front of the drugstore talking with Virgil Evans and Rollie Smith, Rube guessed what the conference was about. Only the day before, Rube had told Virgil about helping Charlie Blackburn fill a railcar full of cattle that had recently belonged to Jap. Gestures and body language suggested the conversation was intense. In bib overalls and brogans and a painful "hitch in his get-along," Rube ran to catch up with Jap and Sam. Out of breath, greetings and questions tumbled forth: "Jap, it's mighty good to see yuh—did Virgil tell you about them there cattle bein' shipped? Ain't they the ones I sold to you when I left the farm last spring? Did you sell 'em to Charlie Blackburn?"

Knowing that Rube meant no harm, Jap launched into his sad tale as the two walked side by side, heading east on Main. Before turning left toward Rube's house, the 2 men and Sam were fully visible from Minnie Blackburn's house no more than 100 yards straight ahead.

For the fourth time within two hours Jap repeated what had happened and his intentions concerning Charlie Blackburn.[1]

The Winfrey's white weather-boarded house, with a wide porch and Victorian gingerbreading, sat on the right, midway down the hill. Anyone coming or going on the north side of town need pass Rube's house. Surrounded by a freshly painted white-picket fence, the house was ideally located for a meddler and a gossip. Stopping at the front gate, Jap had a question for Rube, "How come you didn't let me know about Charlie shippin' those cattle?"

Sadly shaking his head, Rube replied, "Well Jap, I reckoned it was all legit, but I guess I should a' sent word out there to yuh."

Not wishing to hurt his old friend's feelings, Jap quickly relented, "Aw, Rube, that's alright—don't worry about it, you had no way of knowin' what Charlie was up to." For the last time, Jap repeated his "garnishee everything that Charlie Blackburn's got!" threat.[2] He then turned his ire on Virgil Evans and the People's Bank: "I think Virgil Evans is worried that if I go after Charlie in court, I might be gettin' in ahead of the bank's $3,000 loan. As far as I'm concerned, the bank can just go to hell!"[3]

Rube was surprised to hear Jap swear. A mild-mannered man raised in the church, Jap Francis definitely had his dander up:

"You know somethin', Rube, I was perfectly happy with my account over at the Bank of Stoutland and servin' on the board and all, but Marvin and Virgil and Doc Carlton kept a-workin' on me to move over to People's, and you know how good Doc was to Mom and Dad when he was takin' care of 'em before they died—I just couldn't turn him down. Now I'm halfway beginnin' to wish I had!"

Jap's concern was well-founded. In 1911, several Stoutlanders, along with investors from outside the community, chartered a second bank in Stoutland. The People's Bank fought the application tooth and nail, but competition prevailed and the "Bank of Stoutland" was incorporated June 16, 1911. Its life was short. Ironically, both Jap Francis and Charlie Blackburn were founding stockholders of the new bank, with Jap and Charlie's uncle, Smith Blackburn, serving on the bank's first board of directors. But in early 1914, Jap Francis and several other large depositors were persuaded to move their business to the People's Bank. Left with insufficient capital, the Bank of Stoutland was forced to sell its assets to the People's Bank. The ubiquitous Virgil Evans, acting as "Secretary" of the now-defunct bank, duly swore an affidavit, dated February 6, 1914, that the Bank of Stoutland "is no longer in existence" and sent it to Missouri's Bank Commissioner, J.T. Mitchell.[4]

Virgil Evans was a fast learner in the art of putting competitors out of business.

Jap continued, "You know somethin' else, Rube? To tell you the truth, I've never liked that Virgil Evans much—he almost seems to get a kick out of foreclosin' on some real nice people that I know. I feel sorry for 'em. The bank shouldn't let them get in so deep that if they have one bad year they'll lose their farm. If this is all the consideration the bank can show me when I've got troubles, maybe I took the wrong part in that fight!

"Jap, I don't blame you a bit. I feel about the same way."

Jap mounted Sam and prepared to head for home. Before leaving, he wrote Rube a $100 check. Filling in the name of the People's Bank, he steadied the checkbook on a little red "daybook" that he always carried with him. The reason for the payment is unknown, but Rube noticed and remembered that several similar blank checks remained.[5]

Rube urged Jap to stay overnight. "Jap, now it's startin' to get dark already and yore a-gonna have to come right back to town in the mornin'—why don't you just stay here with us tonight? We've got a good extry bed, and Mary will have supper on the table here before long. We don't get many visitors, and we'd shore 'preciate the company."

"Oh, Rube, you know I'd like to, and you know how I enjoy Mary's cookin', but I've got to get home and take care of my livestock—I've been gone all day."[6]

A farmer all his life, Rube knew that "taking care of the stock" always comes first. "Alright, Jap, if you need to go, you need to go, but you take care of yourself—maybe this thing will work itself out—I sure hope so. But I'll tell you what, Virgil Evans may be right—I'd stay away from Charlie Blackburn until you get the goods on him, and then I'd lay the law to him, good and proper!" was Rube's farewell.

As Jap rode away, he turned, waved, and cheerfully called, "I'll probably see you tomorrow." The rhythmic clatter of Sam's hooves striking the hard road slowly faded into the distance. The last light of day lingered in the western sky, framing the brooding darkness of Rouse Hill in the foreground.

Rube opened the gate, limped up the steps, and seated himself in the porch swing, awaiting Mary's call for supper. The time was about a quarter until six. If Charlie Blackburn was still at Minnie's, he would soon pass on foot right by Rube's gate. Had Charlie seen Jap and Rube on their walk down Main Street? Had discretion counseled Charlie to tarry with his beloved wife awhile longer until he was sure Jap Francis was out of town?

As Jap left Stoutland and headed toward Rouse Hill and home, only four people knew of his plan to return early in the morning and "do something about" Charlie Blackburn: Virgil Evans, John Frey, Rollie Smith, and Rube Winfrey. Virgil Evans was afraid that Charlie might be about to skip out on his debts, leaving the bank in the lurch with a large unsecured loan. He was an unlikely candidate to tattle such alarming news to Charlie. Rollie Smith worked for Marvin Calkin, Virgil Evans, and the bank's directors, including Jap Francis. He almost certainly did not relay Jap's intentions to Charlie. John Frey was already uncomfortable with the situation. Giving Charlie Blackburn a "heads up" concerning Jap's intentions seemed out of character. That left Rube Winfrey. Rube had the knowledge, an easy opportunity, and a reputation for being a blabbermouth.

When Charlie passed Rube's house, did Rube hail him? Imagining that he was doing Jap a favor, did Rube inform Charlie that Jap Francis was coming back early in the morning to see if the returns had come into the People's Bank? A retired Rube Winfrey, feeling out of the game and a little irrelevant, might have been tempted to act as Jap's "agent" in telling Charlie that if Jap didn't get paid he was going to "garnishee everything that Charlie had." Still peeved that Charlie had shown so little appreciation for his help in loading the cattle, Rube had learned that his labors may have assisted Charlie's fraud upon a friend. He could have taken satisfaction in leaking to Charlie that Jap Francis was about to lower the boom. No one will ever know for sure.

Events would make it very uncomfortable for anyone who admitted telling Charlie Blackburn that Jap Francis would be on the dark road to Stoutland early in the morning of November 10, 1915. Someone did—and Charlie and his informer took it with them to the grave.

5:45 p.m.

It was "evening rush hour" in Stoutland. People were coming and going on the main road, some on horseback and some in automobiles. Jap was in no great hurry. It would be dark by the time he reached home anyway. He knew that Sam had put in a long hard day and saw no reason to tire him unnecessarily. Jap let the broad-chested speedster pick his pace, slowing to a steady walk as the two began the ascent of Rouse Hill. As Jap moved along, he was met or passed by several people, all of whom he greeted. He even stopped and exchanged pleasantries with a few.

Harry Taylor and Jimmy Marshall worked together in Stoutland and had gotten off work at 5:30. Motoring in Harry's car, the two passed Jap and Sam traveling in their same direction near the bottom of Rouse Hill. Harry slowed the jalopy sufficiently that it was possible to shout over the car's engine. Sam disliked automobiles and turned away from the sputtering and foul-smelling monster. Reining him back, Jap spoke cordially to both and remarked, "Boys, the way it's cloudin' up, it looks like we might be goin' to get some rain."[7] Jap Francis knew his weather. The government's official weather observer at Lebanon would record ½ inch of rain in the area within the next 30 hours.[8]

Harry drove halfway up Rouse Hill and dropped Jimmy off where the Fulbright Road T's in from the left.[9] The Marshall place was but a brief walk down the hill. It was not yet clear whether Jap would go "the other way" as he had told Virgil Evans. If so, he would have followed Jimmy down the poorly maintained Fulbright Road, circled around the Blackburn farm and re-entered the Decaturville Road near the old Craddock School.

Jack Burke, a 31-year-old farmer riding "pretty fast" on horseback passed Jap and Sam moving "tolerably slow" well past the top of Rouse Hill. Hearing Burke approaching from the rear, Jap reined Sam to the side, "kind of getting out of the road to let me pass."[10] Ever the gentleman, Jap tipped his hat and nodded at Burke as he sped by. He reined in a surging Sam who disliked being overtaken by another horse. Sam nickered and snorted as if to say, "This once, I'm giving way—but I'm the king of this road and don't you forget it."

Jap had passed the decision point of "going the other way" down the Fulbright Road. In his conversations with Virgil Evans and Rube Winfrey, he had averred any mention of confronting Blackburn that evening. Yet, he continued homeward by the route leading by the Blackburn house. No witness would ever testify that he stopped, seeking to confront Charlie.

At a point well beyond Rouse Hill and just before turning left on the Decaturville Road, Jap met John "Happy Jack" Jackson and another man in a buggy heading toward Stoutland.[11] "Happy Jack," a portly but agile man, came by his name rightly. Never without a smile and a wink, a joke or a story, Jack was a salesman for the Watkins Company. "Watkins Men" traveled door to door peddling a vast array of products, preparations, and household goods to rural households.

In the summertime, toting a heavy salesman's case, Jack rarely had to conjure up labored breathing and a sweaty brow when knocking on farmhouse doors. The appearance of a hot, tired man "just trying to make a living" never hurt his chances of a sale.

"I don't need a thing," was the inevitable refrain from busy mothers with a baby on one hip, another clinging to her apron, and two or three other bashful "Bobs and Betties" peering from behind the bedroom-door curtain.

Impeccably courteous and formal, Jack replied, "Oh, that's perfectly understandable, Miz Newton! I was just wondering if I might impose on you for a dipper of water—it's mighty hot out today."

"Well now, you just come on in and sit for a spell. Lands sakes, you look like you're just about to have a sunstroke! Jimmy, you run and get Mr. Jackson a cold drink. I just drew it from the well no more than five minutes ago."

Once in the door, a good salesman never leaves without an order. Whether the lady of the house needed a new broom, chamomile-scented hand soap, a bottle of vanilla or lemon extract, or a tin of any spice imaginable, Happy Jack had it. He also had a line of cosmetics "guaranteed" to put the full bloom of youth back on the cheeks of haggard housewives. Miracles awaited those women purchasing a tortoiseshell face-powder compact with mirror, a tiny circular box of rouge for the cheeks, and some rose-scented face and hand cream.

"Why, Elnora Breedlove [the most beautiful woman in the neighborhood, whose pale face had never seen the sun] just swears by this cream! I sold her two sachet jars this very afternoon.

"Oh, and what about some of this coconut-scented shampoo? See this lovely bottle! Looks like little golden drops of rain coming right down the side—now doesn't it?

"Ma'am, just sample the aroma of this wonderful preparation! Smells just like palm trees and the South Seas, don't it? Why, it only takes a little dab to break the hardest water in the Ozarks! That rich lather leaves the hair as smooth and shiny as a baby's!"

By now, curiosity had overcome the apprehensions of even the shyest of the "young'uns," wide-eyed and edging ever nearer the black satchel's seductive contents.

Summoned by the eldest lad, a teenager who had fled out the back door upon Jack's arrival, the man of the house now enters. He smiles and greets Jack, but dreads the pitch of a man making a living "way out there in the blue, riding on a smile and a shoeshine."[12] That's good—both decision makers are in the room—no alibis or excuses now. The kids are begging for something for themselves.

The lady has now transformed from "not needing a thing" to Jack's best ally. She laments, "I know that we can't afford it, Ellis, but just sniff this wonderful shampoo," thrusting it boldly under her husband's wrinkled nose. "You know this old hard well water and hand soap is ruinin' my hair—it's breakin' off somethin' terrible!"

A couple of exotic whiffs had morphed Thelma into the 17-year-old beauty Ellis had married 15 years earlier.

"Well, now, honey, that shore smells purty alright, but you know we're real short of cash money right now." Hasty interjection needed here.

"That's no problem, Mister Newton," reassured Jack. "All I need right now is a mere ten percent down on any lot that you buy. I'll be back for the rest in the fall after the crops are in—you might be needing something else by then anyhow. And on top of that, if you buy five dollars worth or more, Mister Watkins has authorized me to take a special ten percent off—now isn't that an attractive offer?"

Easy credit and a discount to boot! America is a truly wonderful country.

With wills weakened by a master salesman's removal of buyer objections, the family shopping spree gets into full swing.

"I am about out of vanilla and that old straw broom of ours is worn down to the nub, Ellis, and you know the Watkins brooms last twice as long as the others."

"Daddy, can I have a comb?" wails a little girl.

"How about some toothbrushes and tooth powder for these lovely children?" urges Jack.

The "bought" pile in the middle of the floor is expanding by the moment. Throwing in the towel, Ellis splurges on himself, "Jack, have you got a bottle of some of that Sloan's Linnyment? I'm gettin' suh sore lately, I cain't hardly sleep at night."

"No, Mr. Newton, but I've got something even better [withdrawing a large, square, patent medicine bottle]. This'll warm and relieve those old aching muscles—just smell the strength of that! It's cheaper than Sloan's and if it don't fix you right up, I'll give you your money back."

And so it went. Finally, someone had to put their foot down. Thelma, coconut shampoo in one hand and rose cream in the other, shouted, "Now, you kids, you're not gettin' another thing! Do you hear me?"

An endearing stroke of genius is held to the end.

"Miz Newton, you were so kind inviting me in out of that oppressive sun and having that fine little man get me a cold drink of water when I was about to thirst to death! I want to present to you this gift of French cologne (tiny bottle pulled from the back of the case), my compliments—no charge whatsoever."

Losing all control, Thelma grabbed the blue silk-ribboned bottle, dabbing generously behind both ears and a little on the wrists. Once more, she was 17 and in love.

John Jackson wasn't called "Happy" for nothing. He brought magic, fantasy, and a taste of the good life to rural folk. Spirits were a little brighter, the monotony of housework a little less boring, and the drudgery of the fields a little easier after a visit from Happy Jack. When Jack and his partner met Jap Francis in the gathering gloom at "about six o'clock,"[13] November 9, 1915, Jack slowed the one-horse buggy and greeted Jap cheerfully. He then lashed the reins and yelled giddyap! With several hundred dollars of "harvest money" in hand, including the Newtons', the men hurried onward toward Stoutland.

Sadly, Jack's magic could neither detect nor deflect the malevolent evil stalking Jap Francis. John "Happy Jack" Jackson, master salesman and raconteur, was the last person to see Jap Francis alive.

Chapter 11

Minnie Blackburn and her mother, Mary Jane Craddock, seemed unable to agree on Charlie Blackburn's comings and goings on the afternoon of November 9, 1915. Minnie would claim that she saw her husband "a little bit after noon" after she had summoned him with a phone call to her mother. She further stated that after walking into Stoutland and reading the telegram from Clay & Robinson, "He remained only about twenty minutes and then started back to the farm."[1] If true, this would not have permitted Charlie, while in town, to learn that Jap Francis had become aware of his deceit and was threatening to do something about it. Francis was still at an auction some 20 miles away. It would be another five hours before he would tell others that he would be coming to Stoutland early the next the morning.

Miz Mary Jane's recollection was very different. She placed Charlie in Stoutland at a time overlapping with Jap Francis's urgent fact finding mission. In a sworn deposition, Miz Mary would testify that her son in law ". . . went to Stoutland to see about the cattle . . . in the evening . . . leaving about 4:00." She added, "It was between 4:00 and 5:00 when he left the field for Stoutland. [Skip] Archer came in from the field with a load of corn and told me . . . it was after dark and about suppertime when he got back."[2] Mary Craddock had been cooking supper on a farm for nearly 65 years. Like all cooks, she was keenly aware of when her charges came in for supper and when the meal was served. In the country, "after dark" means exactly that.

Given that it was likely an overcast sky (Jap Francis was predicting rain), it's a fair assumption that "after dark" was about an hour after the end of "civil twilight,"[3] or around 6:30 P.M. Leaving Stoutland on the heels of Jap Francis, Charlie Blackburn could easily have conversed with someone and arrived home in time for supper. Following a familiar cross-country path, he would not have been seen by "Happy Jack" and his trainee coming into Stoutland by buggy on the main road.

6:30 P.M.

Jap arrived home and quickly changed clothes. Using an old Frisco conductor's lantern for light, he set about the farm chores. Jap's cows and calves were mooing for attention. His small flock of sheep had already bedded themselves down for the night. He immediately unsaddled Sam and led him to his stall, giving him a big bucket of fresh water, an extra ration of sweet-clover hay, and oats mixed with grain. The cows were then quickly milked and turned in with their calves. The hogs got their usual rations, and then Jap returned to Sam's needs. Using a big bucket of water warmed by the day's sun, a soft brush, and horse shampoo, Jap washed the tired and sweaty horse down. After thoroughly drying Sam, Jap grabbed a bottle of horse liniment and gave the animal a brisk rubdown. Nuzzling the remains of his oats and hay, Sam snorted appreciatively at the attentions from his human companion and provider.

Having seen to the animals, Jap turned to his own needs. His ambition did not extend to kindling a fire and cooking anything. He had taken a liking to the newfangled boxed cereals Kellogg's Corn Flakes and Postum Grape Nuts. A sweetened mixture of both in cold milk with a little sugar and a handful of raisins pleased his fancy. Mixing up a bowl, he sat quietly eating at his parents' round 1890s-era oak dining table. Fitted with elaborately fluted column legs and covered with a worn oil cloth strewn with tiny strawberries, it hearkened to a day when Lucy Francis cheerily presided over her kitchen. In the late twentieth century, auction houses would dub such ornate furniture "Renaissance Revival." Coal-oil lamp turned low, Jap reviewed the events of the day and thought about tomorrow. As those living alone are wont to do, he spoke out loud:

"I wish to God I wouldn't have to deal with this, but I guess Charlie Blackburn's givin' me no choice. He just took my property and he's treatin' it like his own—and I don't see a dollar in sight. I just wonder if he really does have a deal with Joe Givens? That'll be the next thing to do. I'll have Simp call over to Decaturville—I wonder what Joe has got to say? Surely, Charlie doesn't believe that

I'm gonna let 'im swindle me out of a herd of cattle. Does he think I'm that big a fool? How in the world does he plan on gettin' away with this? Maybe Virgil's right—maybe old Charlie is about to fly the coop. I've heard he's got family way out in California someplace—maybe he expects to take my money, and anybody else's he can get his hands on, hop the Blue Bonnet, and head way out west somewhere. Why, he could just disappear and nobody would ever find him."

Jap finished his little soliloquy with a resolute declaration: "If I was married to Minnie, I can't say as I'd blame him for wantin' to leave the country—but he won't be doin' it with my money!"

Rinsing his bowl with a dipper of water, Jap placed it in a dry sink to be washed later. As Jap prepared for bed, his mind wandered back in time:

"Me and Dad and the boys worked too hard on this old place—and us finally gettin' halfway comfortable after all these years—to have people stealin' from us! And what about Mama and Murtie? They worked their fingers to the bone around this house a-cookin' and cannin' and cleanin' and ever' other single thing that women do to make life bearable on a farm—it wouldn't be fair to them either. Shoot, when I die, everything I've got is gonna go to those boys of Ben's."

Jap Francis wound his Westclox Big Ben alarm clock, synchronized it with his more accurate gold Waltham pocket watch, and set it for 4:00 A.M. He then removed the globe from the lamp on the nightstand, blew out the flame, and went to bed. In spite of the unusually warm days, it was chilly after sundown, and Jap appreciated his old featherbed and goose-down coverlet. "I'll get into Stoutland a little after five and go by the 'City' for breakfast and then get over to the depot as quick as John Frey opens up around six o'clock. I'll find out what's a-goin' on and get back here as soon as I can to feed the stock."

In 1910, Tom and Minnie Davis had opened a combination restaurant and tailoring business next to the barbershop in Stoutland. The "City Restaurant" featured, "Steak, Breakfast Bacon, Ham, Chicken, 'Winnies,' Toast, Eggs, Sandwiches, Chicken Gravy, Milk, 'Both Kinds,' Tea, Hot or Iced, Coffee, Cold Pop, Pies and Jelly Rolls." The "City" wasn't Tony Faust's in St. Louis or the Savoy Grill in Kansas City, but it had quite a following among railroad men up and down the Frisco line. Filling out the menu, one could get "Sliced Tomatoes, Hamburger, Fresh Oysters and Chili in season."[4]

Although the "City" didn't make biscuits, Jap loved their steak, gravy, eggs, toast, and buttermilk. He usually finished his breakfast with a slice of Minnie's renowned blackberry jelly rolls and a couple cups of chicory flavored coffee with cream. A steady patron of the "City" since it opened, Jap Francis would be a no-show Wednesday morning.

Tired from his long day, Jap still had trouble drifting off to sleep. When he finally did, his dreams were dark and disturbing, roiling from one bizarre event to another. He dreamed that tragedy had befallen his brother Ben and family on their way back from California. All had been killed in a train wreck. They stood on a hill above the wreckage, beckoning to him. He dreamed of his mother and Miz Mary Craddock. Somehow, it seemed that Miz Mary was working to "pay back" Charlie Blackburn's debts to the Francis family. She was trying to get a giant quilt into Lucy Francis's quilting frames, but no matter how it was turned, it wouldn't fit. It was just too big. Casually, Miz Mary grabbed a pair of sharp scissors and deliberately cut the lovely "Lone Star" quilt top in two and said, "Now, it'll fit."

"Why, you've ruined it," exclaimed Lucy.

"Oh, it's still plenty big enough to cover up Jap—that's all it'll ever be used for anyhow," replied Mary. Lucy was aghast.

Next, Jap found himself running Sam for all he was worth toward Stoutland on an urgent mission. Descending Rouse Hill at a breakneck pace, he overtook and passed Virgil Evans, Rube Winfrey, John Frey, and Rollie Smith, all moving at a leisurely pace. Desperately trying to enlist their help, he called their names. None seemed to notice or hear him. They seemed oblivious to the emergency. It was as if he were invisible. Then, as he passed Charlie Winfrey, his best friend waved at him and shouted a wordless warning. As Sam stretched for maximum speed, his iron shoes striking sparks on flint, horse and rider leaped into a great chasm—falling,

falling, falling into darkness. Jap awoke with a start. He was in a cold sweat. It was 3:30 in the morning.

Jap wanted no more of such dreams. He turned off the alarm, arose, lit a lamp, and, shuddering from the morning chill, prepared for his trip to Stoutland. With distant lightning flickering in the south, Jap was more concerned about getting wet than cold. Nevertheless, he donned two sets of summer cotton underdrawers and an undershirt. No sense in putting on those prickly woolen long johns until absolutely necessary. After washing his face and hands with soap and water on the back porch, Jap pulled on a clean set of dark blue striped trousers and a light blue open-collared broadcloth shirt. Leather thonged suspenders, polished high-top brown shoes, and a dark brown single-breasted dress coat finished the ensemble. Concerned with the weather and knowing the unpredictability of Missouri's climate ("Wait five minutes and it'll change."), Jap tucked his velvet-collared overcoat, along with his business valise, under his arm. He then blew out the light, felt his way from the bedroom to the parlor, grabbed his nearly new gray Stetson hat from a rack by the door, and strode outside. Jap Francis was a man on a mission. Inexplicably, he left his rain slicker draped over a hook.

Chapter 12

Jap Francis wasn't the only one dreaming about his mother. Sam was fast asleep in his cozy stall dreaming of his life as a colt on a horse farm near Mexico, Missouri. It is well known that higher forms of animal life dream. Their dreams surely relive past experiences, pleasant or unpleasant, with other animals, including humans. It's doubtful that animals' dreams are nearly as complex, fanciful, inventive, insightful, or bizarre as those of humankind. But no one who has ever watched a slumbering horse or dog, muscles twitching and legs moving in running sequence, accompanied by muted barks or whinnies, can doubt the vividness of their reveries.

Sam didn't know it, but he was of royal ancestry among horses. The American Saddlebred Horse dates to the 1600s, with almost all registered animals descended from the great Gaines' Denmark. This foundation stallion's sire, Denmark, was a "square" trotting horse, but his dam was a Narragansett Pacer from Rhode Island. Thus all of Gaines' Denmark's progeny carry easy-gaited blood. As they followed the pioneers westward to Kentucky, Virginia, and Tennessee, these horses became the "The Walking Saddle Horse" or "Plantation Horse," later called the "Tennessee Walker." These horses' running-walk gaits were fast and comfortable but not surefooted enough for the rough terrain of the Missouri Ozarks. There, they were bred to local horses, who with their high-stepping "Fox Trot" literally stepped over obstacles. The Missouri Fox Trotter breed was thus born.[1]

Sam's main recollections consisted of his mother, said to be Lucy Mack, one of the most famous Saddlebred mares, owned by Joe McDonald of Mexico, Missouri.[2] His mother's unique smell and memories of coltish cavorting at her side through the green pastures and whitewashed fences of beautiful Audrain County often replayed themselves in Sam's dreams. His other dreams invariably included the only two humans with which Sam had ever spent much time: a colored man by the name of Tom Bass and his current owner, friend, and provider, Jap Francis.

When his father died in 1906, Jap inherited a couple of thousand dollars, along with the homeplace, consisting of a small house and about half of Bill and Lucy Francis's farm. Simp Francis and wife, Ida, received the same inheritance as Jap. Ben and his wife, Lucy (not to be confused with the elder Francis's wife) got an equivalent amount in cash.

By 1912, Jap owned a house and good farm, free and clear of debt. In addition, he had several thousand dollars on time deposit at the Bank of Stoutland. Flush with cash from a good harvest and a reviving cattle market, Jap decided to buy a really fine saddlehorse. People in the know told him that the best horses in Missouri could be obtained in Mexico, Missouri, some 100 miles north and overland from Stoutland. It took him three days to get there, overnighting in hotels in Jefferson City and Fulton, before arriving at the imposing estate and horse farm of Joe McDonald on the outskirts of Mexico. A breeder and trainer of pedigreed show horses, McDonald recognized that Jap was looking for a high-quality working horse and referred him to someone who was already a legend in Missouri:

"Tom Bass has got a hoss of mine over there that I sold him. I just didn't know what to do with him! He's got real good lines, but he was wild as the devil when we tried to break him to the saddle. He's kind of a bastard out of Lucy Mack. We think a neighbor's Ozark fox-trottin' stallion somehow got with her but I can't be sure. I hadta fire one of my best hands for lettin' it happen. There's no way I could give a man a clear pedigree on him. I hated like the devil to give him up but he 'bout killed one of my stable boys—he reared up and tried to kick him, and when the boy ran away, he yelled, 'What in Sam Hill kind of a horse is that!' So we just named him Sam Hill and had him gelded. I sold him to Tom—he thought he might make a good trick horse—you know Tom can teach a horse to do damned near anything. I think if you gave Tom Bass enough time, he could teach a horse to swing on a trapeze! Anyhow, he broke him without any trouble, and now I hear he's as sweet a rider as there ever was. Who knows, maybe Tom'll sell him to you. You tell him Joe McDonald sent you over there."

Jap promptly went to see Tom Bass. Bass was born a slave in 1859 on a large plantation near Ashland, Missouri. Tom's Caucasian features came from his father, a son of Eli Bass, the plantation's owner. As a young man, Tom came to Mexico after the Civil War and got a job as a lowly stable boy, cleaning out stalls on a horse farm. But not for long. It quickly became obvious that Tom Bass had a special gift. Long before "The Horse Whisperer," Tom Bass could break horses to the saddle without beating them, wounding their spirit, or even raising his voice. He even invented a special bit, still in use today, to ease the pain that horses endure during training. It's properly called the "Bass Bit." Bass refused to patent his invention, giving up his lucrative rights to the device. He considered the bit his gift to horses everywhere.[3]

A small, nattily dressed man, Tom Bass was induced to go to Kansas City in 1893 and, while training horses for the city's wealthiest citizens, suggested a fund-raising horse show that would snowball into the "American Royal Horse Show." More than 100 years later, the American Royal is one of the grandest horse and livestock shows in the world. During his three years in Kansas City, Tom Bass's reputation grew such that in 1897, Queen Victoria invited him and his horses to perform for her Diamond Jubilee. Deathly afraid of water, Tom refused the invitation to cross the Atlantic. He then returned to Mexico to buy his own farm, where he continued to show and train fine horses for him and others. In his lifetime, Tom Bass won 2,000 blue ribbons, championships at two world's fairs, and every major horse show in the country. No one could wow the crowd and judges like Tom Bass in tux, tie, and black derby hat, putting Belle Beach, his jet black, high-stepping champion mare through her paces.[4]

If anyone doubts how Missourians feel about their horses and the memory of Tom Bass, take a trip to the State Capitol in Jefferson City. There you will find a bronze bust of Tom Bass standing tall among an elite group of 20 in the Hall of Famous Missourians. The shrine includes General of the Armies John J. "Blackjack" Pershing, artist Thomas Hart Benton, humorist Mark Twain, and another swanky dresser from the "Show Me State," a feisty little man by the name of Harry S. Truman. Not bad company for a former slave.

Today, Tom Bass needed to raise a little money. Tom had a certain eye for the ladies and a game of cards. He was known to sip a little bourbon in colored saloons where piano players in striped shirts festooned with elbow ribbons pounded out the latest ragtime creations of Scott Joplin. Tom wanted the princely sum of $500 for Sam Hill but settled for $300 and the horse that Jap was riding. The two talked for quite a while about horseflesh. Like every horse he ever trained, Tom hated to see Sam Hill go. He bragged:

"Suh, I kin tell by lookin' and talkin' wif you that you is a gente'man and a good man. If I did'na b'lieves it, I would'na sell you this heah horse for nooo 'mount a money! Lordy, duh yuh realize, suh, this heah two-yeah-old colt—why, he's done come outa Lucy Mack? Why, he mightiest be one a her las' foals, she be gettin' priddy old, you knows. Lucy's jes one of the fine'es mares theah evah has bin—an that's all they be to it—plain and simple! This hoss is one of the best ridin' hosses I've evah set a hand to. He's a biggin, moe than sixteen han's and fuh sho is gonna take you wheah evah you wants to go—and in gran' style too! Even though his daddy's prob'ly just a t'ree-gaited fox-trottin' hoss—this 'in's got all five of 'em."

In a soft but animated drawl, Bass exacted a promise from Jap Francis: "Suh, jest swehr me one thing—as a gent'eman. That you wone nevah, evah, raze a han to 'im! Yuh sho'ly wone need to. He'll do evah thing you ask an' a hoe lot moe. When I trains 'em, I trains 'em right!"

Jap kept his promise and never in his life raised a hand to Sam Hill. As he rode away from Tom Bass's big ramshackle horse barn, he patted Sam Hill on the withers and said, "We're a-goin' home to Camden County, big fella. Horses don't have highfalutin' names there. We're just gonna shorten your name up to 'Sam.' That's plenty good enough. Oh, and we've got a little something in common, boy. My mother's name was Lucy, too."

Chapter 13

Sam's slumber was interrupted by the barn door opening. Awareness of his human master moving about pushed aside his dreams of colthood. The joy of reliving time spent with the small human whose gentle sounds allayed his fears of bit and saddle must end. Reluctantly, memories of the training ring at Bass Farm and the excitement of honing his natural high-stepping gaits while learning to serve humans receded. Sam snapped awake. It was long before daylight and his natural clock told him something was unusual. He and his human companion would be going someplace soon—but at a time different than ever before. As horses do, Sam quickly arose, front feet first, pushing himself erect with rear haunches. Most horses sleep standing up, but like a little knock-kneed overachiever by the name of Seabiscuit, Sam relished sleeping lying down in a deep bed of straw.[1]

By the time Jap reached the stall with a lit lantern, Sam was upright and peering curiously over the stall gate. "Sorry I have to get you up at this hour—I don't like it any better than you do." Sam did not understand his master's words but felt reassured by the greeting, accompanied by a cursory nose rub and a pat on the face.

In only a few minutes, blanket and saddle were in place and cinched tight. During the process, Sam helped himself to water and munched a few mouthfuls of hay. He would need them. The relationship between man and animal is more complex than the human side may realize. Sam sensed a combination of impatience and annoyance in the speed, precision, and assertiveness of Jap's movements. It was all business at this odd hour with his human friend, and Sam took his cues. Accepting the bit and bridle readily, he moved eagerly forward, ready to step out of the stall.

Jap finished his preparations by securing saddlebags containing his neatly folded overcoat and business valise to the back of the saddle. Carrying the lantern, he led Sam out of the barn toward the house, where he extinguished the flame and placed it inside the porch door. Leading Sam through the front gate, Jap mounted and turned the big sorrel toward Stoutland. It was 5 minutes until

4:00 A.M. Jap expected to get into town just as the City Restaurant opened at five o'clock.

It was very dark, and Jap let Sam settle into his "fox-trot," combining a fast walk with his front feet and a shuffling trot with the hind. Horses have good night vision, with distinct but colorless images akin to those provided by late-twentieth-century night goggles. Sam would need all the vision he possessed, because Jap could not see his hands in front of him. The waxing crescent moon had set at 6:59 P.M. the previous evening and would not reappear until late morning.[2] A slow moving warm front, some 50 miles to the south had stalled out. A high cloud cover, preceding the front, obscured most of the starlight. Distant glimmers of lightning added to Jap's night blindness. Sam would be both lookout and navigator for this night ride.

Some two miles into the journey and just before crossing a small bridge, horse and rider passed the home of Fred Huff. Jap observed a lamp burning and a figure moving about inside. As Sam's hooves clattered loudly on the bridge's wooden deck, Jap thought, "Ole Fred's gettin' up awful early this mornin'."[3] Jap and Sam continued the slow ride toward Stoutland, arriving near the Blackburn farm at about 4:40 A.M.

Still wishing to avoid Charlie Blackburn, Jap briefly considered circling the Blackburn place by turning Sam at the Craddock School and taking the Fulbright Road. He quickly dismissed the idea. "It's just too danged dark to get through those gates, and I sure don't want Sam to stumble in any of that soft ground—the county never seems to put any gravel in through there! Besides, even if he's up, it's too dark for Charlie Blackburn to see me or me to see him. I'll just let Sam take his head and we'll scoot on by."

And that's what horse and rider did. When Jap sensed Sam make the sharp left turn at the school, a spoken word and a nudge of his boot shifted Sam into his "third gear," a measured canter. With no lights showing, the white Blackburn house was barely visible as they passed. Jap neither heard nor saw anyone. After splashing through a low water bridge at the spring-fed stream at the bottom of the hill, Jap slowed Sam to a walk. Otherwise, he was afraid that he might come unseated in the darkness when Sam made the

90-degree turn onto the Stoutland–Linn Creek road. Worse, Jap could feel the dampness of the mist lying heavy in the lowlands forming the stream bed. "Even Sam can't see much in this fog, and he might run me into a tree limb." Instinctively, Jap hunkered lower in the saddle.

Sam made the turn without incident and resumed a slow trot up and over the two gently rising ridges leading to Rouse Hill. It was still very dark, without a hint of light in the eastern sky. In the middle of November, the sun sets early and rises late in Missouri. It was 4:50 A.M., and the sun would not breech the horizon's edge for another 2 hours. Morning twilight would not reveal objects distinctly enough to be recognized by the human eye until 6:17 A.M.[4]

The unusually warm Indian summer had delayed the migration of night birds. Jap could hear the expressive three-syllable call of a whippoorwill in a hollow not far away. The fluttering wings of a diving nighthawk suddenly caused Sam to jerk his head, mildly startled. Even the frogs, usually buried deep in pond mud for their winter-long hibernation, were croaking as if God had declared perpetual summer. Another bird of prey, the great horned owl, added its strangely melodic call to the anachronistic symphony. Something was odd. Something was out of kilter. It was as if Mother Nature had suspended the rules and would require a sacrifice before the natural order of things could be restored.

Geared down to a walk on the steep climb up Rouse Hill, Sam's shod hooves striking the hard, rocky road could be heard in the morning quiet for at least a quarter of a mile. The sweet morning air was slightly tainted by the faint odor of burning tobacco, carried by a gently gusting southern breeze. Only Sam noticed—it was much too faint for his human rider to detect. Sam didn't like the smell any better than the fumes of motorcars. Snorting in disgust, he never slackened his pace.

At the top of the hill, the terrain flattens for a couple of hundred yards, and it was then that Sam, the lookout, spotted an oddly moving figure. It was the visible upper torso of a man, his arms flailing wildly as if trying to balance precariously on a beam. As the distance narrowed, it became clear the figure was ascending Rouse Hill from the other direction, running up the road directly toward horse and rider. To Sam, ignorant of the poor night-vision of humans, the man appeared acting very strangely. He was carrying a long narrow object in his left hand and moving erratically from one side of the road to the other. On two occasions, he stumbled and fell. It was time for the sentinel to sound a warning.

Sam jerked his head and whinnied loudly. "What is it boy—another horse?" Jap, who could see nothing, had no comprehension of how near animal or human might be. Now on full alert, Sam whinnied again more urgently and, slowing his pace, veered to the side of the road. Fearing that they might be about to collide with another horse and rider or perhaps a pedestrian, Jap stopped Sam with a sharp, "Whoa!" Listening for the sound of approaching hooves, Jap heard nothing. Sam could see that the man, only 25 yards away, had moved a few steps off the road and was standing motionless near a large tree. He was staring intently in their direction. The long object in his hand had been replaced by a smaller object which Sam recognized as a club. Domestic animals, with instincts millenniums old, are fearful of any human with a stick in hand. If the human raises the object as if to strike, almost all will run or shy away. Sam was no different. He snorted and whinnied again and turned his head questioningly to his master.

"Hello! Is anybody there?" shouted Jap. There was no answer. "Aw Sam, aren't you gettin' a little old to be spooked by some old possum or coon crossin' the road? Come on, boy—let's go, we gotta get to Stoutland." Sam stood stock-still. "Come on now, there's nothin' out there, let's go!" demanded Jap, neck reining Sam to the left and nudging his thigh with his boot. Sam had been trained well. In spite of his fear and certain knowledge that a human with a dangerous stick was nearby, he responded to the command and began moving forward at a slow walk on the side of the road opposite the intruder. Two generations earlier, Sam might have been a mount for one of J.E.B. Stuart's cavalrymen. The raised sword of a charging federal trooper would not have deterred this natural warrior.

As they moved closer to the strangely acting man, Jap noticed that Sam's head was tracking something just ahead and to the left. Sam continued to snort and shy to the right side of the road. Jap could see no person or thing. Coming even with the man, Sam saw him move from the tree into the road. The object in his hand was no longer visible. The man called out a soft greeting. Sam stopped, turned toward the man, reared slightly, and whinnied loudly. He was in full defensive posture. Instinctively, the man backed away, bringing the stick from behind his back up to a striking position. Sam reared again and shied to the other side of the road. This man looked and smelled familiar. Sam could not understand why his provider and friend did not seem concerned. If it had not been pitch dark, Jap Francis would have been very concerned.

Sam then heard his rider respond in a questioning voice to which the intruder spoke several more words. Inexplicably to Sam, Jap then dismounted and, gathering Sam's reins, moved toward the human with the hidden stick. Sam followed reluctantly. A brief but quiet conversation between the men followed. Neither could see more than a vague silhouette of the other.

No angry voices, no argument, no harsh tones, no threats, no cursing, no warning. The intruder simply raised the club and swung it with great force sideways across the right side of Jap's head, causing him to fall sideways and bringing him to his knees. Jap cried out with questioning words and attempted to get to his feet. In the darkness, an ill-aimed blow caught him across the bridge of the nose. The same burning sensation of a liquid in his nostrils, just as when he had almost drowned as a child, filled Jap with horror and fear. Now realizing he was in mortal danger, he doubled up in a fetal position, gasping through his mouth. Perhaps he hoped that the attack would subside. It didn't. The pain in his head and his face was excruciating, and he groaned loudly, identifying the position of his head in the darkness. Another mis-aimed blow struck him across the back of the neck, crumpling him to the ground and causing him to roll on his left side.

With legs and left arm paralyzed, Jap was now helpless, unable to rise or reason. Mercifully, he could no longer feel pain or react to the rain of blows directed at his head. He could hear the thudding sounds and sense his body's movement upon impact, but he felt nothing. It was the sensation of surgery with a powerful local anesthetic. The patient senses the pressure and movement caused by the surgeon's manipulations, but they seem distant and painless. Many of the blows missed their target altogether, slamming into the hard, rocky road, sending a sharp pain and numbness up the attacker's arm and bringing forth vile curses. A few did not. Jap continued to moan loudly and mumble audibly.

Unconscious and in the throes of dying, Jap's last and continuing utterances were, "Mother, Mother—where are you? Mother—is that you?" Stubbornly he held onto life, frustrating the assailant who could not see well enough to kill with efficiency. A friend to many and a man who had harmed no one, Jap Francis would be denied the privilege of a quick death, expertly carried out. It was a botched job.

The killer had a major distraction. Sam had become Sam Hill and was rearing and striking at him. Sam Hill could see his human provider upon the ground. He could smell the blood flowing from Jap's fractured nose. He could hear his outcries. If Sam had remained a stallion, he would undoubtedly have rushed the intruder and trampled him to death. But his efforts remained defensive, trying to get between the attacker and his friend. One of his iron-shod hooves caught the man's right hand between the thumb and the first finger, causing a deep cut and fracturing a bone. The pain was intense. "You devil—you get the hell away from here!" the man shouted as he advanced in Sam's direction with club raised. Sam turned and ran a few paces but remained nearby. Turning again to his gruesome task, the man knelt and continued to strike at Jap's head.

A human is sometimes a hard thing to kill. A lesser man's spirit might already have flown. As the blows continued, Jap Francis, with multiple skull fractures, was nearly across the great divide. But not quite. Unable to silence the groaning, prostrate figure on the road and concerned about the noisy fit that Sam was having nearby, the attacker did what he had hoped not to do. The danger that an early morning traveler would happen upon the scene had become too great. The commotion might summon a curious resident from a house located only a few hundred yards away. He must act and act now. Jap Francis must die quickly and surely.

The man stumbled to the side of the road and, after a minute or two of thrashing in the brush amid suppressed curses, found the long object that he had leaned against a tree. He eagerly grabbed it and returned to the execution. Standing astride his victim, the killer instinctively felt for the source of the moans with his new weapon. He placed its end on the back of Jap's neck. The shotgun's muzzle recoiled and belched an orange flame as the large slug propelled its way through soft flesh and cartilage. It then exited the other side, taking a portion of Jap's face with it.

Jap's last visions were those of his mother and father at a great distance, striding purposefully toward him and beckoning with both hands—as an adult offering to pick up a child. Bill and Lucy Francis's mouths were moving, but Jap heard nothing. It was the conclusion of a D.W. Griffith epic. The great reel of Jap's life was slowly and silently winding down. The wide pan of his loving parents, first playing at normal speed, zoomed to a slow-motion close-up. Then slower, frame by frame by frame, came frozen portraits of their faces. Then stop. Then blackness. No credits. No houselights. Jap Francis was dead.

After a few moments of hushed quiet, nature's sounds resumed. The crickets chirped, the frogs hollered, the night birds sang, and the roosters prepared to crow the beginning of another day. A dog rousted himself, barked briefly and unenthusiastically, and then lay down to await the breakfast table scraps. Jasper Francis's departure from this world had gone virtually unnoticed.

Chapter 14

Only one person ever claimed to hear the gunshot that killed Jasper Francis. Her name was Mrs. Henry Kissinger. If pronounced "Kissun-jur," like the name of the distinguished former secretary of state, Stoutlanders look aghast and cast knowing and pitying sidelong glances at their friends. This Ozarkian faux pas invites ridicule and the brand of "city slicker" and a poorly educated one at that. No, the name is properly pronounced "Kis-singer" and please don't forget it!

The wife of a Frisco section hand (member of a repair and maintenance crew assigned a "section" of the track, usually about 10 miles in length), Edna Kissinger said that she heard the report at around 5:00 A.M.[1] She was fixing breakfast for her husband, who was sitting on the bed, pulling on his bibbed denim overalls. The requisite gray-striped, high-crowned railroad cap lay nearby. The modest Kissinger home sat in a hollow about ½ mile northeast of Rouse Hill. The lady thought the report came from the direction of the "Oliver Place," which lay on a southwest line between her house and Rouse Hill. Since it was well before daylight, she remarked to her husband, "It's a funny time for hunters to be out." He grunted dismissively and quickly forgot it. Gunfire is pretty common in rural Missouri, hardly meriting lively discussion at the breakfast table. Later, Edna wasn't sure which day she heard the shot, stating: "During the week following the seventh day of November [Sunday]. I think about the middle of the week."[2]

With the muzzle pressed against Jap Francis's flesh, the report wasn't extremely loud, and residents situated more closely than the Kissingers, including Lem Fulbright and his family, had no recollection of it at all. Even if they had, a single gunshot would not have propelled anyone into the morning darkness to investigate.

Jap Francis's assailant was the beneficiary of luck and his victim's anxiety to get to Stoutland "first thing." Jap was well ahead of other travelers who might have helped him. Most of the year the area would have been well lit by 5:00 A.M. and the "morning rush" to Stoutland would have made it nearly impossible to carry out a murderous assault on Rouse Hill in broad daylight. But not in mid-November. The life rhythms of man and beast take note of the late-breaking daylight and deferred sunrises. Featherbeds, cozy straw-filled barn stalls, or just a dry sleeping place on the ground are occupied awhile longer during the long nights of late fall and early winter. Still, it would not have been unusual for another traveler to have been on the ill-fated Rouse Hill that morning. But there was none. Jasper Francis caught no breaks. Good fortune doth truly smile equally on ". . . the evil and on the good, and sendeth rain on the just and the unjust."[3]

Listening intently for the dreaded sound of approaching human traffic, the killer heard nothing. After rolling the limp and lifeless body of Jasper Francis on its back, he knelt between his victim's legs, hoisted the ankles to his waist, pinning the calves between his elbows and sides. With surprising ease, he then rose and dragged the body into the unfenced woods bordering the roadside on the east. Fretfully pacing back and forth nearby, Sam posed an unseen but well-perceived danger. Time was of the essence. The man's determination to dispose of the body and "tidy up" the scene was fueled by fear and adrenaline. The terrain quickly grew rough with gnarly second-growth saplings, thorny bushes, fallen limbs, old brush piles, and a deep covering of dead leaves. After stumbling several times, the evildoer fell sprawling into a shallow depression about 30 yards from the road. Maybe it was an excavated Indian grave. Maybe it was dug by eighteenth-century French lead miners. No matter, the cavity was a serendipitous find.

Regaining his feet, the man carefully searched Jap's inside coat pockets. Removing his wallet and fountain pen, he then rolled the body into the depression. It came to rest face down with feet extended toward the road. For good measure, the killer lifted the torso and pushed the sprawled arms underneath the body to better fit the hole. Working furiously in the darkness, the killer dragged surrounding leaves into the depression and covered them with small branches. Satisfied, he stopped to consider his next move. "His damned hat has to be out there someplace," he muttered as he navigated his way back to the road and began an urgent search. The faint light of the coming dawn revealed the white hat as an object appearing in the gloom as a large rock. The killer snatched it up and set off for the crude burial site. He heard the soft nicker of a horse. For a frightening moment he froze, believing himself discovered. He then made out the form of Sam, nuzzling the leaves covering his dead master's body.

Sam should have gone home. If he had, the search for Jap Francis would have begun almost immediately, and the horror inflicted on the proud and loyal animal would have been avoided. But a horse's reasoning is instinctive, not intellectual. The finality of death need be proven over time before Sam would leave his source of food and comfort. He wasn't going anywhere. He was prepared to wait a long time until Jap would surely rise and ride him home. He knew no other outcome. A determination not to leave Jap's body brought Sam within an arm's grasp of the killer.

With Jap's hat in hand and a craftily changed attitude, the man slowly advanced. Speaking in soft tones reminiscent of Tom Bass, he was able to maneuver close by the horse. Torn between a desire to flee, a desire to stay with his friend's body, and the confusion of this now gentle-sounding person, Sam decided to stay. He had been thoroughly trained to obey and cooperate with humans. These two-legged, upright creatures were able to move themselves and objects in strangely impossible ways and inflict cruel pain instantly. They must be gods and they must be obeyed. He stood firm.

Reaching for a dangling rein, the man quickly grabbed it and roughly jerked Sam's head around to grab the other. Nervous and skittish, Sam backed away only to be brought up short by a furious yank on the reins, accompanied by a curse. Having shown no mercy for Jap Francis—he had neither patience nor pity for his horse. In the brief tussle, Jap's bloody hat was dropped. Grabbing the reins near Sam's mouth to better control him, the killer led the now-compliant animal east through the woods and down a steep hill until reaching a creek bank. Man and horse followed the stream northerly for more than a quarter mile. Reaching a flattened glade by an old logging road, the man pulled Sam into a thicket and tied him ". . . shoulder high, to a blackjack sapling."[4] He did a superb job. He first drew both reins together, bringing them around the 4-inch diameter tree and tied a double knot between two limbs such that the loop could slide neither up nor down. The loose end of one rein was then run back ". . . toward the bit and tied in four knots and drawn tight."[5] Removal of Jap's saddlebags, containing his valise with checkbook and red ledger, along with his overcoat, completed the job.

Sam was now tightly lashed in a remote low-lying draw, distant from any dwellings and the likelihood of attracting attention. The tree to which he was tied would bend but never break. Blackjack oaks are as tough and unyielding as the settlers who first peopled this harsh Ozark land. Without human intervention, Sam would die. It was just a matter of time.

The man who killed Jasper Francis and left his horse to thirst and starve, hurried rapidly up the hill. He took a beeline course much different than the one that had brought him to this spot. With dawn's light now stronger, he moved purposefully, seeming to know the territory. It was 5:45 A.M. and he was headed due west, back toward the Stoutland–Linn Creek road.

Intent upon robbery, highwaymen seldom murder their victims unless meeting serious resistance. Even then, a desire for a fast getaway argues strongly against painstaking efforts to hide the body. A 20-minute excursion in the dark to secrete and secure Jap's horse seems unthinkable for a common, armed robber. This felon had a greater plan. A plan that could not tolerate the finding of Jap Francis nor his horse any time soon. Hopefully never.

Chapter 15

If Jap Francis had made it to the "City" for breakfast, he would undoubtedly have whiled his time eating and talking with the proprietors, Tom and Minnie Davis, kibitzing with acquaintances and reading the morning paper. A few copies of the *St. Louis Globe-Democrat*, a Republican-leaning newspaper, were thrown from the westbound Frisco Meteor every morning around 4:00 A.M. The *Globe* was eagerly read by Stoutland's ambitious and optimistic "early birds," mainly small businessmen. The reform-minded *St. Louis Post-Dispatch*, an afternoon paper, did not arrive until about 5:00 P.M., announced by the shrieking whistle and billowing black smoke of the highballing "Blue Bonnet" express train headed for Oklahoma City, Dallas, and Ft. Worth. A Democratic rag advocating the interests of the downtrodden, the *Post* was preferred by the town's old-money gentry. These comfortable folk pored over the war news and clucked approvingly at the *Post's* biting editorials. Bounteous suppers, served by poorly paid "hired girls," added to their contentment. Both newspapers cost only a penny.

The *Globe's* headline for Wednesday morning, November 10, 1915 shouted in bold 72 point type: "**Submarine Sinks Liner—212 Perish**" with sub headlines: "**Americans Reported on the Ancona—Bound for U.S.—Attacking Craft Flies Austrian Flag.**" Only 6 months earlier, the *Lusitania*, with 197 Americans aboard had been sunk by a German U-boat, fueling war fever in the U.S. "**Washington Fears Case Will Reopen Submarine Issue**" blared another headline. President Wilson would now have a harder time relying on diplomatic protests to quell the warmongers at home.

A less electrifying but prescient article appeared a few weeks later in the *Sunday Globe*, quoting T. Wells Brex, a British writer:

> Twenty-five million men have taken up arms . . . and 9,000,000 are already slain or disabled. The total destruction of life in two years will be 20,000,000. . . . When the Great War is over, Europe will realize that no

> plague in the middle ages ever ravaged it like the Black Death that came from Potsdam.

Potsdam, a city in northeast Germany, was the home of Kaiser Wilhelm II ("Kaiser Bill") and the birthplace of Crown Prince Wilhelm, commandant of the German armies fighting on the Western Front.

T. Wells Brex got it right. Ten-million combatants were killed in the "Great War," with an additional ten-million civilian deaths resulting from disease, starvation, and "war-related casualties." The techno-military euphemism, "collateral damage," had not yet been invented. The flower of Europe's youth, along with tens of thousands of Doughboys, Aussies, Anzacs, and Canadians would be slaughtered, crippled, mutilated, and gassed for pitifully few reasons. An assassination by a zealot, nationalistic pride, and interlocking treaties unleashed the dogs of a bloody war now commemorated only by stony-visaged and rarely visited war memorials. Today, on Wal-Mart parking lots, generous but disinterested shoppers hand a dollar or two to aging Veterans of Foreign Wars. They are rewarded with a single crimson paper poppy. "Why poppies? An oft forgotten poem of the period answers:

> In Flanders fields the poppies blow
> Between the crosses, row on row
> That mark our place; and in the sky
> The larks, still bravely singing, fly
> Scarce heard amid the guns below.
> —"In Flanders Fields" by Major John McCrae, 1915

Lying in a shallow depression with only leaves and twigs for cover, Jasper Francis, who as a young man had eagerly sought to take up arms for Uncle Sam, occupied no hero's grave that early morning. Nobody seemed to notice his absence in Stoutland. People went about their business doing the usual things in the usual ways. Other than Edna Kissinger, only the town's roosters and a lone dog took notice of the distant gunshot on Rouse Hill. Silenced by the dull recognition of a terrible violation of nature's laws, the cocks decided not to crow that morning in Stoutland. Aroused by the sound, perhaps they thought additional efforts redundant.

Jap Francis, pledged to return to town in the early morning on an urgent mission, never arrived. Evans, Frey, Winfrey, and Smith took no action and made no inquiry. Maybe they assumed that Francis had settled his business with Charlie Blackburn amicably. Maybe they blamed it on the weather. By mid-morning it was pouring rain in Stoutland, making the unpaved streets a quagmire. The government weather observer at nearby Lebanon checked his rain gauge at 7:00 A.M. on the 11th and dutifully reported ½ inch of rain in the previous 24 hours with a low temperature of 50 degrees and a high of 74.[1] The slow-moving warm front that had produced distant thunder and lightning all night arrived at about 10:00 A.M. with a heavy downpour. It then stalled, bringing intermittent showers and thunderstorms throughout the morning. Maybe those who knew Jap Francis's plans figured that he had decided to wait until the weather cleared before coming to Stoutland. It would have been a sensible thing to do. They were wrong.

Simpson Francis had not seen his brother since early Tuesday morning, having observed him from a distance talking with Charlie Blackburn. Since Jap was mounted on Sam, he knew his brother was leaving but did not know the destination. Simp had worked all day on the place, digging potatoes in the morning, fixing himself dinner and gathering corn until mid afternoon. He then went home.

Unaware that the cattle deal between his brother and Charlie Blackburn was unresolved, Simp Francis again arrived at his brother's house Wednesday morning at about 7:00. The cows and calves were bawling and the hogs were milling expectantly around their feeding trough. With team and wagon, Simp was intent on digging more of his bumper crop of potatoes. The reality of the calendar and fear of a hard frost had set him to work. For the next few days, it seems he did little else.

Seeing nothing of his brother, Simp called for him several times. Hearing no reply, he stepped inside the unlocked house. He found no written note below the cobalt blue salt shaker on the kitchen table where such notes were always left. Simp thought,

"He's never left here without asking me to take care of the stock. I reckon he must have gone off early for some reason and he'll be back here pretty quick." Simp observed the cereal bowl in the dry sink and then, stepping into the bedroom, noticed Jap's denim bib overalls hung over a chair and work shoes sitting by the bed. Heading outside, Simp noticed his brother's rain slicker hanging by the door. "If he's gone to Stoutland, he's gonna get himself good and wet!"

By the time Simp had finished Jap's unattended chores, freshets of breeze and rolling thunder signaled an approaching storm. He began to dig potatoes with all his might and main.[2] Wet potatoes in the ground followed by a hard freeze would ruin the crop. With the help of an iron spade, large red-skinned potatoes flew from the good earth and over the wagon's stake and rider sideboards. By 10:00, the first large raindrops inspired Simp to quickly drive team, wagon, and six bushels of potatoes into the barn's big covered breezeway. He tied the horses securely and fled to the house just as the deluge descended.

By noon, the storm had moved north and the rain had lessened to a fine mist. Simp was a little worried. "Maybe Jap went over to Miz Craddock's to see Charlie about the cattle. Or maybe he stopped to check those mules he was telling me about—maybe one of them kicked him in the head." He consoled himself with, "If something has happened, you'd think Sam would have come home by now!"

Deciding to investigate, Simp unhitched his team and using one of Jap's extra saddles, rode one of the horses to the north pasture. There he spotted the two irascible mules innocently munching grass. No brother was in sight. "I guess he's in Stoutland takin' care of business or mebbe he's left on a cattle buyin' trip and plumb forgot to tell me. Anyhow, he's bound to show up sooner or later. I'll just watch his stock until he gets back."

Jap Francis wasn't coming back. The heavy rain, filtering through his leafy shroud, had thoroughly soaked and chilled his dead body. The cold water, slightly tannic from the leaves, cleansed the skin of coagulated blood, leaving it a colorless chalky white.

Standing in a draw some half mile away, Sam was very much alive and terrified. Throughout the morning, he had stood patiently awaiting Jap's return. Then the thunder and lightning arrived in full force. Alone in a thunderstorm, he was scared to death. Beating rain, bolts of lightning striking trees nearby, followed by ground-shaking thunder had terrorized him into a frenzy. He fought with every sinew in his body to free himself.

Sam's efforts pulled the top of the small tree nearly parallel with the ground, but the stubborn blackjack oak would not budge. Fighting the tied reins, he battled to loose himself. He bit and tore at the one-inch leather strips, beginning the mouth lacerations that would later become infected and rotten.[3] With the bit between his jaws, he could not exert sufficient biting pressure to sever the reins. Digging his hind legs into the soft earth, he set his forelegs and pulled with all his might. Collapsing and losing his footing, Sam's full hanging weight of 1,200 pounds slammed into the bit in his mouth. With excruciating pain shooting into his brain, he struggled to regain his feet.

Sam tried a new tack. Angry and frustrated with the now-hated bridle bit and reins, he went after the reins with his front feet like a bear grasping for berries on a high branch. Using the high-stepping range of his fox-trotting forbearers, he somehow got his right hoof and foreleg up and over the reins, pulling down with all his strength. The soaked leather stretched a few inches under the onslaught but did not break. Using his final reserve of energy, Sam somehow got his leg extricated.

As the storm moved slowly away, Sam lapped drops of water from the leaves he could reach and lapsed, fully spent, into a heaving mass of bone and muscle. After regaining his wind, Sam Hill's screaming whinnies were repeated for nearly an hour. Several horses on the main road, high above and some quarter of a mile away, heard the panicked calls coming from one of their own. Startled, they whinnied replies and moved erratically toward the sound, only to be yanked back on course and scolded by their irritated riders. Any hope of rescue moved on. Sam would get no help soon.

Chapter 16

Charlie Blackburn's whereabouts early Wednesday morning, November 10, 1915, remain in dispute to this day. Seventy-five-year-old Miz Mary Craddock, sleeping in the front bedroom off the parlor, gave Charlie an alibi. In a sworn deposition, she would later say that after returning from Stoutland Tuesday "to see about the cattle," Charlie came back to the farm and was there that evening, and she saw him there the next morning. "Not a soul called for Charlie and I didn't hear anyone leave the house. We usually got up at about the same time, between four and five o'clock in the morning," she elaborated.[1] But Mary Craddock was a sound sleeper and noticeably hard of hearing.

Ellen Castile, who lived with her husband on property adjoining that of Minnie Blackburn in Stoutland, told another story. She said she saw Charlie Blackburn early on the Wednesday morning in question. "At about six o'clock [½ hour before sunrise] I heard my husband talking to someone out in the lot, and I walked to the back porch and saw that it was Mr. Blackburn. My husband asked him if he had stayed in town last night. Mr. Blackburn said, 'No, I came in this morning.'" Mrs. Castile said she saw a saddled black horse in the Blackburn yard.[2]

Typical of the male gender, Ellen's husband, Claude, was sure of the distance separating the Castile and Blackburn houses (150 feet), but less sure of the date of his early morning conversation with Charlie Blackburn. "It was sometime between Monday and Thursday," he reported unhelpfully.[3] Neither of the Castiles could tell whether Charlie had just arrived, was just leaving, or whether he was riding the horse tied in the yard.

Joe Piercy contradicted the Castiles. Joe lived in Stoutland, nearby to both the Castiles and Minnie Blackburn. He claimed he spoke with Claude Castile around daylight on the 10th. Daylight would have come at about 6:00 A.M. He said he saw neither Charlie Blackburn nor a horse around Minnie's house at that hour.[4]

Minnie Blackburn denied her husband's presence at her Stoutland residence the morning of Jasper Francis's murder but gave him no alibi. She said that after seeing him for "about 20 minutes" Tuesday afternoon, when he came by to read the cattle telegram, she did not "see him any more that day nor that Tuesday night, nor the next Wednesday morning . . . I went to the farm Wednesday, riding a sorrel pony, using a man's saddle, leaving at about eight o'clock A.M. and arriving at about nine o'clock A.M."[5] Minnie did not explain the purpose of the trip nor why it took her an hour to cover the 2½ miles leading directly past the murder scene. It was a leisurely pace for a walking person but glacially slow on a horse. Minnie said she stayed at the farm until about 3:00 in the afternoon and that her husband was there, working with Skip Archer the entire time.[6]

Fourteen-year-old Ray Blackburn, living with his mother in Stoutland, claimed not to have seen his father there Wednesday morning. He stated that he saddled his sorrel pony for his mother and ". . . left it in the yard tied to a peach tree," before he left for school.[7]

Marvin Calkin, President of the People's Bank, was out and about that Wednesday morning, trying to do a little business before the rains came later. He lived only a couple of hundred yards from the Blackburn town house and sometime between 6 and 7 A.M. saw "a pony in the Blackburn yard with a man's saddle upon it." He described the pony (any horse smaller than 14½ hands high) as either bay or dark sorrel in color. He did not see Charlie Blackburn around the place. Later, in the company of Virgil Evans and a "man from St. Louis," Calkin overtook and passed Minnie Blackburn riding the same pony in the direction of the Blackburn farm.[8] The group all passed by Jasper Francis's still-warm dead body, lying on Rouse Hill, some 27 paces off the right side of the road. It was broad daylight, but apparently no one detected a large dark pool on the roadbed, created by most of Jasper Francis's lifeblood. It had somehow been carefully covered with gravel and leaves. If their horses acted up from the smell, it went unreported.

Others attested to Charlie Blackburn being on his farm that morning. Fred Huff passed the Blackburn farm at about 6:30 A.M. on his way to Stoutland. He saw no one out and about, and did not see Charlie on the road into town. Returning from Stoutland between 8:30 and 9:00, he thought he saw Charlie Blackburn busily at work near his barn unloading corn. Fred had arisen very early, and, while building a fire to stave off the morning chill, had heard a horse, headed toward Stoutland, pass over the wooden bridge near his house.[9] It was undoubtedly Jasper Francis taking his last ride.

L.D. Franklin went to the Blackburn Farm "at about sunup" the morning of the 10th to haul a load of gravel from the creek. He saw Skip Archer and Charlie Blackburn about a quarter-mile away, in a field pulling corn. While there, he saw them move from one field to another and continue their work. By that time, ". . . the sun was about a half-hour high . . . ," or about 7:00 A.M.[10] Charlie was just doing what farmers are supposed to do. They get up early and work hard.

It seems unlikely that a man who had just committed the worst of humanity's crimes would present himself at his wife's house in Stoutland within an hour of the deed. The risks were huge of being observed away from his farm with blood on his hands and clothes. Unless, of course, Minnie Blackburn was complicit in the crime or, in the crisis of the moment, became a reluctant accessory. Was she startled at her door by a panicked husband excitedly whispering words of an altercation with Jasper Francis? "I didn't mean to do it, but I had to!" may have been his claim of self-defense. Did Minnie Blackburn's instinctive desire to protect her family prevail over a desire to do the lawful thing? Prison or worse for Charlie would eliminate her provider and bring shame upon Minnie, her son, and both the Craddock and Blackburn families. Her world, already a financial shambles, would tumble over the edge.

If Ellen Castile was right about Charlie Blackburn's presence at Minnie's house early in the morning of the murder, Mary Craddock's alibi for her son-in-law went out the window. Consequently, prosecutors would later try to prove Charlie was in Stoutland. But the Castiles' testimony was contradicted and uncorroborated. The likelihood of Mary Craddock being either forgetful or coached seems much more plausible. Charlie was, after all, a son-in-law who had never given her a harsh word.

Eighty-seven-year-old Sylvan Mooney was interviewed about the Francis killing in August of 1998. Syl Mooney lived all of his life in and around Stoutland. Although only 4-years-old when Jap Francis was murdered, he remembered many of the essential facts of the case, handed down from older residents and his parents. Syl remembered it being said that Jap Francis was shot at close range "with a shotgun." Interestingly, he added, "There were rumors Blackburn's wife was seen burning his bloody clothes the morning after the murder supposedly took place."[11] But rumors are just rumors. Minnie Blackburn was never charged with any crime and no evidence was ever introduced that she assisted or covered up for her husband—that is, if Charlie Blackburn was the killer.

One does wonder. How did the murder scene, including the bloody mess on the side of the road, get tidied up and concealed so well and so quickly? The killer was frantic to get the body off the road and conceal it. He must catch and hide the horse and then exit the area quickly. He must leave neither of his weapons at the scene. How did he do such a meticulous job—in almost total darkness? One wonders. Did the murderer return later to make sure the body was searched and properly hidden? Or did the killer receive a little family help?

One other person might have been expected to know something about the whereabouts of Charlie Blackburn before daybreak that Wednesday, November 10, 1915. He was sleeping in the Blackburn house in a small bedroom adjacent to Charlie's. He was a notoriously fitful sleeper and easily awakened. In the summertime, Skip Archer, Charlie's dollar-a-day hired hand, slept on the screened porch on the west side of the house. But the chilly and damp November mornings had inspired the always thoughtful Miz Craddock to invite him inside for the coming winter. Skip knew a little something about Charlie's activities that dark and foggy morning. Reluctantly, he would eventually weigh in—but that would come later.

Chapter 17

Thursday, November 11, 1915

The weather front that had brought rain to Stoutland Wednesday morning had retreated southward by mid-afternoon, pushed by a gust of chilly Canadian air. Overnight, the skies cleared and the first frost of the season deposited a lovely sparkling glitter on the hills and valleys of Camden County.[1] John Frey, arriving at the Stoutland Depot before 6:00 A.M., shivered and clapped his hands together as he fired up the big potbellied coal stove that provided heat for the interior. The smell of coal and creosote permeated the building, giving travelers the sensory illusion of having started their iron-railed journey long before the cinder-spewing behemoths clamored into the station. Some thought of Stoutland as just another gritty little stop on the Frisco's 5,000 miles of trackage. But for those boarding trains there, it was a gateway to adventure and romance, Arlo Guthrie's "Magic carpet made of steel."

For those not traveling that morning, home-heating stoves that had sat abandoned since April were put to good use by town and country dwellers alike. The pleasantly comforting aroma of woodsmoke settled into hollows and draws around the town. A few tardy souls shivered as they arose and hurriedly carried in cast-iron models of various shapes and sizes from summer storage in outbuildings. Chimney pipe and nickel-plated foot warmers were hastily located and installed. The huffing and puffing of a fast-drawing wood kindling fire would soon summon reluctant children from their nests of featherbeds and quilts. Enticing smells from the kitchen drew even the worst "sleepyheads" to the warmth of the heating stove. That is, until Mom called, "Breakfast!" Typical fare included salt-cured bacon (or even better, smoked jowl meat), white milk gravy, hot baking-powder biscuits with churned butter, and freshly laid eggs, fried sunny-side-up and laced with black pepper. Apple butter, jams, jellies, hot coffee, and cold, frothing milk with a skim of natural cream finished the farmer's breakfast. Nobody went away hungry. All seemed well.

Sam, standing shivering in a draw north of town, was both hungry and miserable. After the storm had abated the day before, he had waited patiently through the afternoon for Jap to untie him and ride him home. That was the order of things. Humans tied you up and eventually humans came and untied you. Mercifully, animals have neither watches nor an acute sense of time. Sam had stood quietly through the afternoon, dozing. Unable to lie down or even lower his head to the best upright sleeping position, he quickly learned to cradle it in the fork of the tree that held him. It wasn't comfortable but the best he could do. As the sun began to set, stirred by the expectation of being fed and watered, Sam became wakeful, moving about and pawing the ground. Several whinnies produced nothing.

As darkness descended into the woods, new fears entered Sam's consciousness. He had never been left alone at night, even in a familiar pasture. Now the dark forest and the sights and sounds of creatures moving about were unsettling. A harsh reality was slowly sinking in. Maybe *nobody* was going to come looking for him. With hunger pains unabated, Sam positioned himself with his backside to the wind and tried to sleep. Surely his human benefactor would come for him in the morning.

Through the night, it got colder and colder. Without a winter coat and still damp from the downpour, Sam was chilled and shivering by sunup. Awakened several times in the night by the movement of possums and raccoons, Sam slept only fitfully. A curious red fox had crept within a few yards before bounding away.

At dawn, the big fox-trotter awoke and stamped about to loosen the stiffness in his muscles. As the sun rose higher, it melted the frozen drops remaining on the small branches within his reach. Thirsty, Sam licked the little moisture and wet his lips. He then gently bumped the branches with his head, causing more drops to descend. Scrub oaks hold their leaves until late winter or spring and the tree imprisoning Sam still had its full compliment, albeit deadened and brown. The tree's ability to collect and hold some moisture would be Sam's salvation, but he was in for the fight of his life and he had few survival skills. He had never needed them. After all, he was the prized foal of Lucy Mack. Humans had always been willing to barter pampered care for his beauty, speed, and endurance. Sam was going to need a lot of the latter.

As his dark sorrel color soaked up the meager heat from the rising sun, Sam positioned himself to collect as many of its warming rays as possible. By 10:00 his body heat, along the with sun's radiant energy, had warmed and dried him, easing the shivering. The chilly wind had abated in the protected glade, but like a child having played too long outside in the cold, Sam had a runny nose. It needed a good blowing and wiping.

Jasper Francis, who only 24 hours earlier had ". . . lived, felt dawn, saw sunset glow, loved and . . . [was] . . . loved,"[2] lay dead on Rouse Hill where he had been dragged and dumped. The heavy rain that had cooled and cleansed his remains the day before had been replaced with a light frost on the leaves and branches covering him. The body was now almost completely chilled through. A lack of direct sunlight and the slow evaporation of moisture would continue to cool and preserve his remains.

Worried about his potato crop after the cold night, Simp Francis arrived at Jap's house around 9:00 A.M. and discovered the ground completely thawed from only a light freeze. Seeing nothing of his brother, he turned the calves in with the cows, fed the animals, and finished digging potatoes. Returning in the afternoon to gather corn and again seeing nothing of his brother, Simp did the evening chores. "I sure do wish Jap had a-told me where he was a-goin' and when he was a-comin' back!" Simp was a little peeved.

11:45 A.M.

The door of the People's Bank opened abruptly, and Charlie Blackburn strode in. Ignoring the opportunity to wipe his muddy boots on the rough jute mat just inside, he moved quickly to the massive, marble teller's cage. Charlie's right hand was neatly bandaged with white cotton strips up to his wrist, secured with a safety pin. Only his fingertips and thumb remained exposed.

Virgil Evans was in the back of the building, adding wood to the crackling blaze in the ceramic-tiled fireplace that both adorned and warmed the boardroom. Natural light was provided by two leaded-glass skylights. A dozen green leather upholstered chairs and an electrically lit brass chandelier completed the opulent decor. It wasn't Mercantile Commerce Bank in St. Louis, but the People's Bank was the finest business establishment in Stoutland. Remnants of this finery from another age remain in the building to this day. Virgil would soon be laying out closing papers for a farm loan on the big circular walnut table. The eager and naïve borrowers, anxious to sign, were due into the bank at noon.

Ever the glad-hander and ambassador of goodwill, Rollie Smith cheerily greeted Charlie with uninterrupted patter.

"Howdy doo, Charlie! It's mighty good to see you! You haven't been in for quite a while! What'd you do to your hand? How's Minnie and Ray?"

If Charlie noticed the unintended sarcasm that neither he nor any interest payments had crossed the Bank's threshold in several months, he ignored it. Creditors with non-performing loans rarely hang out, smoking and joking, at the bank sending them demand letters.

"They're doin' alright, Rollie—I just dragged it acrosst some barbed wire,"[3] was the brusque two-for-one reply. Dispensing with any pretension of sociability, Charlie came immediately to the point: "I want to trade some paper with yuh and pay the bank off. How much am I owin' right now, interest and all?"

"Why sure, Charlie, I'll be happy to figure that up for you—I'll be right back," replied Smith as he headed through the doors to the boardroom and the president's office.

In addition to a large steel-doored walk-in vault in the front service area, a similar vault on the back side could be serviced only from the boardroom. Here, in fireproof safety, were kept the bank's charter, board minutes, loan books, and other important papers.

With a lowered voice tinged with a hint of excitement, Rollie demanded Virgil Evans's attention: "Charlie Blackburn just come in and he says he wants to pay off his entire loan with us!" The retirement of a substantial unsecured loan, after many months of accumulating interest with no principal repayments, would be a relief to the bank's stockholders.

"Well, Jap Francis told us that he was sellin' his farm and for us to make sure we got paid—it sounds like old Charlie's savin' us the trouble of garnishin' the proceeds," was Virgil's laconic response.

"Good for him. I wonder if he's gonna make that check to Jap Francis good too?"

"I don't know—he hasn't said nothin' about it," replied Rollie.

"Well, the bank's standin' in line first and we've got us a fuh-doochee-airy responsibility—so just let that ride unless he brings it up," instructed Virgil. "I'll be out there in a minute to look everything over."

Having done the same math for Jap Francis only eight days earlier, Rollie quickly calculated the loan pay-off total and returned to the teller's cage. "If you want to pay 'er all off today, Charlie, it'll be $3,311,[4] even. That's what it'll take to wipe 'er clean alright."

"That's exactly what I aim to do, and the sooner the better," replied Charlie evenly. "Me and Minnie has sold the farm to Jap Francis, and I've got a couple of checks and Jap's note. It's plenty enough to pay my loan and more."[5]

Alarm bells were going off in Rollie Smith's mind. Hadn't Jap Francis, a director and stockholder of the bank, told him that Charlie intended to sell his farm to Joe Givens? Jap had even said he had helped Charlie prepare some of the papers. Hadn't Jap been in the bank two days before, claiming that Charlie had shipped his herd of cattle without his knowledge? Wasn't the bank holding Charlie's $1,200 insufficient-funds check made out to Jap Francis? What sort of turn of events was this? Come to think of it, Jap was supposed to have come in yesterday to send a telegram and look into the cattle matter. Rollie hadn't seen him. Maybe Virgil had. Puzzled, Rollie hesitated, rubbed his temple with his first finger and opened his mouth to speak when Virgil Evans stepped up. "Virgil, Charlie says he's sold his farm to Jap Francis and is in to pay off his loan," spoke Rollie slowly and deliberately, expecting Virgil to grasp his meaning and seek an explanation.

"Fine, fine, that's just fine!" exclaimed Virgil in his usual bumptious fashion, expressing no surprise. "Let's see what you've got there, Charlie."

Charlie withdrew a hand-tooled and laced wallet from his hip pocket with his left hand. Holding it with his wrapped right hand, he produced two checks and a folded piece of paper which he slid across the marble slab under the brass barred divider.

"Yep, here's a check for $1,500 and then here's another one for $1,200—it's just a bonus check on the farm deal."[6]

"Fine, that's fine," replied Virgil agreeably after giving the checks a perfunctory glance. "Now then, let's just look at this here note." Scrutinizing it briefly, Virgil continued, "I see that Jap made her out for $3,000 and signed it—that looks just fine—very good! You know Jap's notes are as good as gold around here—we won't have to discount it a bit."

In full command, Virgil snapped instructions: "Rollie, you go on back and get Charlie's note and mark it 'Paid in Full' and give it to him and zero out the balance in the loan book. While you're back there, bring Charlie's check up here, and we'll just trade it for this one from Jap." Turning back to Charlie, who was leaning nonchalantly against the massive counter, Virgil spoke breezily, "You've got $5,700 here—Charlie, I reckon you're gonna put the balance on deposit with us?"[7]

Glaring at Virgil for a moment, Charlie responded coolly, "I reckon I will—it's always nice doin' business with yuh, Virgil."

Warmed by the rare compliment, Virgil unctuously responded, "That's what we're here for, Charlie—we're just here to serve."

Rollie returned shortly with Charlie's $1,200 check and, after handing it to him, reached down and, one by one, perused the signatures on the two checks and note. He considered going and comparing them against Jasper Francis's authentic signature card but thought better of it. His boss had already accepted the checks and note as authentic. Further scrutiny could be interpreted as questioning Charlie's honesty—an insult. Although slow to repay loans in years past, Charlie had never been accused of swindling, and the bank had always gotten every cent.[8]

Second-guessing of one's superiors, especially in public, is not the path to rapid promotion in the business world. Rolla Smith was a good foot-soldier who took orders and carried them out faithfully. And, well, frankly, the signatures seemed to look OK. They were written uniformly in the same ink with the same pen. It seemed a little odd that the two check signatures looked exactly the same, but the note signature, although similar, seemed more hurriedly written and crude.

As Charlie turned to go, Virgil's curiosity finally surfaced. "Charlie, we'd kind of heard through the grapevine that you was a-plannin' on selling your place to Joe Givens. Jap hadn't told us a thing about buying your farm."

Charlie was glib: "Naw, I never had any intentions of sellin' to Joe. I guess you wonder at it, but I've been holdin' the papers for some time on account a' Jap. For some reason or another, he wanted to wait to finish up the sale and didn't want the word to get out. Why, I don't care if the whole world knows about it. I'm catchin' the train to Leb'non this afternoon to see Kellerman [a Lebanon attorney] about gettin' the deed drawed up. Jap's gonna meet me down there."[9]

Only half-listening to Charlie's monologue, Virgil had more important things on his mind—namely, the incoming deposits to the bank. Squeezing and rubbing his chin with thumb and forefinger, Virgil prodded: "We've been lookin' for those cattle returns, Charlie; will they be comin' in pretty soon?"

"Aw, no, Virgil, I sent 'em on down to the bank at Leb'non. I've got a little loan down there that I'm gonna pay off."[10]

Virgil Evans knew in a second that the "little loan" was with Judge W.I. Wallace. Hypocritically, Virgil both envied and railed about the "yew-sir-rus" rates of interest charged by Wallace.

Slamming the door shut, Charlie Blackburn took his leave of the People's Bank. The deal was done. Charlie Blackburn walked in owing $4,511 dollars and walked out owing nothing with $1,189 deposited to his virtually empty account.

"Of all the people in the world, it just seems odd that Jap would come in here and mislead us about Charlie selling his farm to Joe Givens with him intendin' to buy it himself—and why would he be so mad about the check and the cattle trade if that was just gonna be part of the farm deal?" wondered Rollie aloud to Virgil after Charlie left. "It all just seems odd. Did you notice that both of the $1,200 checks are dated the same date? That seems like an awful funny way to do business."

Virgil dismissed Rollie's concerns with:

"Oh, Rollie, people are just funny—maybe it started as a cattle deal and then Jap decided to make him an offer on his place—who knows? Anyhow, the bank is danged lucky to get its money back!

To tell you the truth, I'm not sure that we'll be lendin' Charlie any more money any time soon. Shoot—he may be leavin' the country for all we know—we may never see him a-gin."

Virgil Evans was wrong. Charlie Blackburn wasn't going anyplace. He was paying his debts and acting in every respect like an honest man wishing to live out his days in Stoutland with reputation intact. But he would be returning to the bank in a few weeks under very different circumstances.

Later, Rollie noticed that the $2,700 in checks presented by Blackburn, after making Charlie's $1,200 check good, had overdrawn Jap Francis's account by a few dollars.[11] "That's odd—very odd, just not like Jap."

12:30 P.M.

Charlie Blackburn bought a 50-cent one-way ticket to Lebanon from John Frey at the Frisco Depot. Frey didn't inquire about the cattle shipment and Charlie volunteered nothing. Charlie's presence reminded Frey of Jap Francis's avowed intent to appear the prior morning and inquire about the returns. Frey dismissed Jap's absence with a silent, "I guess it got settled alright."

With the Southwest Special running on time and due in at 12:42, Charlie stepped outside, his boots crunching on the gravel-and-cinder-covered passenger loading area. He passed Wes Scrivner, chewing tobacco and lounging strategically on a bench just outside the door. Wes was Rube Winfrey's competition for the nosiest busybody in Stoutland. Actually, it wasn't much of a competition. Wes, to the irritation of some and amusement of many, was the hands-down winner. True to form, he wasn't about to let Charlie Blackburn escape his inquisition.

Well acquainted with Charlie's sour disposition, Wes loved to get under Charlie's skin. For Wes, it was a satisfying sport. Waiting until Charlie had passed him by without acknowledgement, Wes spoke to Charlie's retreating backside: "Charlie, looks like you've been in a fight and got the worst of it!" jabbed Wes, leering at his victim.

Charlie stopped, turned, and glared at Wes. Pursing his lips as if to whistle and nodding his head knowingly as if to say, "My hand is none of your damned business, you old blowhard," Charlie replied icily, "No, Wes, I just had a little 'set to' with a roll of barbed wire. I reckon I'll be *just fine* in a couple a' days."

With exquisite timing, Wes waited until Charlie turned on his heel to walk away and then spoke again: "I thought you wuz gonna rent me your farm, Charlie?"[12]

Stopped in midstride, Charlie turned again. Knowing fully well that Wes had no intention of getting back into farming and was only poking around to plumb his business, Charlie concluded the game might be advantageous. He decided to play. "Well, I'm just real sorry, Wes, but I can't let you have it."

"Why, shorely you could rent me a measly 10 or 15 acres so a man could run a few head on it!" exclaimed Wes.

"Now, Wes, you know that if I could, I would," lied Charlie in a sarcastically sweet tone, "but I can't—I've done sold the farm." The question was properly begged. With pursed lips and a knowing nod, Charlie waited patiently for the inevitable.

"Well then, who did you sell it to? I haven't heard a thing about it." Wes spoke incredulously with more than a hint of skepticism. Heavens! How could such an important transaction have escaped Wes's inquiring mind and tireless toils in the land of scuttlebutt?

Enjoying the little test of wits, Charlie became the cruel persecutor: "Why, I'm surprised you hadn't heard, Wes; I thought everybody in the country knew about it by now."

Squirming between a rock and a hard place, Wes Scrivner, the most well-informed geezer in Stoutland, knew checkmate when he saw it. To admit that he actually didn't know the business of every living soul in town (and the outlying provinces) was a painful admission, but it must be made for the greater good. After eyeing Charlie for a moment and spitting tobacco vigorously into a nearby bush, the CNN of Stoutland threw in the towel and admitted defeat: "Why, Charlie, I ain't heard a danged thing about it," he announced indignantly. Refusing to ask the previously unanswered question twice, he inquired feebly, "If I was a needin' to rent a few acres of your farm, Charlie, who am I gonna have to see?"

Slowly inhaling through clenched teeth, Charlie shook his head and held the pause for a brutally long moment. "I reckon you'll just have to see Jap Francis about it, Wes—by the way, have you seen him in town? We're supposed to be goin' to Leb'non this afternoon to draw up the papers."[13]

Sharp-eyed Wes Scrivner had failed to see Jap Francis that Thursday. Only death could separate Stoutland citizens from Wes's prying attentions. "No, I ain't seen a thing of Jap—but he better get here pretty durned soon—didn't I just hear the "Special" blow for Garnsey [a crossing four miles east of Stoutland]? She'll be here pretty quick."

As Charlie wandered away, he helpfully added details for Wes's consumption: "It doesn't look like he's comin' in—he said that if I didn't see him here to go ahead anyway, that he'd just ride through the country and meet me there."[14]

Charlie Blackburn boarded the Southwest Special and rode the 18 minutes it took to get to Lebanon. Once there, he didn't spend a lot of time looking for Jasper Francis. He walked to The State Bank of Lebanon and confirmed that the proceeds of the sale of Jap's cattle, $1,014.35 to be exact, had been received by mail from Clay & Robinson Commission Company. As ordered, it had been deposited in the name of "Chas. Blackburn."[15] The returns made Charlie $185.65 and two mangy mules short of breaking even on his cattle trade with Jap Francis. He couldn't have cared less.

Charlie then hustled over to Judge W.I. Wallace's stately Victorian mansion on the moneyed north side of town. Only a few blocks from the red brick Laclede County courthouse and deeply shaded by towering elms and sweet gum trees, Harwood and nearby Michigan streets were populated by the "arrived," the "arriving," and a few over-borrowed pretenders.

Charlie was admitted at the side "business" entrance by Rose Duffy, a young Irish servant. Only the "better" citizenry of the town who came calling used the front vestibuled entrance. Certainly not debtors in default. Dressed in a starched black dress, petticoats, and white linen apron, Rose was one of several young female servants in the Wallace household over the years.[16] Rose briskly ushered the visitor into the plush-carpeted presence of the great man.

Seventy-five-year-old Judge Wallace, comfortably ensconced behind a large oaken rolltop desk, greeted Charlie with the genial condescension of the learned and wealthy. Wallace and his wife, Louise, were of eastern aristocratic stock, he having been born in Massachusetts in 1841 and she in the Empire State of New York in 1843.[17] Wallace's pinched nasal tones, clipped vowels, and dropped "R"s signaled his New England roots. His air was that of the *noblesse oblige* but without much of the *oblige*.

Judge Wallace helpfully filled out a check for Charlie's $1,014.35 deposit at The State Bank of Lebanon and dated it November 11, 1915. Charlie scrawled his signature on it. When presented for payment the next day, the bank stamped the check, "Paid, Nov. 12, 1915."[18] But Judge Wallace needed a little more money.

Charlie and Minnie owed Wallace $2,223.80,[19] consisting of a $1,000 second mortgage on the farm and town properties with $1,223.80 interest in arrears. The loan had been outstanding for three years. It's amazing how fast interest compounds at 2¼ percent per month. W.I. Wallace didn't get to be a millionaire arguing with his conscience. With the loan on the farm and the Stoutland residence in default, the kindly judge was calling the entire amount immediately. Left unpaid, Wallace, along with the State Savings Bank of Springfield, would foreclose and evict Charlie, Minnie, and their coddled son. Miz Mary Craddock would be equally homeless. The Blackburns' façade of propertied affluence would come crashing down.

Renting a farm and sharing the produce with the owner was not Charlie and Minnie's cup of tea. The dreaded "sharecropper" word gave them the heebie-jeebies. Worse, Minnie might have to share a bed with her husband whom she had come to loath. Privately, she had sworn never to "know" him in the biblical way again. Perhaps most distressing of all, there would be no more day-long excursions to the hoity-toity dress and millinery shops of Lebanon and whatever else occupied Minnie's long afternoons in that fair city. It would all be "just so very intolerable."

Charlie wrote Judge Wallace a check on the People's Bank of Stoutland for $1,209.45, paying off the good justice "fair and square." Wondrously, the $4,500 from Jap Francis, along with the $1,014.30 in returns from the sale of Jap's cattle, came within $20.50 of ridding Charlie and Minnie Blackburn of their most pressing loans. Charlie felt a lot better. He was an impulsive man who rarely pondered the consequences of his actions. Large ego intact, he wasn't worried about the destination of the train he had set in motion.[20] It had left the station and would soon build speed, but he wasn't concerned. Charlie decided to celebrate financial freedom by slaking his thirst at a local saloon.

As Judge Wallace lead Charlie toward the door, he casually inquired, "And just how is your lovely bride?"

"Judge, she's doin' just fine," replied Charlie with the aggrieved tone of one who pays the bills for a big spender.

"Well, Charlie, now that you're all caught up, if you should happen to need a few hundred now and again, you just have that better half of yours come in and see me just like she always does. You know, I find it very difficult to turn down lovely ladies. Fine women have so many little needs and wants—and they do cost money, now don't they?"

Charlie ignored the rhetorical question. Shaking Charlie's hand, Wallace mused out loud, "Charlie, you're a very lucky man. Such a fine specimen . . . yes, indeed, very lucky!" As if awakening himself from a pleasant reverie, the aging judge dropped Charlie's hand and spoke these parting words: "Charlie, you take care of yourself now and give my very best regards to that charming spouse of yours."

Mumbling, "G'bye, judge," Charlie turned and trudged toward downtown.

By 9:00 that evening, some 6 hours after leaving Judge Wallace's dignified presence, Charlie had achieved a mellow and conversational mood in the less refined "Ozark Hitchrail" pool hall and saloon. Jim Sullivan, proprietor and bartender, asked Charlie how the farm business was and if he had sown any wheat. Charlie replied that he had not planted any wheat and did not intend to. "Come spring, I expect I'll seed at least a part of it in grass."[21] It was a peculiar response for a man intending to relinquish ownership of his farm in only a few days.

Later, Charlie tipped a Frisco brakeman two bits and hopped an eastbound freight train scheduled to drop a car in Stoutland. Walking home to the farm, he arrived after midnight and sank into his bed a tired and contented man. It had been a good day. Everything had gone as planned.

Chapter 18

Sunday, November 14, 1915
10:00 A.M.

The church bells were ringing in Stoutland, summoning Baptists, "Campbellites" and Methodists alike to morning services. It was the coldest morning of the autumn, with the ground frozen solid by an overnight temperature of only 17 degrees.[1] Woodstoves, fired early in the morning, made the churches habitable, as talkative worshipers hustled into the buildings, their breath leaving little puffs of fog in the bright sunlit chill.

After a rousing hymn or two and an opening prayer, the adults stayed in their seats for Bible study. This consisted of each person reading a verse from a selected chapter of the King James version. The ensuing discussion, lead by a wizened and holy elder of the Church, attempted to divine what it all meant. As the reading progressed, bizarre pronunciations of biblical names and places sometimes brought uncontrolled titters, followed by cleared throats from the deacons' bench. Miscreants quickly straightened their reddened faces and stifled further outbursts. Decorum must be maintained in Sunday school, but those infernal "fill-us-steins" will trip a person up most every time. Woe to the poor parishioner stuck with "Sadduck-sees," "Far-as-seas," and "King Nab-yur-knee-zar."

With reluctant steps, youngsters were shooed by their mothers to a remote corner of the building for "young folks class." These benches, since time began, have been presided over by ancient spinsters or widows who "just love children" while instilling the fear of God in every one of their juvenile prisoners. Blithely confident of heaven's reward for their frightful ministrations on earth, these ladies seem uniformly turned from the same mold: a prim nose, surmounted by wire rimmed glasses through which they peer menacingly down at their helpless charges. Tortoiseshell combs, dating at least to Luther's 97 Theses, hold tightly knotted hair in a silver bun.

The apprehensive little sinners were immediately tossed upon the tempest of reciting verses assigned the previous Sunday. In panic, most forgot the words. Many stuttered and cast their eyes heavenward. Some had not even attempted this cruel and demanding exercise.

"Well, alright, Herbert, can you please recite *any* verse in the Bible? Any at all?"

"Uhh, uhh," a sly smile crept its way across little Herbie's freckled face. "Uhh—Jesus wept!" he blurted triumphantly.

Miss Sour Pinched Face had been cannily defeated by the "old reliable." John, with his inspired wisdom, must surely have written that simple verse, full of wonder and meaning, just for the purpose of saving children from such humiliation. The doors to the kingdom of heaven would remain ajar one more Sunday for young Herbert—but only just a crack.

Salvation for Sam was nowhere in sight. He had now stood for more than four days in the weather, through a hard rain and two plant-killing frosts. He had no food and only a little water dripped from the leaves and bark of the tree that restrained him. A horse in poorer condition might have already been on the brink of death. But Sam had been Jap Francis's pride and joy, and the legacy from his dead master would serve him well. He had gone into his ordeal well nourished and physically fit. The saddle and blanket kept some rain off and conserved body heat. Nevertheless, Sam had started to weaken noticeably. He had already lost 50 pounds of body weight, and his saddle, tightly cinched 4 days earlier, had loosened to the point that any vigorous movement might dislodge it.

Sam was very hungry and had munched all the brown leaves within his reach. Bitter and full of tannin, they provided almost no nutrition but brought some moisture to his dry mouth. He hadn't yet resorted to ripping at the bark for any tiny shreds of cellulose. That would come later.

Much like a sentinel posted in the cold, Sam's lot had become a routine of shifting his weight and stamping his feet to keep leg muscles from cramping. The repetitive movements burned enough calories to help keep his body temperature up during the cold nights, staving off pneumonia, shock, and a certain death. Sam longed to lie down for a while, but the reins, tightly knotted to the tree at nose height, gave him little leeway. Instinctive efforts to pull himself free had drawn the leather knots lock tight and the black-jack sapling, iron strong, would bend but never break.

Sam spent most of his time dozing. His dreams were filled with visions of romping through the green summer fields of his birth-place in Audrain County. Other times, he distinctly heard his master calling him from the pasture. "Oh, Sam!" "Sam, boy!" "Here, Sam!" Drooling from the thought of the awaiting treat, be it apple or pear or sugar lump, Sam would turn and drive his feet toward the barn. The sharp tug of the bit in his scabbed and sore mouth rudely awakened him. He screamed out in pain.

Sam had now accepted the fact that his human friend and benefactor was not coming for him. If a horse has a heart, and all horse lovers believe they do, Sam had forgiven Jap for abandoning him. Knowing that he was now on his own, he waited for better prospects. Maybe another kind human would come his way before it was too late. Survival was the only option.

Simp Francis skipped church that Sunday. He went over to Jap's place early in the morning, as he had all week, and did the chores.[2] He had searched the house and barn several times for any clues of his brother's destination and had found nothing. His work clothes were draped over the iron-railed foot of the bed. He had dressed to go somewhere, taking his nearly new hat and his best overcoat. Inexplicably, he had left his rain slicker.[3] "This time a' year there's just no way he'd a' gone off on a long trip without that slicker," muttered Simp out loud. He had been anxious all week, but as Simp walked about his brother's house that morning, he was suddenly seized with a strong sense of foreboding. It was quiet—dead quiet—in the house, and the floor squeaks from his footfalls seemed amplified and ominous. It had been too long. Just too long! Something bad was the matter. No letter, no telegram, no word of any kind had arrived.

"Jap wouldn't have just walked off and left this place!" A slow-moving, stoic man, Simp had wrestled long enough with doubts and uncertainty. It was time to find his brother.

He started by calling Virgil Evans at his home in Stoutland. Evans told him some things that he already knew. That his brother had sold cattle to Charlie Blackburn and had been awaiting payment on a check placed at the bank.[4] The record is vague about what else Evans disclosed that afternoon. The disquieting news that Jap Francis had disappeared and had been missing for several days may have tightened Virgil's lips about everything he knew. Specifically, that Jap had not appeared in Stoutland as expected Wednesday morning. Virgil almost certainly did not impart the jaw-dropper that Charlie Blackburn had shown up at the bank Thursday with $5,700 worth of checks and notes supposedly signed by Jap. He surely left unsaid his own duplicity in ignoring Jap's interests by authorizing payment of the checks and notes after only a glance at the signatures.

Driven by a greedy desire to recover the bank's money, Virgil Evans had turned a blind eye to patently suspicious circumstances. Instead of a brief delay to verify authenticity of the note and checks, Evans was more than pleased to rely upon Charlie Blackburn's good faith—the very same man, whom only days earlier he had suspected of planning to leave the country to avoid his debts! It was a litany that Virgil didn't wish to recite, so he ducked the task. "Simp, according to Charlie, he's done sold his farm to Jap. I would give Charlie a call and see what he knows."[5]

That's exactly what Simp did. The wires of the Stoutland Independent Phone Company were burning that Sunday afternoon.

Charlie denied any knowledge of the whereabouts of Simp's brother. However, he confirmed that he had agreed to sell his farm to Jap. "He was supposed to meet me in Leb'non on Thursday [to see about paying off the second mortgage on the farm]—but he didn't go."[6] Charlie continued:

"Me and Jap was plannin' on meetin' in Linn Creek on Tuesday to finish up the deal. Simp, you be sure and let me know if he gets in tomorrow? Shoot, I don't wanna ride all the way to Linn Creek if he ain't gonna show up."[7]

Knowing that the whole world was likely listening on the party line, Simp declined to ask the question that would have raised his anxiety to a full red alert: "How much did my brother agree to pay for your farm, Charlie?" Eleven thousand, five hundred dollars for a seven-thousand-dollar farm would have been an attention-getter.

When he got off the phone, Simp spoke heatedly to Ida:

"Charlie Blackburn says Jap is gonna buy his farm! Why, that doesn't make a durned bit of sense. He's never said a thing in the world to us about it. Good God! Jap has got more farm now than the two of us can take care of. Besides, the last thing that Jap told me when we wuz a-fixin' fence was that Charlie was sellin' his farm to Joe Givens and couldn't pay him for the cattle until Joe paid him. And now Jap's a-buyin' it? That's some fine how-do-you-do!"

Standing and shaking his head for a while, Simp exclaimed resolutely, "Ida, I don't believe a word of it! I don't know why, but Charlie Blackburn is a-lyin' like a dog a-trottin'. I'm worried about Jap—real worried!"

Simp then rode into Stoutland and mailed off the following notice published in the *Linn Creek Reveille* and the *Laclede County Republican* at Lebanon:

> Information Wanted[8]
>
> Information is wanted of J.J. Francis who disappeared November 9th or 10th, 1915, from his home about 6 miles north of Stoutland, Mo. He is about 5 feet six inches high, weighs 150 lbs., dark hair and mustache and gray eyes. He was riding a large sorrel horse with white hind feet and blazed face.
>
> Address Simp Francis
> Stoutland, Mo.

While in town, Simp wrote up several placards and slipped them under the doors of the general stores and other businesses to be placed in their front windows on Monday. The same "Information Wanted" notice was left at the office of an upstart weekly newspaper, the *Stoutland News*. This fine little publication claimed to be the "Real Local Newspaper, one fit for your children to read." Within a week, the words "Murdered" and "Assassin" blared forth on its front page, hardly the stuff for those of tender years.[9] The edition sold like hotcakes.

Simp questioned the few people that he met on the street but learned nothing. Remarkably, neither Wes Scrivner nor Rube Winfrey was out and about that quiet Sunday afternoon. If so, Simp would have been enlightened at warp speed. Unfortunately, the near-freezing outside temperature and the lack of "action" downtown kept them indoors. It was just too danged cold! Where are the busybodies when one really needs them?

Arriving home at about 3:00, Simp decided that it was time to call the Law. "Ida, ring up central and let's see if we can get the Sheriff's office at Linn Creek; I don't care if it is long distance, we've got to let them know. I may look like a danged fool later, but I'd rather not wait any longer."

Amazingly, the phone lines were not down and W.T. Salsman, Camden County Sheriff, answered the phone at his living quarters located in the first floor of the jail.

Hearing the facts, Salsman said, "Sir, it sounds to me like we better start looking for your brother. There may be a good explanation, but maybe not—I'll send my deputy, Sam Paxton, over there tomorrow and see what he can find out. And Mr. Francis, since Stoutland is right on the county line, I would advise you to alert Sheriff Hufft over at Lebanon, too. He's a good man, and I think he'll want to help."

Sure enough, the "Montreal Items" published November 19 in the *Linn Creek Reveille*, noted that, "Sam Paxton, of Linn Creek, was in town Monday." On his way to Stoutland to investigate a missing person, Paxton stood out in the little crossroads hamlet of Montreal. The Senior Deputy Sheriff of Camden County was bigger than life. Standing 6'2" and weighing a compact and muscular 240 pounds, Sam had bright blue eyes, a ruddy face, and a walrus mustache. Sporting an oversized silver star on his "duster" overcoat, a broad brimmed Stetson hat, scuffed boots with ringed spurs, and a heavy gunbelt holding a long-barreled Colt 45 with full compliment of cartridges, Paxton presented an intimidating presence. A double-barreled shotgun, sheathed in a saddle holster, completed the arsenal.

Like a Nimitz-class aircraft carrier offshore of a third-world country, Sam Paxton projected the power of the State to the outer reaches of Camden County. Long before the creation of a state police force, Sam Paxton represented the full weight of Missouri law in the hinterlands. He had a role to play on a big stage, and he fit the part.

Seated on a large gray American Saddlebred horse resembling Robert E. Lee's "Traveler," Sam Paxton could put the fear of the Lord in malefactors. One desperado decided, with guns blazing, to flee to the woods rather than submit to an arrest warrant. After fair warning, Paxton shot him dead. When dealing with honest citizens, Sam was an amiable man with a hearty laugh. With those of other persuasions, Sam was short on patience. Sam Paxton didn't suffer fools or lawbreakers lightly. Sam would later be elected Sheriff of Camden County and become something of a legend. Today, he just needed to find Jap Francis.

Arriving at Simp Francis's farm shortly after noon, Paxton learned that the last time Simp had seen his brother was the previous Tuesday as he departed for the Peters sale at Toronto. After penciling a few notes, Paxton invited Simp to accompany him to Stoutland. Stopping at each house along the way, including the Blackburn place, they turned up no useful information. Charlie was nowhere to be found. Skip Archer volunteered that he had seen nothing of Jap since he had briefly stopped by the farm 9 days earlier, Saturday, November 6.

Paxton and Simp interviewed most of the merchants and farmers in Stoutland but learned nothing. Stepping into the People's Bank, Paxton's imposing presence loosened Virgil Evan's tongue, and Rollie Smith was more than happy to disclose his last conversation with Jap and how it seemed to conflict with Charlie Blackburn's presentment of $5,700 of Jap's checks and notes to the bank in payment for his farm.

"Why, Jap said that Charlie was a-sellin' his farm to Joe Givens and for us to be sure and get the bank's money!" exclaimed Rollie.

Simp Francis asked to see the checks and notes, but Virgil Evans put him off. Stuttering for once, he replied, "W-Well, Simp, y-yuh know they're filed away in the safe. We'd have to open it up and look—it might take us uh, uh, a little while to find 'em."

Puzzled by his boss's reluctance to produce the documents, Rollie Smith, a young man who believed in Sunday school and doing the right thing, blurted out, "Simp, the last thing I heard Jap say when he was in last week was that he was a comin' back the next day to find out where the returns on his cattle had went, and we ain't seen a thing of him since."

The words chilled Simp Francis to the bone. A premonition that he would never see his brother alive slipped through the door of his consciousness and took a seat.

Anxious to move on, Paxton commanded, "You boys keep your hands on all that there paperwork—we might need it later."

"Oh, yes sir, Sam, we will—we sure will," chirped Virgil Evans respectfully.

For the rest of his life, Simp Francis would regret not demanding to see the checks and notes right then and there.

Stopping in the *Stoutland News* office, Paxton had a stack of "Missing Man" posters printed off. "Simp, you put some of these around town, and I'll tack 'em up all the way from here to Linn Creek."

It was getting late in the afternoon, and Sam Paxton had little to go on other than Jap Francis apparently had a business deal going with Charlie Blackburn. Conflicting versions of the transaction had surfaced. The best way to settle the matter was to find Jap Francis—one way or the other. Paxton learned that Jap occasionally traveled away on stock-buying trips. But he had never left without telling his brother where he was going and about when he expected to return.

"Maybe he just plumb forgot," said Paxton. "Yuh know, we all get a little forgetful in middle age."

"I reckon it's possible, but I sure doubt it," replied Simp.

"Sooner or later, most missin' people show up safe and sound, and it's usually just a misunderstandin'," continued Paxton. "If his horse threw him somewhere or he got waylaid by somebody, you'd a' thought the animal would have come home by now."

Simp Francis wasn't satisfied and shook his head, his face stricken with worry. Paxton laid out a plan of action:

"We'll notify the Sheriff's offices of every county between here and Springfield and have 'em be on the lookout for a man of his description—maybe he'll turn up—but I'll tell you what, Mr. Francis, if your brother ain't showed by the end of the week, you let me know, and I'll come back over here, and we'll organize us some search parties and cover the countryside. There's a lot of territory 'tween his farm and Stoutland or 'tween here and Leb'non. Shoot, there's a million places to look for him, but by God, if we have to, we'll search every square foot of Camden and Lay-clede Counties. We'll find 'im—I guarantee it!

The sheer force of Sam Paxton's pledge heartened Simp but didn't relieve the worry.

Leaving town, Paxton tacked one of the posters on a tree on Rouse Hill near the Fulbright Road. The cold body of Jap Francis lay only about 30 paces north and east of where they stood.[10] As the pair rode north over the hill, Sam heard the hoofbeats on the ridge above but didn't attempt to nicker his presence. He had grown too weak.

Another attempt to interview Charlie Blackburn at his farm proved unsuccessful. Mary Craddock said that she didn't expect him back until after dark. Later, after parting company with Deputy Paxton, Simp called Charlie on the telephone. Intending to tell him that Jap had not returned and that it would be futile to go to Linn Creek, he thought better of it. He counseled Charlie: "If Jap told you he'd meet you tomorrow to sign those papers, he'll be there! My brother'll sure do what he said he would do." And then meaningfully, "Unless something bad has happened to him."[11]

After a pause, Charlie replied, "Yeah, I reckon I will, and if you don't mind, I'll just stop by your place on my way—just in case you've heard anything."

That evening, Billy Frederick and Ray Eddington left Stoutland and were ascending Rouse Hill with a team of mules pulling a wagon. Just as they passed the Fulbright Road, a shackle holding the front axel to the wagon came loose. Yelling "Whoa" to the mules, Billy set the brake, lit a lantern, and the men went to work. Stepping into the woods with an axe, Billy cut a small tree and trimmed it to use as a pry pole. Hoisting the wagon up, the two were able to refit and tighten the shackle back in place. Billy would state: "I was about as close as a man could be and still be in the wagon track . . ." to where Jap Francis lay. Neither of the men saw nor smelled anything unusual.[12]

The rain, followed by chilly weather and a prevailing westerly wind, were conspiring to hide the remains of Jasper Francis.

In Stoutland, a kerosene lamp burned late into the evening at the People's Bank. The window shades were carefully drawn, but a silhouetted figure could be seen moving about inside. Passersby assumed it was the cashier, Virgil Evans, catching up on important paperwork. They were right.

Chapter 19

Early Tuesday morning, Charlie Blackburn met Simp Francis at Jasper's house. Simp confirmed that he still had heard nothing from his brother. By all appearances, Charlie was on his way to Linn Creek to meet Jap at the Camden County courthouse.[1] There, they would record the deed for the farm sale—assuming that Jap Francis materialized out of the ether.

Simp had a few probing questions for his visitor. "Charlie, how much did Jap agree to pay you for your place?"

"Eleven thousand, five hundred dollars altogether, takin' into account the cattle and the mules,"[2] confidently replied Charlie.

Stunned, Simp stared open-mouthed at Charlie for a long moment. Composing himself and with the tone of a man who has made up his mind about something, Simp responded, "That's a pretty penny for your farm, Charlie. Just how long have you and Jap been talkin' about this deal?"

"Oh, quite a while, I reckon a month or two," replied Charlie. "He finally decided to put his cattle in on the bargain instead of just sellin' 'em outright. It took us a little while to get 'er all firmed up."

"Did Jap sign anything on this—have you got a contract with Jap?"

"Why, I reckon I do—you know he wrote the partiklars all up in that little red book he's always got with 'im. Shoot, he already wrote me a couple a' checks and a note for a lot of it, and he's gonna take over my mortgage, and then he'll just give me a second mortgage and some money for the rest."[3]

Simp Francis had heard enough. He wasn't buying a word of it. It was inconceivable that Jap would have spent several weeks negotiating the purchase of a farm without mentioning a word to his brother and closest confidant.[4] Simp Francis had never read *Hamlet*, but if he had, he would have blurted: "The lady doth protest too much, methinks."

Casting his hands palms out toward Charlie in the universal body language of disbelief and dismissal, Simp interrupted Charlie's monologue: "Like I said, Charlie, if Jap agreed to this deal and said he'd meet you in Linn Creek—he'll be there! I suggest that you go on to Linn Creek—he may be waitin' for you right now."

Mounting his horse, Charlie took an ominous new tack: "I ain't sayin' anything bad has happened to Jap and a' course we hope not, but if it turns out that somethin' has, I reckon that you and the family would go ahead with the sale, wouldn't yuh? It's a finished deal, agreed to fair and square!"

Leering at Simp, Charlie pursed his lips as if to whistle. Simp chewed at the corner of his mouth, staring intently into Charlie's eyes. After several uncomfortable seconds, the interrogator averted his gaze. Nodding his head slowly up and down, as if divining Charlie's thoughts, Simp Francis quietly replied in a voice honed as sharply as Damascus steel, "I don't expect it'll come to that, Charlie; I don't expect it'll come to that."

Charlie shrugged and, without farewell, urged his horse north toward Linn Creek. But no one ever recalled his presence in that fair city Tuesday, November 16, 1915.

Dissatisfied with Deputy Sam Paxton's leisurely plan to search for his missing brother, Simp called Sheriff John Hufft of Laclede County. Hufft, a Republican, had been elected in 1912 and would serve out his four-year term in 1916. A long-time acquaintance of the Francis brothers and a fellow member of the Odd Fellows Lodge, Sheriff Hufft sensed the worry in Simp Francis's voice. They agreed to meet in Stoutland that very afternoon. Hufft would come to Stoutland by flagging the first eastbound freight out of the county seat at Lebanon. The Frisco was required by law, if safety permitted, to provide emergency law-enforcement passage. Hufft boarded the caboose and rode along with the conductor and brakeman.

Simp was urgently playing catch up. It was time to view the checks and the note purportedly signed by his brother. He would brook no further delay. Arriving at the People's Bank around noon, Simp again asked to see them.

"Well, Simp, we don't ordinarily open up the books to anybody but people on the account or the law," whined Virgil Evans.

"My brother ain't ordinarily missing, with somebody claiming to have sold him a farm for a hell of a lot more that it's worth," replied Simp.

Discretion being the better part of valor, Virgil made an exception. In a matter of seconds, the checks and note that only the day before seemed beyond reach were tossed under the bars of the teller's cage.

The $1,500 and $1,200 checks had been written on identical unnumbered preprinted People's Bank of Stoutland checks. The checks were printed on fairly flimsy translucent paper. The $3,000 note was written on a "fill in the blanks" promissory note form printed on heavier cardstock paper.

Simp Francis had signed and received many checks and a few notes in his lifetime. He had never seen any cancelled in the manner of the note before him. The blue ink signature had been neatly stamped over twice with a black ink stamp with the following words encircled:

> Paid
> Peoples Bank
> of Stoutland
> Nov. 11, 1915

Jap Francis's signature had been virtually obliterated.[5] Turning the documents over, Simp noticed that the same "Paid" stamp had been placed in the usual location, below the endorsement block on both the checks and the note. Turning a quizzical eye to Virgil, Simp commented, "'Pears to me like the Bank was mighty happy to accept this note—somebody stamped all over it, includin' the signature."

"Oh, that's just the way we do 'em—we always stamp notes on the front and the back," replied Virgil in his best officious banker manner. "Rollie musta been doin' a bunch of 'em at the end of the day and happened to hit the signature on that one—ain't that right, Rollie?"

Standing nearby, Rolla Smith had lost his bouncy, upbeat approach to customer relations. With averted eyes and in a soft monotone, Rollie replied, "I reckon that's right, Virgil, I reckon so."

Examining the note carefully, Simp found the filled-in portions reading "Charles Blackburn" and "$3,000" seemed to be in Jap's handwriting and written with his newly acquired fountain pen. The signature, or at least the portions visible under the bank's stamps, appeared similar to Jap's but somehow stilted, as if written slowly and carefully. Likewise, the body of the $1,500 check seemed to be in Jap's handwriting, but the signature, although similar to Jap's and a better facsimile than the note signature, looked somehow too "pat." The body of the $1,200 check, written in pencil, was clearly in the hand of someone other than Jap. Jap's signature, however, was in the same blue ink as the others.

Holding the one check over the other against the sun streaming in the ceiling skylight and aligning the signatures, they appeared to be nearly identical—too identical.

Simp Francis decided to keep his suspicions to himself. At this point, he did not know who to believe and who to trust. His brother was inexplicably missing, and Charlie Blackburn was claiming to have sold his farm to Jap at an exorbitant price. Jap had told the Bank that he was coming in on the 10th to see where the money for his cattle had gone, hardly the action of a man selling his cattle as part of a farm deal. To top it off, the checks and note paid by the People's Bank of Stoutland on his brother's account looked suspect.

The urgent, repetitive whistle of a Frisco freight making a screeching unscheduled stop at Stoutland interrupted his thoughts. Tossing the documents back across the counter, Simp announced, "I've got to go see a man." While opening the front door, Simp reminded Virgil, "Don't forget, Sam Paxton told you to hang on to these papers—there may be some people who'll need to see them again."

"We'll keep 'em safe and sound, yes sir, yes sir, safe and sound," was Virgil's reassuring reply.

Simp was already gone, slamming the door and rattling the windowpanes as he departed. He nearly tripped over Minnie Blackburn passing by on the sidewalk.

Surprised, but ever the gentleman, Simp tipped his hat and greeted Minnie with a respectful, "How do you do, Miz Blackburn?" Sensing opportunity in this unguarded moment, he quickly asked, "Say, I understand my brother is intendin' to buy the old Craddock place from you and Charlie. You know, Minnie, that's sure a surprise to me. Jap hasn't told me a thing about it. When did you first find out about it?"

Waving her gloved hand dismissively, Minnie replied, "Oh, Simp, you know Charlie never tells me what he's up to—why, I've only known about it a day or two myself."[6]

Minnie then swished away in a cloud of Coty perfume. It was a breathtaking admission. Later, Minnie Blackburn would vehemently deny "saying any such thing."

Sheriff Hufft of adjoining Laclede County was as polished and buttoned-down as Camden County's Sam Paxton was scuffed and disheveled. With highly shined ankle-length dress shoes, blue vested serge suit, and a dark Homburg hat, Hufft could easily have been mistaken for a haberdasher of fine men's wear. A warming trend early in the week had brought the afternoon temperature to a pleasant 63 degrees. Overheated by the coal stove in the train's caboose, Hufft had removed his gray wool herringbone overcoat and draped it over his arm. A trim mustache and brown twinkling eyes completed the picture of a man who liked meeting and greeting people.

John Hufft was a man of action and a problem-solver. Although he appeared something of a dandy, pinned on his suit coat was a sterling-silver star signifying the arrival of a powerful civilizing influence on barroom fights and battles-of-the-sexes turned violent. A Smith and Wesson .38 Special revolver, tucked discreetly away in a shoulder holster, provided the necessary firepower if reason fell victim to ignorance, malice, or strong drink.

With an athletic step, Hufft bounded off the steps of the caboose's trailing platform. The brakeman, waving a green flag, immediately signaled the engineer to proceed at maximum speed. A glance at the Frisco's train orders for the day informed the crew that they were being followed by a passenger train only 15 minutes behind. With little time to lose, they would be siding at Crocker, some 20 miles east, to permit the faster train to pass.

Simp greeted Sheriff Hufft just outside the depot and they walked quickly to the City and ordered the plate special and black coffee. Out of his jurisdiction just over the Camden County line, Hufft was dispensing with technicalities. He wanted to help find his friend, Jap Francis. Well known in Stoutland, Hufft was greeted by several well-wishers offering to help.

"Sheriff, you put out the word, and we'll have 50 men out at Jap's place headin' in any direction you want us to go," offered Dave McClure, a neighbor of the Francises.

What Hufft heard didn't sound good.

"Maybe I'm just imaginin' things and have got me a bad case of the jitters, but none of this adds up," complained Simp between forkfuls of roast beef and mashed potatoes. "I don't believe Jap had any thought of buyin' Charlie Blackburn's farm, yet there's a check and a note over at the bank written out by him to Charlie, and another one, too, that maybe he signed. I don't know about the signatures. They don't look right to me, but the dad-burned bank stamped 'Paid' all over one of 'em. Who knows whether he really signed 'em or not? Rollie Smith says Jap had planned to come into town last Wednesday to see about the money on the cattle that he sold to Charlie Blackburn, yet Charlie says that was all just part of the farm deal."

As the words came tumbling out, Hufft listened carefully, slathered a hot yeast roll with fresh butter, and quietly began to eat. Simp speculated, "Maybe he's off on a cattle-buyin' trip. Maybe he got robbed. Maybe he's a-layin' hurt or dead in a ravine somewhere!"

Finally, speaking low to not be overheard, Simp voiced his darkest fear, "John, somehow, I just wonder if Charlie Blackburn knows where Jap is?"

Finishing his cup of coffee and fastidiously wiping his mouth with a napkin, Hufft summed it all up: "As much as I hate to say it, Simp, I think we've got to accept the fact that something bad may have happened to Jap." In a quiet, sober voice, he continued, "If what you say about his habits is true, it sure seems to me he'd a let you know he was leavin' or he would have sure been home by now. And you know very well that big horse of his would have come home if he could."

Leaning forward, almost whispering, Hufft looked Simp in the eyes and voiced what was on Simp's mind: "Simp—I always like to look on the bright side and hope for the best. But at this point, we may just be lookin' for a body. If we are, we're way too late now anyhow." Hufft offered some advice:

"Before we round up a bunch of search parties, why don't you go back to Leb'non with me today and we'll ask around town—maybe somebody remembers seein' Jap since he disappeared. If I was you, I'd catch the early train tomorrow to Conway and see if anybody around the stockyards has seen him.

"When you come back through town tomorrow evenin'—you come by my house. If nobody has seen him, we better go over and see Don Vernon, he's a damned fine lawyer, and it don't hurt a bit that he's a good Republican! Don and his partner, Claude Mayfield, will know what to do about Charlie Blackburn and this here farm deal. We'll call 'em—it don't matter the hour."

Simp agreed to the plan, paid the check, and walked with Hufft back to the depot where John Frey flagged the next westbound freight. The sun was already low in the sky.

Sam was indeed in a ravine, hurt and starving to death. He hadn't gone anyplace. He was so stiff, he could hardly move. The warming of temperatures from Sunday morning's frigid cold had given him some relief, but he was losing weight fast and so desperate for nourishment that he had begun to strip the bark from the tree that held him. Holocaust concentration-camp inmates boiled and ate their shoes, seeking to put something—anything with the slightest nourishment—in their stomachs. In desperation, Sam choked the coarse bark of the blackjack oak down his dry throat. This indigestible form of wood cellulose brought on painful stomach cramps, but the feeling of mass in his stomach, no matter how foreign, briefly relieved his raging hunger.

But it was not hunger that was about to kill Sam. He had not been watered in six days. A couple of pints, licked from tree vegetation during the rainstorm, could not sustain him. Soon, without more water, dehydration would shut down his organs. A brief high fever would follow, and then he would die. Moist breezes now streaming up from the Gulf of Mexico, colliding with a fast-moving "Alberta Clipper" sweeping down from Canada, would inevitably produce precipitation. But when and what form would it take? Nature's clock was nearing midnight for Sam.

The man who consigned Sam to a slow, agonizing death by tying him to that blackjack oak was a coward without a conscience. Afraid to free Sam but equally afraid to put a bullet through his brain, he tied him up and just walked away. As the days wore on, fully aware of Sam's life or death dilemma, he did nothing. He chose to just wait it out.

Sam's mouth was swollen and infected from the bit in his mouth and the tearing of tissue from violent attempts to escape. His head was down and he was motionless. A pair of coyotes had passed nearby the night before. Upwind from Sam, they had not noticed him and continued their meandering trot through the woods, noses down, seeking much smaller game. Unknown to Sam, he had been staked out by a more serious predator. Observing him with curiosity, a ferocious hunter was calculating when to make a move. Sam's last reserve of strength, bequeathed to him at foal from his high-bred mother and his powerful but unknown sire, would soon be needed.

Chapter 20

Returning from Lebanon late Tuesday evening, Simp Francis rode north over Rouse Hill toward home. For the third time in three days he passed close by where his brother's mortal remains lay and within a "half a quarter" of where Jap's prized fox-trotter horse stood with dry, swollen tongue, dying from thirst.

Simp had run into a passing acquaintance, Guy Stanton in Lebanon, who claimed he had seen a horse and rider matching the description of Jap and Sam in Lebanon a few days earlier. He said he had later seen the same horse "up near Phillipsburg."[1] For Simp, it was a straw to cling to and a reason to take Sheriff Hufft's advice to inquire around the stockyards of Conway and Phillipsburg.

Simp's older brother, Thomas Benjamin "Ben" Francis and his entire family, bag and baggage, were due to arrive in Stoutland by train the following Tuesday. They had made a two-year odyssey to South Dakota and California, grown homesick, and were returning to their farm.[2] Simp had posted a letter to his brother on Monday hoping to break the news of Jap's disappearance before the family left California. He valued Ben's judgment and wished he would arrive sooner. "Ben's always had a good head when there's trouble, and we've got trouble a-plenty," mumbled Simp to himself. "Maybe Jap'll turn up or at least we'll know something by the time they get here." They would.

Arriving home, Simp told Ida what he'd learned and his planned trip to search for his brother. She was not impressed. "I've heard that fellow Stanton is just a big wheeler-dealer windbag. I don't think you're gonna find out a thing by goin' all the way down to Phillipsburg. If he had gone there, he'd a' been back by now," she argued. Voice trembling, Ida continued, "You'd do better lookin' closer around here—God knows what somebody's done to Jap! I don't think he's very far from here—we just don't know where!"

Putting his arms around her, Simp tried to give comfort:

"Honey, I know—I know, but the word's been out since Sunday and I've looked everywhere I know to look. We're gonna start a search with a bunch of men on Thursday. Maybe there's an explanation. Maybe he'll still show up. But I've just gotta make sure that nobody saw him down thatta way. Maybe somebody waylaid him and robbed him and took Sam. Lord only knows. If they did, he could be anywhere between here and there!"

The dam holding Ida's emotions broke. Between labored breaths she sobbed out what had been on her mind all day. She spoke in the earnest, heartbroken tones of a little girl who had broken her favorite china doll: "The last time I saw Jap—he said he reckoned he wouldn't want to go to heaven—if he couldn't—if he couldn't take some of my raisin pie with him. And now he's a-missin'! And I'll never be bakin' him nothing ever again in this old world!"

Ida ran and threw herself on the bed, crying without consolation. In her woman's intuitive heart, she knew Jap Francis would not be coming home. His throat constricted and burning, Simp did not attempt a reply. He quickly turned away and, wiping his eyes with his shirtsleeves, headed for the barn to tend the animals. There was comfort in that. They waited expectantly to be fed, watered, curried, and milked. Simp could do something for them. He would try to do something for his brother in the morning.

In bed by 8 P.M. and before sinking into a fitful and unrewarding sleep, Simp heard the arrival of gusty winds and the first few large raindrops on the sheet-iron roof. By 9:00, the squall line had passed, leaving a steady, gentle drizzle that would continue most of the night.[3] A rain that falls slowly, soaking into the subsoil and resting there, replenishing wells and waiting to nourish newly planted crops in the spring. The kind of rain that is God's blessing to farmers. Rain welcomed by all creatures, great and small. Simp yawned, turned on his side, wrestled with his goose-down pillow and thought, "I'm sure gonna need my slicker and rubber boots in the mornin'."

Wednesday, November 17, 1915
11:00 A.M.

Charlie Blackburn had no knack for avoiding his nemesis, Wes Scrivner. After the rain had eased to a light mist, Charlie had ridden into town in the late morning. He stopped by Minnie's house and then headed to Burhams Drug Store to buy some headache powder for his ailing wife. He never made it—at least not for a while. With the predatory cunning and split-second timing of modern day paparazzi, Wes swept open the front door of Calkin and Evans General Store. Charlie's leisurely stroll was unexpectedly blocked. He either had to stop or step off the elevated sidewalk into a mudhole. Wes Scrivner could have taught the Viet Cong a thing or two about ambushes. Charlie never had a chance.

"Well, if it ain't Charlie Blackburn! Whud-duh-yuh-know, Charlie?" Without a millisecond hesitation, Wes got down to business: "I hear Jap Francis is turned up missin'? It's all over the country. I expect there a'lookin' for him right now. I reckon that'll queer up your deal to sell him your place? Is that about right?"

Wes waited with cocked head and squinted eyes while holding the door ajar, permitting his companion chewers and spitters within to hear every word. Charlie's look was that of a cornered cobra confronting a mongoose—dull hatred mixed with cool appraisal. Aware that his reply was being monitored, he chose his words carefully: "I don't reckon so a-tall—I figger the deal is gonna go through just fine." Assuming his pursed-lip mannerism, Charlie stood glaring at Wes, wondering what was coming next.

Columbo could not have devised a craftier gambit than Wes Scrivner, a man with a fourth-grade education:

"Why sure, Charlie, Jap is gone but he ain't dead! He'll undoubtedly turn up one of these here days—why I'll swear, I saw him in Leb'non just yestidy. He was a movin' away from me, but hit shore looked like that big, white stockin'ed geldin' of his'n to me! Shoot, Charlie, if the trade is like Minnie said it was, you couldn't blame old Jap for takin' to his heels!"[4]

Charlie Blackburn was not amused. Either Minnie had been running her mouth to the biggest gossip in town or Wes was lying, feigning knowledge that he didn't have, hoping to sucker Charlie into disclosing details of the farm sale. With flushed face, he chose to change the subject: "Mebbe so, Wes, mebbe so—look here, I gotta get to the drugstore; Minnie's got a splittin' headache."

When Charlie tried to step around his antagonist and be on his way, Wes dropped the bomb. "I suppose you fellers have a contract to the effect of that there trade?" Inside the store, heads with cupped ears leaned forward expectantly.

Charlie Blackburn blew his cool. Pointing and shaking his finger at Wes, Charlie angrily exclaimed, "We damned sure do have a contract and that contract is wrote out on two sheets of paper and folded together and is put down in that little red book that Jap always carried in his pocket!"[5]

Charlie's finger was now pecking on the elderly man's chest. "And when they find Jap Francis, they'll find that little book with that contract in it."[6] Charlie then shoved the door aside, rudely pushed past Wes, and stalked away.

Score one for Wes Scrivner and he knew it. The old can be bold, and he had successfully goaded Charlie Blackburn into a statement that would be duly noted at a later time and a different place. With a satisfied possum grin resembling none other than Lyndon B. Johnson at his manipulative best, Wes stepped back inside and returned to his place on the communal bench next to the potbellied stove. Instant analyses from Wes's little coterie of supporters signaled a big "thumbs down" for Charlie.

"He seems awful durned sure that when they *do* find Jap, they're gonna be searchin' his body," hotly declared an old-timer with a high-pitched voice.

"Hit seems like he may know some things that we don't!" offered another.

If their aged ears had not been so tinny, they might also have noticed that Charlie had used the past-tense verb "carried" rather than "carries" when describing the little red book.[7]

The amateur investigators duly assembled in the general store next to the Odd Fellows Hall weren't aware of the discrepancy between Charlie's description to Simp Francis of the contract as "partiklars all wrote up in that little red book he's always got with him" to the expanded claim of a contract "wrote out on two sheets of paper."

A lie is a wonderful thing. It is soft and malleable and alluringly attractive. It has perfect elasticity. It can expand without boundaries or contract into a black hole, sucking its protesting victims at the speed of light into an oblivion where reputations find their resting place. Truth is hard and brittle. It is lonely and homely and hard to look upon. It has fixed boundaries. If stretched, it cannot still be called truth. It has mass and form and staying power. Truth is never as popular as a lie. Its tellers are left naked and vulnerable, dressed only in the clothes of their convictions. Truth demands courage. Any coward can spin a lie.

Ida Francis was right about the futility of her husband's journey down the Frisco Line to the cattle towns of Phillipsburg and Conway. Beef was "king" in the flat terrain and grassy fields of southern Laclede County. A prime location for breeding herds producing feeder calves, the towns were often destinations for men like Jap and Simp Francis. Such men used their land to grow and fatten the weaned calves to an age of 14–18 months. They then shipped the steers and heifers to slaughterhouses in St. Louis, Missouri, and East St. Louis, Illinois. If, like the Francis brothers, a man's land was unencumbered, he could absorb one or two or maybe even several bad years in the cattle markets. If he was mortgaged to the hilt like Charlie Blackburn, the cattle business was fraught with risk.

Quick access to the Frisco Railroad for both buyers and shippers of cattle was crucial. Much of the line's corporate slogan, "Ship it on the Frisco," was earned by the hundreds of loaded cattle cars, reeking of crowded and frightened beef on the hoof, winding their way to the bloody and foul abattoirs of Chouteau, Vandeventer, and North Market Streets in St. Louis. Swift, Morrel, Krey, Wilson, Independent, and other slaughterers and packers of meat formed a giant maw, taking in live cattle and producing sliced, chopped, and ground protein for the masses. The packers prayed for "good runs" (big supply) to lower prices and fatten profits. Raisers prayed that their peers would produce few cattle, pushing prices higher. Demand pumped up by an occasional war made both parties happy, at least for a while.

Simp alighted from the train at the Phillipsburg depot by 9:00 A.M. Wednesday morning. The local auctioneer and cattle hands were acquainted with Jap Francis but hadn't seen him in months. A tour up the main street, checking at restaurants, rooming houses, stores, and even the barbershop, produced uniform results. Blank faces turned to concerned faces. Hats were removed and scalps scratched. Heads slowly shaking in the negative told the story. Nobody had seen Jap Francis. All were politely concerned. "I sure hope you find him" and "He'll probably turn up" were the phrases of choice. Simp was appreciative but little comforted.

Discouraged, Simp hired a sturdy horse from the livery stable and rode down the road to Conway, some 3½ miles distant. He asked the same questions all over again and got the same answers. He rode back to Phillipsburg, turned in his horse, and had a hot meal at the white stucco café with blue trim next to the depot. He then settled in for the long wait to board the eastbound local that would return him 32 miles up the line to Stoutland. It was a chilly afternoon with intermittent showers, and the station agent had a cozy, warm fire burning. Exhausted of possibilities and out of ideas, it was time to get a lawyer. Using his folded slicker as a pillow on the hard bench, Simp lay down, turned the collar of his mackinaw coat up, pulled his hat over his eyes, and took a two-hour nap. Oblivious to the occasional thundering freight train, it was the best rest he'd had in days.

Chapter 21

Wednesday evening, November 17, 1915

Returning from his failed mission to Conway and Phillipsburg, Simp Francis shared supper with Sheriff Hufft and his wife at their modest but well-furnished home in Lebanon. Laura Hufft was accustomed to drop-in guests and graciously set another plate. After eating, the men trudged the few blocks to meet with attorneys Mayfield and Vernon.

A law office is a wonderful place. The smell of stale cigars, old leather, an unemptied spittoon, and a touch of mildew can brace up the softest of milquetoasts to sue his neighbor with confidence and impunity. Or, by God, prosecute those S.O.B.'s to the full extent of the law!

Donald O. Vernon and L.C. "Claude" Mayfield shared Spartan quarters located above a furniture store on Commercial Street. "Mayfield and Vernon—Attorneys at Law," painted in prominent black letters and shadowed in red, was displayed on a shingle at street level and on the office's second-floor plate-glass windows. Inside the door, a steep flight of wooden steps led those eager for legal remedies onward and upward. There they were deposited into the middle of seeming chaos. Every horizontal surface, as far as the eye could see, including the floor's perimeter, was stacked high with files, folders, law books, transcripts, and correspondence. Blue-backed case files, punched and penetrated with two-pronged brass retaining clips, topped individual stacks. Proof of a large client base and lots of billable hours was displayed everywhere.

One side of the 20' x 30' room was lined with shelves burdened with the lifeblood of justice, the Missouri Statutes, complete, annotated, and revised. In addition, row upon row of leather-bound and gold-stamped case-law books—filled with decisions, citations, and esoteric distinctions—instilled prospective clients with wonderment and awe. These records and relics of jurisprudence inspired confidence. *Black's Legal Dictionary* and various ancient scuffed volumes, seemingly as old as the English common law they contained, finished off the library.

The woman's touch was singularly lacking from the office decor. This was a male domain and looked it. A mottled maroon linoleum rug, dull and unwaxed, covered the center portion of an otherwise unfinished and splintery wooden floor. A dusty, framed copy of the Magna Carta, written in old English script, totally unreadable, graced one wall. Adding dignity to the setting was a yellowed copy of the Mayflower Compact. This venerable document, signifying the arrival of government (and, of course, lawyers) to the new world, hung tipsily with binder twine from a large nail. It seems no self-respecting law office then, or now, can accept business without displaying these seminal documents. The nicked-up frames suggested second- or third-hand provenance from venerable firms long since closed or merged.

A single, naked electric bulb hung by its cord from the pressed-tin ornamental ceiling of the era, painted slate gray. It illuminated a battered but sturdy oak partners desk with kneeholes on both sides. A four-legged stool on one side served the junior partner. A more comfortable slatted-back chair, with armrests, accommodated the wizened and often dozing senior partner. A fine, old, slant-front tabletop desk, a coatrack, and two spindle-backed client chairs completed the sparse office suite.

The Mayfield family comprised a substantial portion of Laclede County's legal talent in 1915, and more were on the way. In the Progressive Era, when initialed monikers were *de rigueur* for businessmen and professionals, L.C. "Claude" Mayfield, I.W. "Irwin" Mayfield, and W.C. "Waldo" Mayfield comprised nearly half of the county's entire supply of lawyers. Claude and his older brother, Irwin, practiced separately. Waldo shared an office with his father, Irwin. The Mayfield family's roots run deep in Laclede County. A township in the northeast corner near Stoutland is named after an ancient forbearer of the clan.

Donald O. Vernon, veteran E.B. Kellerman, a 24-year-old upstart by the name of Phil M. Donnelly, and the State's Attorney, D.D. McDonald, rounded out Lebanon's largess of legal advisors. When Simp Francis came calling, the worried innocent just needed a little advice. But this case would offer more—so much more. Legions of barristers and jurists would soon be summoned to battle.

Mayfield and Vernon were solid country lawyers, well versed in civil and criminal procedure. The vast portion of their work involved civil matters of real estate, wills and probate, divorces, a few business incorporations, and run-of-the-mill lawsuits. Most criminal cases involved nothing more serious than hot checks, a little livestock rustling, or common assaults incited by liberal quantities of John Barleycorn.

With a long face made longer by a drooping Winchester mustache, Claude Mayfield, 47, could hardly be called handsome. But his weathered visage, hardy and masculine, punctuated with keen blue eyes, inspired trust, the coin of the realm for a good lawyer. Mayfield possessed a rumbling voice and a contemplative disposition. When Claude spoke, people listened. Dressed in a rumpled suit and western-style ribbon bowtie, Mayfield could have been cast as Wyatt Earp in an early Hollywood Western.

Don Vernon, 44, was as direct and verbose as Mayfield was circumspect and reserved. Clean-shaven, with a chiseled, handsome face, Vernon cut a distinguished figure around town. Always dressed in a neatly pressed suit, tightly knotted Windsor, and a starched shirt, he could have been the Van Heusen shirt model.

When Jap Francis and Sheriff Hufft arrived, pleasantries were brief. The exchanges quickly became as intense as the subject was sobering. Fraud and possible murder focused the minds of everyone in the room as Simp Francis poured out what he knew of his brother's mysterious disappearance. The antennae of both lawyers went up as Simp described the presentation of checks and notes by Charles Blackburn, emptying Jasper Francis's bank account less than two days after he was last seen alive. Jap's threats of legal action against Charlie Blackburn raised eyebrows. Vernon jotted down voluminous notes and asked a number of clarifying questions. When it was all out, Simp waited for the lawyers' reaction. Mayfield and Vernon exchanged glances. Vernon cleared his throat and spoke first:

"Mr. Francis, if your brother should show up, this could be nothing and we shouldn't jump to conclusions. But if he doesn't, this is a very serious matter and we need to proceed carefully. The facts, as I understand them, suggest that Mr. Blackburn can produce no bonafide contract in which your brother agreed to buy his farm at any price, leave alone the stated price of $11,500, which you believe to be outlandish. There's been a lot of money changing hands here for which there seems to be no basis in law. At the moment, it seems to me that the recovery of those funds is something that we can try to do something about. That's a civil matter. If, as you suspect, it turns out that Mr. Blackburn was involved with your brother's disappearance, that's a criminal matter. That would be taken up in due course by the authorities within the appropriate jurisdiction, depending upon, well—to state it plainly—where he may eventually be found."

Vernon then deferred to the older Mayfield, who had been listening quietly, fingers laced, chin resting on thumbs. "What do you think, Claude?"

Uncrossing his legs and pushing his hat back on his head, Claude Mayfield already had a plan:

"Given what we know, I believe that time is of the essence. I would recommend that you and your brother Ben Francis file to be named as administrators of Jasper Francis's estate just as soon as possible. If Mr. Francis should turn up, it'll all be moot. But if he doesn't, his assets are in need of a conservator. I believe a judge would grant it in these unusual circumstances. My God, the man's bank account may have been pillaged without any proof of contract whatsoever. Now then—Mr. Francis, you and your brother, as administrators, need to file what we call an "attachment suit." That suit will seek a writ claiming any and all funds and property of Mr. Blackburn and his wife, up to the amount that may have improperly changed hands. That needs to be done just as fast as it can be prepared—while these assets may still be liquid. If Blackburn's in as much debt as we think, he may go illiquid pretty durned soon—if not already. If he does, it may take years to get it back and it'll probably only be cents on the dollar."

Vernon interjected, "I think you're right, Claude, and just by summoning Charlie and his wife before a judge, they may be persuaded to settle this case out of court—that would be the best thing. That is, if we can come to a fair agreement."

Simp agreed to engage Mayfield and Vernon to prepare the suit against the Blackburns on a contingent basis. The lawyers would be entitled to 30 percent of any or all of Jap Francis's money recovered from Charlie and Minnie Blackburn.[1]

After shaking hands, Simp prepared to depart into the night to reclaim his horse for the long ride home. Rousing himself to a standing position, Mayfield had two more recommendations: "You stay away from Blackburn—don't you talk with him or meet with him unless you've got counsel present. Furthermore, don't you or your wife discuss this lawsuit with a soul until it's filed."

Punctuating what he was about to say with a stunningly accurate assault on the brass spittoon, Mayfield offered one last piece of advice:

"Mr. Francis, if it turns out that your brother has been the victim of foul play in Camden County, you had better be prepared to hire a good attorney to help the prosecution. That new fellow, Lodge, at Linn Creek, is wet behind the ears and not up to a murder case. With your permission, I'd like to contact Sid Roach; he's the best attorney in Camden County. I'll put him on notice that we may be needing his services if this thing turns out bad—that is, Mr. Francis, if you know what I mean?"

Grieved by the talk of his brother's possible demise, Simp slowly replied, "Yes, Mr. Mayfield, I know what you mean—I sure do. You go right ahead."

The prosecution's team had now been formed. All it needed was a body and some evidence. John Hufft stepped front and center with an action plan to find Jap:

"Simp, you meet me in Stoutland tomorrow morning at nine o'clock. I'm gonna bring a car and a deputy. We'll get that telephone operator to crank those party lines, and we'll get us some good old boys on horses, and we'll start searchin' the countryside for any sign of Jap. He's somewhere around there and so is that big horse of his. We've just gotta find the right place! By God, if Camden County won't do anything 'til Saturday, I'm packin' a suitcase tonight and I'll stay over there as long as it takes—until we find him."

Tears welled in Simp's eyes as he grabbed Hufft's hand and looked him square in the face.

"You're a mighty good friend to do that. My brother, wherever he is, thanks you. I want you to know, I'll never forget it."

Sheriff Hufft would find his man. It would just take awhile.

Thursday, November 18, 1915

Anyone in Stoutland who did not know that Jap Francis was missing was either deaf or off visiting Uncle Arley and Aunt Nellie in Pulaski County. Individuals and small groups of men had ridden or walked over their own and adjoining farms, looking for anything odd or suspicious. Traveling to Stoutland or other nearby destinations, they kept their eyes peeled for strangers. Untethered horses resembling Sam were rustled up and ownership established. On Main Street, small groups of men and women huddled together in subdued, anxious conversations. Nerves were unsettled and a whiff of fear was in the air.

Fear of the unknown is the natural enemy of rational thinking. Asleep, the unconscious mind slips effortlessly into a swirling black pit of paranoia. Formless, nameless, roiling terrors, buried and reburied in Freud's Id since the dawn of humanity, skulk from their uncovered crypts. Their exhumation comes effortlessly and without license. The rapid-firing synapses of the "old brain" rush at nearly the speed of light, screaming "fight or flight?" We can do neither. The heart races. Adrenaline is mainlined from the urban arteries to the distant provinces of the capillaries, grasping and twitching and paralyzing each muscle along the way. It's life or death, but movement is impossible. In full conflagration, the nightmare explodes into the deep, guttural, unworded growls of that frightened primate suppressed within us. "Maybe it can be scared away. Let's just make a lot of noise. Let's sound like we will kill it and eat it if it comes any closer!" *It* is not impressed. *It* is not intimidated. *It* has come for us. Our own vocal chords, hoarse from being pushed to impossible extremes, startle us awake. The nightmare is over, but a sweaty residue of fear leaves us sleepless and fatigued.

Locked doors and tortured dreams would be unbidden guests in Stoutland soon enough. For the present, people stood in clusters on Main Street: farmers, merchants, housewives, seamstresses, section-gang men, canning-factory workers, and common laborers alike, speculating the fate of Jap Francis.

Everybody in town knew and liked Jap. A bachelor by choice, he was respectful to women to the point of chivalry, regardless of their age, station, or reputation. He was a practicing Christian even if his attendance at church was a little irregular. When Jap hired men to help plant or cut corn, haul and pitch hay, or pick the apples, pears, and plums from the Francis orchards, he always seemed to know who was in desperate need of a "job of work." He not only hired them, but employed their frail 10- and 11-year-old boys to help. These "tagalongs" were determined to show they could work as hard as their wiry, stoop-backed fathers. "Slow down there little man—you don't have to work that hard," was Jap's repeated entreaty. "You get yourself a dipper of water, and sit over there in the shade and rest awhile."

Jap always overpaid a little and was never without help when he needed it. At butchering time, a ham, a fully salted slab of bacon and plenty of lean sausage, laced with black pepper and sage, went home to the helper's hungry family. Many a steady churchgoer could not be trusted to send more than a few spare ribs, a little dab of sausage, and the neck bones. Jap Francis's kindness to his neighbors was not going unremembered. More pointedly, they "danged well wanted to know what the Law was gonna do about it."

Promptly at 9:00 A.M., a sputtering Ford automobile ("Any color you want as long as it's black"[2]) marked with a large gold star and lettered "Laclede County Sheriff" chugged into town. The law had arrived and the people felt reassured. Sheriff Hufft and a deputy parked the sputtering contraption in front of Calkin's store. A curious crowd quickly surrounded the first police car ever seen in Stoutland, a spanking new "C" cab pickup truck.[3] The rear seat had been reinstalled to transport prisoners, and the entire bed and cab had been enclosed with enamel painted sides and a rubberized top. Two double-barreled 12-gauge shotguns, buckshot loaded, hung in a rack from the cab ceiling. These deadly firearms, along with handcuffs and other law-enforcement paraphernalia, received whispers of admiration and wonder. Law-abiding citizens took pride in this high-tech display of the stern face of the law. A vicarious shiver or two was felt by those anxious but unable to join the posse. Eager volunteers stood waiting for instructions.

Within minutes, Simp Francis arrived on horseback. By this time, several witnesses, including "Happy Jack" Jackson, had come forward. It was decided that the search party would start from where Jackson had last seen Jap and work both sides of the Decaturville road westerly all the way back to his farm. The Sheriff's car would be the moving "command post." The engine's hiccups and backfires, along with an occasional "Ahhhoooogah" from the flivver's raucous horn, would identify Hufft's location.

The telephone switchboard, located in a private home, was put into service. The good woman cranked out one long, continuous ring, normally reserved for fire emergencies, and then put Sheriff Hufft on the line. It brought results. By 10:30 A.M., 12 men on horseback, armed with an assortment of firearms, were assembled at the road intersection ¼ mile east of Charlie Blackburn's farm. Neither Charlie nor Skip Archer was among them. Hufft laid out the situation and a plan:

"Boys, Jap Francis has been missing more than a week. There's posters out on him, and Simp here has looked for him on both their farms and checked with the neighbors up and down this here road. He's been all the way down to Phillipsburg and Conway lookin' for him without any luck. Jap has flat-out disappeared without a trace. His horse, a big sorrel named Sam, never came home.

"Now then, the last anybody saw him was right where we stand, a week ago Tuesday, at about six o'clock in the evenin'. We don't know if he made it home or not. I hate to say it, but if he and that horse were harmed or tied up, they may be in an awful shape by now. We want to search everything within about a half a quarter of the road. You need to look anywhere that a man or a horse, dead or alive, could be hid. Check anything that looks suspicious—'specially any turned-up ground lookin' like maybe somethin's been buried lately. If you find anything or need me for any reason, you fire two shots, five seconds apart, and I'll come a-runnin'. A single shot will mean for everybody to come straight back to the road. We'll plan on pulling you all back in at about one o'clock."

One rough-hewn Samaritan had a question: "What about ridin' all over these folk's farms? Hell, if we have to get pur-mission from everbody along heah to look all over thur places, we'll nevah git a mile down this heah road."

"You tell 'em you're serving as official deputies of the Sheriff's Department on a missing person's search, and if they don't like it, have them come see me. I'll be easy to find right out here on this road. Now then, spread out on both sides and don't miss anything." Operating well out of his jurisdiction, John Hufft wasn't letting legal niceties get in the way of a manhunt.

Simp Francis pulled two of his most trusted friends aside. "Don't you ever repeat anything that I'm sayin', and I can't tell you why right now, but I would appreciate it if you would give Charlie Blackburn's place a real good goin' over." Simp's meaningful look told these amateur lawmen everything they needed to know.

"We won't miss a thing, Simp—we'll work 'er over with a fine-tooth comb."

It was slow, tedious work. The weather was starting to turn sour. And they were headed in the wrong direction. The locations of Jap and his horse were as obvious and as obscure as Poe's "Purloined Letter." Often, the best place to hide something is right under people's noses. Sheriff Hufft and the other searchers were fixated with the six miles of territory from where Jap was last observed, all the way back to his farm.

The notion that Francis had met his fate within hollering distance of downtown Stoutland, with his horse led away to die, escaped them. In the next few days, the searchers would ride back and forth over Rouse Hill a dozen times, always on their way to the distant and remote places where killings are supposed to take place. Places far removed from civilized folks and civilized doings. Places where dead horses are left to rot—their bones bleached by the wind, rain, and sun. Not just over on Rouse Hill, up the road and around the corner from the Fulbright place. Not just down in the rough woods by the creek on Old Man Oliver's place.

By noon, the searchers had moved only to the vicinity of the Craddock Schoolhouse on the western edge of the Blackburn farm. It started to rain and rain hard. Some searchers had slickers, most did not. Sheriff Hufft and his deputy parked at the school and fired a pistol into the air. People heard it for miles and wondered if Jap had been found.

Entering the building, Hufft reassured the teacher, Miss Georgia Laquey (pronounced "Lakeway"), that there was no reason for alarm; his men just needed shelter from the rains.

"Oh, that will be just fine, we were about to put down our books for lunch anyway."

The 16 or 17 children, ranging in ages from 5 to 16, gazed with open mouths and wide eyes upon their adult visitors, packing guns and flashing five-pointed stars of law officers.

"Children, we'll all be eating at our desks today so our visitors can use our lunch tables."

A few children carried their lunches in buckled lunch boxes designed for the purpose. Most used one-gallon lard buckets carried by the bale. The contents ranged from hard-boiled eggs to biscuit and bacon sandwiches to nothing more than a slab of cornbread with a little molasses and plenty of butter. An apple or a sugar cookie was an added luxury.

The damp and hungry men dried themselves by the woodstove and withdrew makeshift sandwiches, stuffed in pockets and saddlebags by wives eager to help.

Soon the children's awe of their adult visitors wore off and the happy din of confined and energetic little scholars had to be quieted by the gentle and lovely Miss Laquey. A few children offered surplus tidbits to the hungry searchers. The men drew strength from the youthful energy and innocence in the room, far removed from the grim search for death and the attendant evil that had brought them there.

It continued to rain. With no break in the weather in sight, at 1:30 Hufft decided to call the search off. They would convene the next morning at the school and continue their work. Some vowed to bring more men to speed the search.

In a nearby ravine, the blessed rains of Tuesday and Thursday[4] had given Sam a few reviving rivulets of life. One last reprieve before nature would carry out the sentence imposed by the man who had tied him where he stood.

Chapter 22

Sunday, November 21, 1915

It was nearly dawn and freezing cold at 30 degrees. A large cat, trekking over its hunting range, leaped across the small stream that flowed some 150 yards east of Sam's forest prison. Following a zigzag pattern, he had searched all night for food without success. Tired and hungry, he suddenly paused, alert, head up and ears perked. Crouching nearer the ground, his nose investigated the aromas wafting in the predawn breeze. Included was a scent that had become familiar. The scent of nearby game. Big game. Too big—much too risky. The stealthy hunter had detected this large animal several days earlier, standing quietly in a clump of bushes and small scrub trees. He had given it a wide berth.

More recently, foraging at evening twilight, the cat had noted the same creature in the same spot. Creeping closer, he observed the animal standing quietly, head down, but occasionally raising its legs at the knees and shifting positions. Downwind and undetected, the tawny feline had twitched its tail a few times, slouched closer to the ground, and in a few quick bounds had gotten within 50 feet of the subject of his curiosity. The cat stood with one paw raised, considering, calculating, measuring his chances. Courage failed. Unlike his lion cousins, he did not have the pride's ferocious females to do the hard work of the kill. He was on his own. This loner would have to finish what he started. Reluctantly, he had turned away and with a series of leaps, vanished into the night.

This time it would be different. Something clicked in the predator's arithmetic mind. Feeble body language plus lack of visible movement plus same exact location for several days equals a trapped and dying animal. The cat's hunger was nearly as enormous as his prey's. Forget the size. Take a chance. The stomach gnaws.

Bounding silently from log to bush to tree, the cat crept to a final attack position. Belly to the ground, its tail twitched slowly and evenly, a metronome for music both suspenseful and ominous.

Now, only feet away from the helpless prey, there was still no movement. Dwarfed in height, the cat's instinct drove him to higher ground. He needed elevation and the kinetic force of his entire body mass targeted at the neck and the jugular. Emboldened by the complete lack of response of this large prize, the cat quickly clawed his way up a nearby scrub oak and stretched his supple body on the only limb that would support him. Bent by the live weight, the tree shook violently. Taxed to its limit, the branch began to crack. Fast losing his balance, the cat could no longer wait. A missile beyond recall, he coiled on his haunches and, with a vicious snarl, leapt.

Briefly revived by the welcome rains earlier in the week, Sam had reverted to a point lower than any of his captivity. He simply could not capture enough water, free-falling in his mouth or licked from the branches and trunk of the tree that held him, to sustain life. It seemed that the tiny, inadequate ration of the precious liquid had only prolonged his agony.

Much like a hapless human falling through ice, quick-chilled in frigid water, Sam's body had gone into a similar survival mode. He was in a suspended state of animation, all but unconscious, senses dulled, unable to perceive the approach of danger. Respiration had slowed almost beyond detection. Electrolytes out of kilter from lack of sodium and potassium salts, his big heart was pumping weakly at only 20 arythmic beats per minute. Edema from poor circulation and lack of exercise was starting to fill his lungs. The digestive system was completely shut down from nothing to process and lack of osmotic fluids. His body temperature was an alarming 96 degrees, having dropped from a normal 99.7. Sam, the prized possession of those who had owned him, was a dead horse standing.

Lethal trajectory altered by the breaking limb, the big cat missed Sam's neck and landed sideways atop the saddle, still resting astride his back. Perched with his four clawed feet pulled together on the saddle's curved seat, he crouched again to make the final leap to the neck and the violent rending of the carotid arteries. With the belly cinch completely loosened by Sam's radical weight loss, the saddle gave way.[1] Instead of striking a fatal blow, the cat found himself desperately clawing to stay atop his prey. The moving carousel was a losing proposition—like a climber with failing handholds on the sheer face of El Capitan. With a yowl, the cat was deposited rudely and awkwardly on the ground. Insult to injury was delivered by the saddle's opposite-side stirrup. Drawn up and over the horse's back by the weight of the slipping saddle, it became a flail, striking the attacker's head with force sufficient to make a convincing case for flight.

Amazingly, a revived Sam was contributing to his own defense. Drawing on reserves that should not have existed, Sam roused himself from a terminal sleep. A horse is a prey animal. Big cats are the ultimate predator. Horses are terrified by the crouching, stealthy, darting movements of cats, detected at any distance. Awakening to a snarling archenemy, literally on his back, brought Sam a miraculous revival of strength and courage. Swamped with massive doses of adrenalin, his stiffened muscles rose to the challenge. Bucking like the best rodeo outlaw, Sam aided the failing saddle's slide, dispensing the cat from his back. Then, sensing movement around his feet, a well-aimed backward kick of his foreleg struck home on the startled animal, sending it rolling into the nearby bushes. Lucy Mack would have been proud! Enough was enough. The cat fled, disappearing in the blink of an eye. He did not come back. If he had, his success would have been assured.

Mountain lions, pumas, panthers, and catamounts are all the same animal; technically, *Puma concolor*. The last recorded killing of a mountain lion in Missouri was in 1927.[2] By 1915, no one had seen nor heard one around Stoutland in years. The screams in the night and the mating yowls that could make the hair of grown men stand on end had long gone silent. Women and children no longer cowered sleeplessly in their beds, behind locked cabin doors, with the coal-oil lamp left burning all night. Reportedly, the "painters" had all been killed or migrated away. Maybe. But then perhaps a lone male, ranging far from his deeply wooded lair on the Roubidoux Creek, had terrorized Sam. Maybe. Most likely it was a large, but far less lethal, bobcat. Sam didn't discern the difference. In a final frenzy, desperate to escape, Sam reared and fought the tied reins with his forelegs for the last time. Like a punch-drunk boxer jabbing at his adversary, he somehow got one leg up and over the seemingly unbreakable leather strips. Entangled at the knee, he fought to retrieve his right leg. This time he couldn't do it. Hog-tied with all of his weight bearing on only three legs, Sam was on empty, unable to move. Now, after 11 days in the woods on the back side of Rouse Hill, help was nowhere near. People were looking in all the wrong places.

Chapter 23

Delayed by rain on Thursday, the search for Jap Francis and his horse had continued on Friday and until almost dark Saturday evening. Names and faces of volunteers changed, but Sheriff Hufft, his deputy, and the weary Simp Francis remained constantly vigilant. Saturday, they had been joined by Deputy Sam Paxton of Camden County and Charlie Manes, Constable of Auglaize Township, both on horseback. A warm day with a high of 65 degrees brought out almost 50 searchers.

Hufft, the senior lawman on the scene, asked Francis's immediate neighbors to search the roadsides and overland route that Jap Francis may have taken to Lebanon. This presumed that Charlie Blackburn was telling the truth when he stated that Jap had promised to meet him there on the Thursday prior.[1] This effort proved futile.

Paxton and Manes organized other volunteers, on foot and on horseback, to search from Jap's farm back to where he was last seen. Retracing the steps of other searchers on Thursday and Friday, this hopeful group cut a nearly half-mile swath on both sides of the road, finding nothing but barbed-wire fences, curious cattle, an angry bull or two, and the bleached bones of long-dead animals.

By Saturday evening there still had been no organized search of the stretch of the Linn Creek Road from its intersection with the Decaturville Road, over Rouse Hill, and into Stoutland. It was too obvious. No one thought a man would be accosted so close to town on the well-traveled main road. No one had seen nor heard anything in this area. Besides, Francis was last observed heading in the opposite direction. It was time to begin thinking "inside the box."

The searchers agreed to suspend the search on Sunday, the Lord's Day. If nothing was found Monday, the hunt for Jap and Sam would be ended. There are limits to seeking those who vanish in thin air. Neither man nor animal had been seen in 12 days. They could be a mile or five hundred miles away. No one knew. Preachers in the pulpits of Stoutland churches prayed for Jap Francis's "safe return to the arms of his loved ones" and urged their charges to join in the search the next day.

Sheriff Hufft returned to Lebanon Saturday evening, tired and disappointed. He was at a loss for what to do next. He had promised to stay until his friend was found, but Simp Francis insisted that he go home to his family. Hufft appreciated the reprieve. Besides, the rope bed and straw ticking at Stoutland's only rooming house was treating his back with extreme prejudice.

Harold Bell Wright, the world-famous author, served as minister of the First Christian Church of Lebanon for two years before his acclaimed novel, *The Shepherd of the Hills,* was published in 1907. He promptly moved to California and stayed. By the time he died in 1934, the novel had sold 2,000,000 copies[2] and is still considered the fourth most successful novel of all time.[3]

Many in Lebanon thought the thinly disguised characters in another Wright novel, *The Calling of Dan Matthews,* reflected poorly on some of the more prominent members of his former congregation. Not Fred Hufft. Fred had known Wright well, and his thoughts turned to the preacher's book while a less-inspirational minister droned on during Sunday services.

The words of Psalms 121:1, the source of spiritual strength of Sammy Lane, *The Shepherd of the Hills*'s heroine, kept repeating themselves in John Hufft's mind. Its glorious and lofty lyric kept echoing as he thought about the search for Jap Francis. "I will lift up mine eyes unto the hills, from which cometh my help."

Charlie Blackburn, a man who should have been very interested in the whereabouts of the buyer of his farm, had disdained every opportunity to look for the good man. Searchers had been up and down the road in front of his house. They had tramped on, around, and over every square foot of his property. Charlie had looked on with sullen disinterest.[4] He and his vassal, Skip Archer, just kept on about their business. Such cold indifference had rankled Simp Francis and puzzled Hufft.

Neither had Marvin Calkin nor Virgil Evans of the People's Bank seen fit to search for their board member and courted depositor. But then, they had only acquiesced in the plundering of Jap Francis's bank account—not scaled the ramparts and battered the vault door open. Rollie Smith had shown up on the Decaturville

Road Saturday afternoon after the bank closed at noon and offered his help to find "old Jap." Along with the others, he had tramped the fields and streams until dusk—to no avail.

Mulling the hypothesis that Charlie Blackburn was connected with Jap's disappearance set Hufft off on an exciting line of self interrogation. What if Charlie Blackburn was seeking to defraud Jap Francis out of his cattle and perhaps much more? And what if he had learned, by whatever means, that Jap could no longer be conned and was about to lower the legal boom? Perhaps murder had become the option of choice for a panicked Blackburn. Or maybe it had been calculated and in the cards all along. Jasper Francis had not been bashful about telling everyone he met that he was coming to Stoutland early in the morning to find out "what was what" and take action. Maybe Blackburn had learned Francis's travel plans for the dark and rainy morning he disappeared.

Seeking to get inside the mind of a killer, Hufft reasoned that, like a rat not wishing to stray too far from familiar territory and a protective hole, Blackburn may have decided to do the deed nearer rather than farther from town. If things went bad, he could quickly flee into the dark, finding quick refuge and alibi at his farm or Minnie's home in town. Hiding a body and disposing of a horse required nearby cover, hardly like the areas already searched: cleared fields, patches of woods and sycamores, and willow-lined streams. No, what was needed was rough, wooded, hilly terrain, right next to the road. A place with steep slopes falling off into hollows and draws. A place that could swallow a man or a horse.

"I will lift up mine eyes unto the hills, from which cometh my help."

Fulfilling deaconly duties, Hufft was passing the communion trays, filled with tiny cups of the "fruit of the vine" and unleavened bread wafers, to the congregants. Suddenly, inexplicably, he blurted out in full voice, "My Lord! Why, of course!"

"Amen, Brother!" responded his fellow elders and deacons in unison. They then turned in their seats to see what spirit had moved the good apostle.

Sheepishly taking his seat, Hufft appeared as struck as Saul on the road to Damascus. "How could I have been so blind?" he exclaimed to himself. John Hufft now had a plan, and it involved the hill whose somber visage stared down at the town of Stoutland. Rouse Hill.

If there are guardian angels for poor, brutalized animals, Sam, barely alive, must have been hearing a whole heaven's choir. The sisters and brothers of Lebanon's First Christian Church, accompanied by the strains of an old Hammond organ, sang:

> "Faithful til death said our loving master,
> A few more days to labor and wait.
> Toils of the road will then seem as nothing,
> When we sweep thru the beautiful gate."
>
> "Farther Along"
> —Rev. W.B. Stevens

Would Sam's fate be the exalted freedom of life? Or the sweet delirium of death? Either way, his suffering would soon be over.

Chapter 24

Monday, November 22, 1915

Jim Hooper, a 48-year-old Laclede County Sheriff's deputy, resided in the Spring Hollow community, near Bennett Spring. Monday morning he was a long way from home and in unfamiliar territory. Hooper's keen eyes and curiosity would soon prove invaluable.

Accompanied by his boss, Sheriff Hufft, Hooper had arrived in Stoutland by car to assist in the search for Jap Francis. Hiring a horse at Mooney's livery stable, he set out in the direction of Rouse Hill to meet the search party. Sam Paxton and another deputy sheriff from Camden County were already on hand. The deputy was driving a well-worn Model-A Ford. Paxton was aboard his trusty saddlebred horse. It seems that word had gotten back to Linn Creek that Camden County's finest were being upstaged by their sister county. Elections would be coming up in 1916, and a show of force seemed in order. Constable Manes filled out the Camden County contingent.

The badged officers were joined by 15 or 20 volunteers at the intersection of the Linn Creek and Decaturville Roads. Keeping his record of unconcern unblemished, Charlie Blackburn made no appearance. It had not gone unnoticed.

The morning was crisp and sunny at 28 degrees. The searchers were bundled in long johns, heavy shirts and trousers, and a hodgepodge of woolen or denim work coats with brass buttons. A few had lined, linen dusters, extending to their ankles.

Among the group was Dr. C.E. Carlton, the 39-year-old physician who had labored valiantly to prolong the life of Jap's mother. At a time when the average height of a man was only 5'7" inches, Carlton, at 6'2", stuck out in a crowd.[1] "Old" Doc Carlton, bespectacled and as bald as a cue ball, had a disposition as cheery as a redbird in the snow. He would skillfully tend the sick and deliver babies in the Stoutland area for another 41 years until his death in 1956. His simple tombstone in the Stoutland cemetery has no epitaph. No chiseled words commemorate a lifetime of service. His memory is etched only in the hearts and minds of generations of Stoutlanders still living. Today, as always, he would be on hand when a life needed saving.

Hufft delivered the marching orders:

"Boys, we've been at this for quite a while now, and if we don't find anything today, we're gonna wind it up. We've looked high and low from right here where Jap was last seen, all the way out to his farm. But today, we want to search back towards Stoutland through these woods and up and over the top of Rouse Hill. Simp, here, tells me that the ground falls off to a branch back there on the east side. We want to get all the way down to that creek and even on the other side of it. I sure 'nough hate to say it, but if something has happened to Jap Francis, we're prob'ly not gonna find 'im alive. So look sharp for places a man or a horse could be covered up and hid. If the tables was turned, you know Jap would be right out here with us, a-lookin' for you or your loved one, so spread yourselves out and try not to miss anything!"

After a few questions, Hufft continued, "I'll fire a shot along about noon. Remember where you were and come on back to the road. Lem Fulbright's wife, bless her heart, is gonna cook dinner for all of us and give us a chance to warm up."

And they were off. By 11:00 A.M. the party had moved, on line, only about a mile. The going was rough with steep ridges and draws dotted with cedars and scrub oaks. Jim Hooper migrated down the hill and discovered the traces of an old wagon road.[2] Finding the way easier, he urged his horse along the faint trail. Within minutes, scanning to his right, he saw the faint silhouette of a horse standing in a thicket of small trees and bushes.

Thinking one of the searchers had dismounted, he pulled his horse up and waited a moment or two, not wishing to interrupt a call of nature. But nothing moved. Seeing no one, he softly spoke "giddyap" to his horse which picked his way carefully up the steep shoulder of the old road and into a flat bottom glade. Urging his mount closer, Hooper was surprised at the lack of reaction from the strange horse. No greeting whinny. No sweep of the tail. No movement. Just silence. Jim Hooper had been around horses all of his life, and a sudden apprehension, bordering on fear, gripped his stomach.

Drawing nearer, he saw a horse that matched the description of Sam, about 16-hands tall, sorrel in color, with a starred forehead and three white-stocking feet. Everything else was wrong. Everything else was a horse lover's nightmare. The animal's head was down, and it appeared dead. One of the restraining reins had come loose or broken, but the other remained securely tied through the fork of a 4-inch blackjack oak. In a furious effort to escape, the horse had entangled its right foreleg over the remaining rein, creating a constant tension on the bridle bit. The loosened saddle hung limply below the creature's belly. Its mouth was black and swollen, reeking of raw infected wounds.[3] Poor to the point of emaciation, the horse's ribs protruded and its hindquarters were misshapen by a radical loss of weight. Starvation is an ugly thing. The bark and leaves on the restraining tree had been shredded off as high and as far as its prisoner could reach.[4]

"My God! This hoss has been here a long time—this has gotta be the one," Hooper spoke grimly to himself. Looking about for signs of the missing rider, he reined his horse away, moved off a few paces and stopped. Withdrawing a lever-action Winchester 30:30 rifle from a saddle holster, he aimed it skyward and fired. Levering another cartridge into the chamber, he triggered another round. The second report caused hearts to leap all over the Stoutland countryside. Finally, something had been found! Sam Hill had been found. Oblivious to the rifle reports only yards away, Sam had not even flinched. He may have been only minutes from death.

Men soon converged on the scene from all directions. Each was shocked and repulsed by what he saw. Some turned away with sadness and anger. Horse lovers all, they recognized what a fine mount Sam had been. They had never witnessed such abuse to a dumb animal. "They oughta shoot the son of bitch that tied this horse up," growled one stubble-bearded farmer.

"Yeah, and I just might be the man to do it," murmured another.

Sam was aware of distant human voices but was too weak to acknowledge their presence. They sounded as if underwater, the slowed, distorted sound of an Edison phonograph, its spring winding down to a stop. His eyes were closed, lids glued together with hardened mattering of the eyes.

Sheriff Hufft, out of wind from running on foot, came crashing through the deep leaves and underbrush. Simp Francis appeared, fearing what he might have to witness. He was accompanied by Sam Paxton. Grabbing a couple of men, Hufft began a canvass of the immediate area, looking for signs of the missing man.

Spitting a liberal stream of tobacco on the ground, Deputy Paxton took a practical approach to the horse's plight. "Fellers, it looks to me like he's way past helpin'. I reckon it'd be a mercy to put him out of his misery," drawled the burly man with the big star.

Slowly and reluctantly, all present shook their heads in agreement. Simp Francis, pale as a sheet, stood before the deteriorated remains of his brother's prized possession. The realization that the awful facts of Jap's disappearance would soon be revealed had left him shaken and shivering in the morning chill. Like a warden's signal to a hangman, Simp gave his assent with a single downward nod and turned away. He could not bear to watch.

"Cut him loose there, I won't shoot a tied horse—besides, he ain't got no place to fall," ordered Paxton. With two quick motions, someone with a sharp Barlow knife accomplished in seconds what had eluded Sam for almost two weeks. Free at last! His right leg remained frozen in its high-stepping position, a bizarre reminder of this highly bred animal's training from the master, Tom Bass. Sam would go down resembling his dam in all her show-stopping equestrian glory.

Paxton unholstered his old Naval Colt 45, cocked the hammer, and, carrying it at arm's length, muzzle down, strode slowly toward Sam. The end must be quick and sure—for the animal's sake.

"Whoa there! Now, you wait just a minute!" Sam's death sentence had been stayed.

Nothing died unnecessarily on Doc Carlton's watch. He was in the life business. At the age of 24 he had taken the Hippocratic Oath, vowing to "Relieve suffering and do no harm." Armed only with a small black bag, strong compassionate hands, and a joke and a quip, he had gone about his profession. Instinctively, he reasoned,

"Jap Francis may well be dead—we'll get to him in time. But for now, I've got a live creature that needs me."

A comic figure on a tragic stage, Carlton's feet nearly dragged the ground as he rode into the clearing. Nobody laughed—that would come later. Astraddle a small Hackney horse, part of a team that usually pulled his buggy, he dismounted with ease and set about his work. No modern ER physician could have matched his performance on Rouse Hill that day.

"Well, what are you waiting for? Go get this horse some water out of that creek—and be quick about it! Get that saddle off his belly and put that blanket and as many coats as you can get on him—can't you see he's about dead from exposure?"

Happy to take directions in a last-ditch effort to save Sam, the men stepped to, running about, working furiously. Sam Paxton, deprived of his lethal chore, took the long overcoat off his back and placed it over Sam's withers. Others did the same—they would shiver now, but speak proudly of it later.

Barking out orders, Carlton was a man in charge:

"You, and you—get a-hold of that horse's stiff leg and give it a good rubbing. See if you can get it down and straightened out. Lean up against him there! If he goes down, we'll never get him up. Rub this horse all over—let's see if we can get some circulation going. Get that bit out of his mouth! Easy with it now! You there, you ride to the nearest house and get me some table salt, a whole shaker full! Young fellow, you ride to Stoutland and get Chase Mooney [teamster and liveryman] over here. You tell him that C.E. Carlton told him to come right now! Bring a couple a' buckets and a few oats and some bran. D'ya hear me now? Get going!"

Decisiveness is a wonderful thing.

The physician then set about his examination. Pulling clean compresses out of his bag, he soaked them in glycerine and began dabbing at the dried secretions bonding Sam's eyes closed. Mission accomplished, he pulled the eyelids up with his thumb and was relieved to find the eyes focusing—not fixed and dilated. Nevertheless, Sam was far from out of the woods. His mouth and tongue were dry as cornstarch, and his labored breathing was wheezy. Deep probing of the belly disclosed an empty stomach and intestines with the bowels blocked and hardened. The liver was distended from overwork converting diminished body fat to blood sugars. But the immediate problem was dehydration. The animal needed fluids, and fast.

Young Keller Barr, a tall gangly lad, came to the rescue. He had filled his floppy felt hat to the brim from a clear pool of water in the nearby stream. Carlton swabbed Sam's dry mouth with it and told the boy to run for more. The good doctor then reached for a secret weapon that had brought relief to a multitude of patients. He kept a large cobalt-blue bottle of the miraculous remedy with him at all times. Sugar-filled placebo pills. A little water, a little sugar, a pinch or two of salt—no ICU nurse could have hung a better IV bag for what ailed this animal.

Using the bent hat brim as a spout, the physician literally poured a trickle of sugar water down Sam's throat. Coughing and sputtering, the animal made movements and showed signs of life. Like a half-drowned man pulled from dark waters, Sam retched and coughed, trying to adjust his eyes in the dazzling sunlight. Sam had come to. The sweet taste in his mouth was associated with his master. Was it a winesap? Twitching his ears, he nodded his head and sought to plunge his nose into the hat. Doc Carlton nodded back and exclaimed, "Yes, sir! Yes, sir! Gentlemen, I think this horse just might make it!"

Then came a little petroleum jelly, mixed with oils of camphor and eucalyptus, rubbed on Sam's scabbed and sore mouth and around his nostrils. He didn't like it, turning his head away. Perfectly normal. The salve would help heal the lesions while the vapors opened the bronchial tubes, easing the labored breathing. A little more water with sugar. A little more with a dash of salt. "Not too much now." A regimen of a pint of sugared water with a pinch of salt about every 15 minutes was begun. No more than a gallon or so right now. Sam was greedily taking liquids and nourishment.

The body massage was loosening Sam's muscles, but more importantly, the human touching did what it always does. It gives life, love, hope, and security. Sam Hill was indeed going to make it.

Chapter 25

Combat veterans of every war get used to viewing the dead. Lives ended violently and instantly by a grenade fragment or razor-sharp shrapnel or a speeding bullet. Forever soundless to its victim—a report never filed. Sometimes it's the man right next to you. Maybe it's the buddy you've had since basic training. Maybe it's the kid who minutes earlier had spoken fondly of mom and dad or sweetheart and "getting back to the world." At first there is horror, shock, and throwing up. Then comes a hardening to the realities of life and death and survival. Trust your comrade in arms. Just don't get too close to him. Euphemisms ease the psychological agony. "He took a bullet," "got zapped," "dinged," "wasted." They all work.

When describing those wrenched from life into death in the blink of an eye, warriors speak of oddities. First, how very small the dead appear. Stripped of their life and soul, they seem strangely and suddenly diminished, as if downsized in some peculiar way by the grip of death. And how pale they look—paler than chalk. A white so unnaturally pure and definitive that no medic glances twice. Better to move on to those with color. Those with hope. And finally, the puzzled expression on their faces. Some unknown, unvoiced question lingers on their lips. "What happened?" "Where am I?" "Why's it so dark?" "Am I dead?" No one can ever find out. Jasper Jacob Francis was no exception. He had died wondering why, seeking an explanation.

After finding Sam hidden and tied in a thicket, searchers redoubled their efforts to locate the missing man—or his remains.[1] Surely he must be nearby. Like bloodhounds finding a scent trail, they knew they were onto something. Excitement of the hunt was matched in full portion by apprehension of what they might find. Each longed to solve the great mystery of Jap Francis's disappearance, but dread supplanted any hopes of glory. It was a job that needed to be quickly finished.

Clint Fulbright was a bachelor living with his parents, Sam and Ella Fulbright. Their farm was over the Laclede County line, some two or three miles south of Jap Francis's farm. Fulbright, a skinny and energetic fellow, appeared considerably younger than his 27 years. Dave McClure, a 56-year-old farmer and family man, was a close neighbor of the Fulbrights. The two men were riding together[2] and that suited them just fine. Clint was a good friend of Dave's sons, Ray and Ralph, who were searching some distance away.

Dave pulled his horse up in a lightly wooded area on a flattened plateau that topped Rouse Hill about ½ mile southwest of where Sam had been found.[3] He and Clint had ridden up the steep backside of the hill on an angle that would intersect the Linn Creek Road. They were only a hundred yards above where the Lem Fulbright road tee'd in from the west. As Clint approached, Dave pulled his pocket watch from his vest. "I sure as the devil thought we'd a-found 'im by now. It's nigh onto noon—I reckon they'll be callin' us in pretty quick for dinner."

"And none too durned soon either, for my part," replied Fulbright. "That poor old horse has got my coat, and it's still danged chilly, especially up here in the wind."

McClure withdrew a packet of cigarette papers and a tin of Prince Albert tobacco from his pocket. Shaking some short cut burley on a paper, he licked the edges and rolled himself a smoke. Wasting a couple of matches in the breeze, he sheltered his light with a cupped hand and took a long, satisfying drag. Young Fulbright had healthier and more nourishing business on his mind. He happened to know that his great-aunt Lizzie Fulbright was one of the best cooks in the country.

"Oh my Lordy, Mr. McClure, I think I can taste Auntie's chicken and dumplings right now! Why, she feeds the threshin' crews ever year—and I ought to know."

"That ain't the half of it," was McClure's knowledgeable reply. "Ever'body knows that woman makes the best apple pie in Camden County and prob'ly Lay-clede too."

Preparing to move on, Fulbright looked to his left and at some distance noticed a blue object in a small pile of brush. "It probably ain't nuthin, but I'm goin' over there to see what that is," he remarked while urging his horse away. Avoiding brambles and scrub brush, he circled around, moving slightly downwind from his destination. He sniffed the unmistakable sweet, nauseating smell of decaying flesh. Quickly dismounting and with excitement edging his voice, Clint yelled, "Mr. McClure, you'd best come over here!" Edging closer, he identified a patch of blue fabric where covering leaves had been dislodged by the stiff breeze. Grabbing a stick, he stirred away more leaves, exposing more fabric. As McClure approached, Fulbright reached down and, wresting a branch away from the pile, exposed a brown boot. The blue-striped cloth was the cuff and blouse of a man's trousers.[4]

Looking over Fulbright's shoulder, Dave McClure had seen and smelled enough. "Good God, Clint—that's gotta be Jap. We've found him right here in this brush pile!"

Young Fulbright had come well armed for the task at hand. He yanked a Savage pump-action .22 from his saddle and squeezed off two rounds, five seconds apart. They may have not been the "shots heard round the world," but they surely stirred Stoutland and its environs. Coming so close to the noon hour and from the direction of the Fulbright house, a few thought the reports were only an errant call to dinner. John Hufft knew better. He gunned Laclede County's fancy police car to the top of Rouse Hill where he was met by McClure and Fulbright. A quick inspection confirmed to a certainty that they had found their man.

Within minutes all the searchers had arrived, including Doc Carlton. As a professional courtesy, Carlton dispatched Clint Fulbright into Stoutland to summon the town's other physician, Dr. W.O. Pool. Leaning over his horse's neck and whipping his rump like a Pony Express rider, Clint covered the 1¼ miles in less than 3 minutes. Startled by the clattering hooves of the fast-approaching horse, idlers on Main Street turned and gawked as Clint announced the long-awaited news. Sweeping by, he shouted, "We found Jap Francis on Rouse Hill—I'm a-goin' for Doc Pool!"[5]

That's all it took. The town emptied. All able-bodied men and boys, half the women and girls, and every untied dog in Stoutland headed for Rouse Hill. No one seemed to know if he was alive or dead, but they were not about to miss the most exciting event in Stoutland's history. As the throng passed the high school, professor and part-time minister H.C. Clark dismissed classes and told the pupils to go home immediately. Almost none did. Most joined the double-time march to see Jap Francis, dead or alive. One young scholar did as he was told. Ray Blackburn went straight home, taking no more than five minutes to get there.

Ray was surprised to find his mother's house full of people. His father, his mother, his grandmother, and his uncle James A. "Jimmy" Craddock were all assembled in the front room. Ray would later say they were "talking about J.J. Francis."[6] Skip Archer arrived momentarily—perhaps to collect his back pay. Charlie and Miz Mary Craddock had arrived that morning by team and wagon. From that day forward, not one of the group ever spent another night on the Blackburn farm. Miz Mary moved in with her son Jimmy and his wife. Always dutiful, Skip Archer returned to live with his parents.[7] Unlike most of the living populace of Stoutland, they all shunned Rouse Hill that day. In fact, Charlie and Minnie did not stray from the house until subpoenas arrived the next afternoon.

Watching the searchers with disinterest for days, Charlie Blackburn chose this morning, when search parties finally set out in the right direction, to move himself and his mother-in-law into town.[8] The same morning, he dismissed his hired hand and summoned his brother-in-law to look after Miz Craddock. He had sold his farm to Jap Francis at a very satisfactory price. The corn had been harvested and most of the animals sold. He had quit farming. Why hang around?

When searchers started combing the hills and draws of Rouse Hill, someone knowing the whereabouts of Jap Francis and his horse would have realized the game was about to change. The bodies would surely be found. A deadly gambit had been played, and the authorities would soon be making countermoves. Jap's last days and utterances would be scrutinized. If Charlie Blackburn was playing a charade, it needed to be convincing and acted out with decisive actions. Having sold his farm, he needed to be visibly out of the business. Was it only a coincidence that Charlie, Minnie, Miz Craddock, and Jimmy Craddock were assembled together in Stoutland the hour that Clint Fulbright thundered into town with the shouted news that Jap Francis had been found? Or were the wagons being circled and the party line being memorized?

With the Camden County lawmen assembled, J.L. Jackson, acting as coroner, appointed Doctor Carlton and H.W. "Harry" Singleton to search the body.[9] Lying in a depression about 27 paces from the road, the corpse was face down, mostly covered with leaves and brush, with its feet toward the road. The hands and arms were neatly tucked under the torso. The body's location was nearly 3/4 of a mile closer to Stoutland and 1/8 mile closer to the road than where Sam was found.[10] The good doctor prepared a weak solution of carbolic acid and dampened the examiners' handkerchiefs with the liquid. They then covered their noses and mouths. It seemed to help.

When turned over, the body was stiff as a board, in full rigor mortis. Some newspaper accounts left the grim details of the body's state of deterioration to the reader's imagination. Others didn't. A "correspondent" for the *Laclede County Republican*, claiming to have viewed the body, reported, "The body was in pretty bad condition, especially the head, shoulders, and breast." The *Springfield Republican*, quoting second-hand accounts, reported the body was "found decomposed." The *Linn Creek Reveille*, a weekly published at the Camden County Seat, provided full graphic details in its Friday, November 26 edition: "The body was turned over and the eyes eaten out and the flesh badly eaten by maggots." In 2005, Lucille (Alexander) Gregory, 84-year-old daughter of Jap Francis's friend, Neal Alexander, had this to say: "The story was [from eye witnesses] that Jap's mustache literally fell off the body when it was moved."

Sam Paxton urged Simp Francis not to gaze upon the corpse of his brother. "You'd best not look upon it, Mr. Francis—it'll shore 'nough give you night sweats for the rest of yore natural life!" he implored, placing his hefty presence between Simp and the body.

"I've got to see—I've got to identify my brother!" demanded Simp.

"He's right, Sam; we need us a positive identification—go ahead and let him through," ordered the Coroner. "Brace yourself, sir; this man has been dead quite awhile. Now then, is this your brother, Jasper Francis?"

Simp gasped, nodded, and stumbled away. Sam Paxton's warning proved prophetic. Simp Francis would carry the awful sight in his mind and dreams for the rest of his days. Then and there he determined that no other member of his family would share his grisly burden.

Dr. Pool arrived shortly and assisted in the preliminary search and examination. Jap's long waistcoat had been pulled up "as far as the band of his pants and partly over his head," apparently from the body being dragged, feet first and face up, from the road to where it was found. It had then been pulled around, feet to the road, and rolled or dumped into the depression. There was a hole "such as a bullet might make" in the back of his neck. Blood stains were visible on his coat and shirt collar, on the right side of his coat at the bottom, and on the underside of his left coat sleeve. His hat, nearly new, was found lying near the body as if placed there. It was discolored by the rain and had bloody fingerprints on the top and inside "like it had been picked up." No bloodstains had been found on Sam or the saddle, suggesting that Jap had likely been dismounted when attacked.[11]

The body was dressed in a brown coat, a pair of blue pants with "a small stripe," two pairs of light summer drawers, a light undershirt, and no vest. His rain slicker was missing but found later in his house. Given the threatening nature of the weather, it seemed odd that a prudent man would have left it behind. On his last day, Jap had a lot on his mind. He was not wearing his gray overcoat with a black velvet collar. Neither was it found at his home.[12] For unknown reasons, his assailant took it from his body or his saddlebag.

A search of Jap's person disclosed three silver dimes, a piece of chewing tobacco, a bunch of keys, a livestock shipper's contract and a handkerchief. No knife, pocketbook, fountain pen, wallet, checkbook, nor "little red memorandum book" was found. A search of his house disclosed none of these items. A watch was found in his pocket with the hands stopped at 3:00. A dog-eared hat check from his last train ride concluded the meager list of personal effects.[13]

Examination of the body by Doctors Carlton and Pool disclosed that Jap Francis had been shot. A large caliber bullet had entered below the right ear and exited through the left jaw. In addition, it was obvious that the skull and facial bones had been struck with a blunt object. The forehead was completely caved in.[14] It would be left to Dr. Carlton to do a careful dissection of the body later that evening[15] by lamplight in a small room in the back of Palmer's Dry Goods and Furniture Store. Such stores sold coffins and did a little undertaking business on the side. Palmer's would later bill Jap's estate $25.00 for "embalming" the body.[16] Most believed this consisted of sloshing the body with formaldehyde and providing a plain oak coffin. It would, of course, be a closed-casket funeral.

With a crowd estimated at 200 people tramping over the crime scene, any identifying objects that the killer might have dropped were trampled into the soft, leafy ground.[17] Ubiquitous yellow crime-scene tape of *Eyewitness News at Six* had not yet been invented. No reliable ballistics tests had yet been devised. Blood and DNA tests were unknown. Fingerprint evidence was not yet admissible in court. Nobody but Sam had witnessed the crime. Jap Francis's killer would receive justice only through circumstantial evidence, if at all.

By 2007, as many as 250 vehicles a day come and go over Rouse Hill. Motorists are oblivious to what took place there so long ago. The blacktopped highway, with no shoulders and few turn-ins, is uninviting to those who wish to stop and walk about. The wooded area where the body was found has long since been cleared. An electric substation surrounded with a chain-link fence stands nearby. Ninety-two years have come and gone since the killing. One wonders if any person has ever walked this ground at 5 A.M. on a November 10 morning, shivering in the pre-dawn chill—and then stood quietly in the darkness, watching and listening. Perhaps no one ever will.

By 2:00 P.M., crowds of people, automobiles, teams and wagons, tied saddlehorses, and lots of dogs filled the woods and spilled out onto the Linn Creek Road. Curious onlookers pressed forward to get a glimpse of the corpse. It seemed nobody wished to live the rest of their lives without having seen the body. The sheriff and deputies sought valiantly to keep onlookers from interfering with the examiners' duties. Efforts to give Jap Francis a small degree of dignity in death were mostly vain. Although volunteers formed a protective ring, the remains lay in full view.

A small man in life, Jap appeared smaller in death. Many commented that he appeared as only a slight boy lying there in the bright autumn sunshine. And yes, he was pale, whiter than most sheets. If anyone had bothered to look, they would have discovered a large bloodspot on the roadside nearest the body ". . . about three feet from the wagon track."[18] The surface was trampled by onlookers and crushed by the rubber tires of several Model T's and one or two Gardners or Moons. The black, coagulated pool, about 5 inches by 6 or 7 inches, contained most of Jap Francis's lifeblood. It had soaked several inches into the hardened road fill. An unknown party had covered the spot with ". . . leaves and fine gravel."[19] Cattle drover W.W. Cox, curious as to why his herd started bawling and attempting to stampede, found the blood six days later on the 28th of November.[20] Cattle hate the smell of blood and will do almost anything to avoid it.

Rumors soon ran rampant. A killer was "on the loose" in the area. Doors would be locked and lamps left burning at night for weeks. Shotguns remained loaded and cocked. Pressure to determine what happened and identify Jap Francis's killer would force a coroner's inquest the very next day.[21]

For now, it was time to move the pitiful remains. A team of horses and a wagon had been commandeered for the purpose. The body was rolled into a canvas tarp[22] and loaded gently onto the wagon bed. As the crowd waited for the sad procession to begin, they beheld a wonderment they would never forget. Jap Francis's horse, led by liveryman Chase Mooney, came into sight over the crest of Rouse Hill. Two able assistants flanked Sam, supporting and encouraging him along.

Mooney had administered Doc Carlton's prescribed regimen of liquid to Sam. He had then slowly fed the hungry horse a couple of quarts of warmed bran mash. The concoction provided liquid, some nourishment, and acted as a mild laxative.[23] Leaves had been cleared away and a small fire—built for the purpose—provided welcome heat for both Sam and his rescuers. The smell of woodsmoke lingered in the air, signaling human occupation and control of this wild spot. Later, a thin gruel of cooked oats, water, and a couple spoonfuls of dark molasses had tempted Sam. He had greedily lapped it up and wanted more. Sam was then coaxed to take a few stiff, labored steps. Unwatered and unfed for 12 days, he would have to climb a nearly 100-foot elevation to get back to the main road. Slowly, one step at a time and with frequent rests and switchbacks, he made it. Once upon the hard road, the going was easier but the gaited track star, Sam Hill, appeared as an old man with Parkinson's. Covered with the coats that had helped save his life, he shuffled along with reluctant and halting steps.

The sight of the once-beautiful animal in such a dilapidated state was painful to watch. Grown weary of the rituals of unnatural death, those assembled on Rouse Hill saw something in Sam that touched them all. Pathetically plodding toward them was a creature that by all reasoning should have been just as dead as the man lying nearby. But the flickering spark of life had not gone out. Just in time, it had been fanned and rekindled. Against all odds, Sam Hill had lived. If Jap Francis had been raised, Lazarus-like, from the dead, the crowd could hardly have been more awestruck.

As he came even with the death scene, Sam's head suddenly came up. He looked directly into the woods where his master lay covered in the wagon. Sidestepping, he shied to the opposite side of the road, stumbled and nearly fell.[24] All eyes were upon him. As Sam righted himself, a lone person started to slowly clap her hands. And then another and then another. The smattering of applause began to build and became a continuous wave of sound echoing throughout the nearby hills. Some even whistled and hooted their admiration. Sam, descended from the finest of show horses, seemed to know just what was expected. His demeanor was suddenly transformed. He visibly arched his neck, nodded his proud head, picked up his feet, and attempted an energetic sideways canter. He was, after all, a Missouri fox-trotter from Audrain County and the son of Lucy Mack. Second fiddle was not in his repertoire. He had to be restrained by his grooms. Dry eyes were few on Rouse Hill that day. A few women and children cried out loud and had to be comforted.

The sad procession wound its way toward Stoutland, led by a weakened and riderless horse and followed by the wagon bearing Jasper Francis's dead body. It resembled another cortege at another time and another place. That was a crisp November day in 1963. Then, a skittish cavalry horse named "Black Jack," as inconsolable as the Nation, followed a wheeled caisson to Arlington Cemetery.[25] Boots of a fallen leader were reversed in the stirrups as the procession marched to the unrelenting cadence of muffled drums. Evil carries no expiration date.

It would now be all downhill for Sam—all the way to Stoutland and for the rest of his life. Later, after Sam was safely placed in a stall at Mooney's Livery Stable, men who had lent their coats to warm him and help save his life, came by to reclaim them. Many kept them for a very long time. They wore them, frayed and patched and stitched, to honor their fallen friend, Jasper Jacob Francis.

Chapter 26

The world, it has been said, is made up of only three kinds of people: technocrats, bureaucrats, and functionaries.[1] In short, technocrats conceptualize and actually *do* things. A broad array of productive and creative people fit into this group, from plumbers to physicians and including farmers, authors, factory workers, entrepreneurs, composers, soldiers, teachers, and artists.

Bureaucrats, on the other hand, report, file, record, criticize, comment upon, litigate, manipulate, massage, arrange, shuffle, count, convey, and categorize those things that productive technocrats *do*. Bureaucrats include newspaper reporters, columnists, journalists, commentators, critics, government workers, bankers, accountants, lawyers, realtors, inspectors, archivists, historians, and so forth. Their jobs do not begin until a technocrat makes or creates or does something of value. Bureaucrats may be necessary, but they annoy and are often despised by the *doer* class. A visit to one's kindly DMV office never fails to reaffirm such sentiments.

Alas, our functionaries sit atop the food chain. They neither *do* anything nor report on what others *do* other than taking credit for such doings in the form of self-aggrandizement. They spend most of their time making appearances as human symbols of something or another. They happily preside over dedications to monuments to achieving *doers*, built by *doers* while having been constantly hindered by legions of bureaucratic *do nothings.* Politicians, corporate CEOs, heads of state, useless and anachronistic royals, religious prelates, and most military general officers fit nicely into the functionary category. Functionaries are envied, resented, ridiculed, and, fascinatingly, *aspired to* by both technocrats and bureaucrats.

When he arrived in Stoutland by train, William H. "Billy" Reed was a happy, purposefully occupied technocrat. To be precise, he was a civil engineer specializing in road building.[2] Of his own free will, he would step across the forbidden line into bureaucracy. Acting as a reporter, he scooped the local press and broke the story of the murder of Jasper Francis in the distant *Springfield Republican.*

Reed, 36 years old, lived in Springfield, 71 rail miles southwest of Stoutland. Tuesday morning, November 23, he arose early and caught an eastbound Frisco passenger train. Billy was due in Stoutland by noon to address a community group on the subject of good roads. Billy knew a lot about road-building, acting as a consulting engineer to cities and counties. Most recently he had worked with the "Greater Springfield Committee" in creating the "Eight Mile Special Road District,"[3] constructing the first continuously paved "parkway" approaches to that fair city. By 1915, it was clear that the automobile was the wave of the future. Cities and towns not accessible by good roads would soon be left behind.

It is said that the definition of an "expert" is a fellow in a pressed suit at least 100 miles from home. Billy Reed truly was an expert in surveying, grading, road materials, compacting, bridging, and all things necessary to speed Tin Lizzies along. In 1915, Model Ts were rolling off Henry Ford's assembly line at more than 1,000 per day. By 1923, Ford would make 2,011,125 Model Ts, or one every 16 seconds.[4] America was going to need a lot of roads and a lot of Billy Reeds.

Reed hoped to induce merchants in Stoutland to foot the bill for paved streets and improved roads entering the town. He would prepare the plan, supervise construction, and draw a nice consulting fee. He had his script, a few charts, shined shoes, and was prepared for plenty of Q&A. What he wasn't prepared for was the aftermath of cold-blooded murder.

As the miles clicked and swayed away, Billy noticed a family sitting in the forward part of the coach. It was obvious they had come a great distance and would be arriving at their destination soon. A mother, father, and four sons, ranging in age from about 14 to perhaps 20, were all dressed in their traveling best.

When the train neared Stoutland, the parents and youngest son became more animated, pointing out familiar landmarks. "Look there, Ben, we just passed Sleeper," exclaimed the plain but neatly dressed woman.

"Yep, I figure we'll be there in about 10 minutes," responded the handsome gray-eyed man. The set of his cheekbones and angularity of his nose hinted strongly at American-Indian ancestry.

Even the older boys, asleep or lazing in their seats, managed to arouse themselves and show a modicum of interest. One well-tanned teenager unhappily opined: "Well, I guess we're back in old cold Missouri—as soon as I get a chance, I'm headed back to California."

"Ward, now you just shut that up and improve your disposition—I reckon you'll get back to that gal friend of yours soon enough!" warned the father.

The train clamored to a hissing stop at the Stoutland Station. There is something about reunions that is irresistible to human curiosity, and Billy Reed waited to let the family step off the train first. Sure enough, there was a couple of similar age, perhaps a little younger, waiting just outside the depot door. As they approached to greet the arrivals, it became obvious to Billy that this was not a typical joyous homecoming. The man's face appeared frozen. Tears streamed from the woman's eyes. They moved forward timidly, seemingly in no hurry to embrace their loved ones.

As Billy grabbed his leather briefcase and stepped down on the conductor's box, he heard snippets of conversation, including "I guess you didn't get my letter?" "Bad news," and "Your brother's dead."

Among cultured observers, the public pain of others is to be quietly and courteously avoided unless assistance can be rendered. Those with manners avert their eyes, lower their voices, and solemnize their faces. Billy Reed quickly discerned what to do and stepped carefully around the family group now standing speechless in disbelief. As he moved away, he heard the words, "murdered on Rouse Hill," a gasp from the newly arrived woman, and the exclamation, "Jap's dead? —oh, no, it can't be true!"

Walking quickly toward the depot entrance, Billy cast a sideways glance at an old man in bib overalls and flannel shirt, standing uncomfortably close to the openly grieving family. Cocking his head to hear each shocked expression, the man stared at each stricken face. Some are beyond teaching.

Reed waited inside the depot, warmed by a coal fire kept perpetually burning by John Frey. Frey was busily assisting the train's porter and the conductor with unloading the numerous trunks and baggage of Ben Francis, his wife Lucy, and their four sons: Leonard, Ray, Ward, and Silas. They were home from California, and what a sad homecoming it was. Finally, the entire grim-faced group, with the exception of Simp Francis, departed the station by wagon and hack. Simp had important business in town and his brother Ben vowed to return later.

When Frey returned, Reed asked the whereabouts of L.F. Fulbright and H.D. Evans who had invited him to speak to the Stoutland "Better Roads Committee." "I expect you'll find 'em over at the Odd Fellows Hall, one block over and down on your left," informed Frey. Shaking his head, he added, "I doubt as how there'll be any road meetin's there today.[5] We've got us a murder on our hands, and the town is full of sheriffs and deputies and lawyers. I hear there's gonna be an inquest startin' this afternoon right where you was goin' to meet."

As Reed turned to leave, he was collared by "Mr. bib overalls and flannel shirt." "Say, mister, looks like yore from the big city. Are you a lawyer here for the big murder doin's?" Anxious to dispel any misconceptions, Reed began to explain his business. He was quickly interrupted by Wes Scrivner:

"Sit down, mister, you ain't goin' nowhere for a while no how—I'll tell you all about it. They got Jap Francis's body over in back of Palmer's store, and it's just a sight to see! I really liked old Jap! I don't know who in the devil would a kilt 'im but [lowering voice] I got me some suspicions."

A mannerly fellow, Reed sat down and listened attentively. And listened. And listened. Some 30 minutes later, he knew as much about the case as most of the attorneys and lawmen assembled in Stoutland. "Sir, I really must be going—to let my hosts know of my arrival," Reed politely interrupted.

"Well, you go on and see about yore business—but if I was you, I'd stick around. I hear that Sid Roach is over here from Linn Creek. He's with that there new prosecutor and a couple a' lawyers from Leb'non brung in by Simp Francis. Old Sid is the best dee-fense lawyer in these parts. He knows his stuff! I sure as the devil wouldn't want him a-turnin' the tables and a-prosecutin' me. They're gonna question ever'body around Stoutland that might know somethin'. Shoot! I may get me a suh-peena myself."

Edging close to his rapidly escaping quarry, Wes tugged Reed's suit lapel, pulled him closer, and whispered, "Some of us think that a feller by the name of Charlie Blackburn might a' had somethin' to do with the killin'. And if he did, there could be some mighty quick justice around here!"

Billy Reed took the advice and stayed.

Chapter 27

> As a result of the disclosure of murder in the finding of the body of J.J. Francis, a prominent farmer who lived near Stoutland, Camden County, Monday afternoon, residents of that community are highly excited and threats of a lynching are heard, according to W.H. Reed, consulting engineer . . . who returned Wednesday evening from Stoutland.
>
> —*Springfield Republican*
> November 25, 1915

> The Camden County officials in charge of the inquiry wished to postpone the inquest until a later date but the residents are said to have opposed it, desiring that the investigation be brought to a speedy end and the responsibility placed.
>
> —*Springfield Republican*
> November 25, 1915

> . . . at times, great excitement prevailed among the people and any positive evidence of guilt on the part of any person or persons would have taken the sad affair out of the reach of the courts.
>
> —Stoutland News, *Linn Creek Reveille*
> December 3, 1915

Sidney Crain "Sid" Roach was 39 years old and at the top of his game as a practicing lawyer in 1915. When he was born July 25, 1876, he had big shoes to fill.

Sid Roach's father, Littleberry J. "Jack" Roach was a legend in Camden County. Roach was born in 1837 in a nearly uninhabited portion of Pulaski County that would first become Kinderhook County and finally Camden County in 1843. Orphaned at the age of four, "Little Jack" was apprenticed to one Hiral Bagley, mistreated, and then re-apprenticed to a farmer, James A. Crain, until

1854. With a formal education of only 4½ months, 17-year-old Jack Roach became a night watchman on an Osage River steamer. There, much like Mark Twain, he was adopted by a steamboat captain and taught navigation. By the beginning of the Civil War, Roach was a boat pilot licensed to run from St. Louis, up the Missouri and Osage Rivers, beyond Linn Creek to the last navigable landing at Warsaw.[1]

Abandoning the river to serve in the Union Cavalry, Jack Roach would return to river piloting after the Civil War. In 1866, he married Miss Frances M. Crain, the only daughter of his former employer. Jack would go on to win elections for nearly every Camden County office, including Sheriff, Collector, County Clerk, Circuit Clerk, and Probate Judge. Later, he was admitted to the Missouri Bar, served terms as Prosecuting Attorney, and was adjudged by his peers as an "ornament" of his profession. While attending to public affairs, he was engaged in several successful business ventures. Acquiring a large tract of land adjoining Linn Creek, Judge Roach built a "handsome and well constructed" Victorian home with more gingerbread, widow's walks, gabled roofs, cupolas, and sweeping porches than any one human ought to have. The self-made servant of the people died June 27, 1886.[2]

To this day, being a descendant of Littleberry "Jack" Roach bequeaths a measure of aristocracy unmatched in Camden County. Roach, a tiny hamlet named after L.J., survives, as does the Roach Cemetery, which still collects the patriarch's descendants who come home to Camden County to be buried in the soil of their renowned ancestor.[3]

Sid Roach hadn't done so badly himself. Born only a month after Custer's loss of the Seventh Cavalry at the Little Big Horn, Sid had been educated in the public schools of Camden and Pulaski Counties and the law department of Washington University in St. Louis. He married Miss Edith King of Osage County in 1899. By 1915, Roach had served as Prosecuting Attorney of Camden County from 1898–1909 and then devoted himself entirely to private practice except for election in 1908 and 1910 to the Missouri Legislature in Jefferson City.[4] His years spent prosecuting malefactors apparently gave Roach an edge in defending the same.

His grandson, Jackson King Roach II, quoted his mother, Sylvia, first wife of his father, Jackson King Roach I: "If you ever got in trouble, at least in terms of a crime, you called Sid Roach!"[5]

Photos of Sid Roach, contemporaneous with the Francis killing, disclose a handsome but rather stern, scholarly looking fellow. He had dark, deep-set eyes capable of delivering a withering, even menacing, stare. Sid Roach was not the kind of man to whom one wished to tell a lot of fibs. He seemed capable of looking right into one's guilty soul, sorting and counting and weighing the lies.

In school, Sid was the tall, pale kid with all the answers. He helped the slow learners and protected the little tykes from school bullies. A quiet, introspective man, he took the measure of new acquaintances by listening to them with a quizzical, slightly bemused expression. He seemed to be classifying, parsing, figuring people out. In relaxed moments, he was an amusing raconteur. His specialty was long, detailed jokes building ever more intricately to an unexpected knee-slapping punch line. He never laughed at his own humor. He just flashed a sly grin and walked away.

Roach's prosecutions were the same, a slowly developing, logical and methodical presentation of the facts, building to a climax. He skewered defense witnesses with insinuating skepticism, scathing irony, and outright scorn. His summations were full of theatre. Commencing with a voice so low that jurors need lean forward to hear, he became a painter, filling the canvas with deft verbal strokes. No impressionism here. His pictures were drawn clearly in the monochromes of black and white. Even the dullest of jurors could understand this kind of art. Building speed and volume, flourish upon flourish, Roach filled the landscape, squeezing out all space for doubt or rebuttal. The miscreant shifted nervously in his seat. The jurors glanced toward the jury room, impatient to do their duty. Then it came time to close the deal—a final impassioned asking for the order:

"For the protection of your families! Civilized society cannot abide such crimes! For the defense of the weak and lowly, send a message of what will not be tolerated! You must be resolute in doing your duty!"

Those piercing eyes demanded justice. Sid Roach was good—very good.

By 3:00 P.M., near-chaos prevailed on the second floor of the Odd Fellows Hall, a two-storied brick building on the north side of Stoutland's main street, three doors down from the People's Bank. The newest building in town, it housed a store on the first floor and a large meeting room on the second. The upper floor was accessed by an outside double-door entrance leading up an enclosed stairway.[6] Seventy-five years later it would become a vacant fire hazard and was demolished for the value of its bricks. In 1915, it was a temple of justice. Using his "out of towner" dress and official demeanor to advantage, Billy Reed was able to move up the crowded stairwell into the packed room. Once there, a hospitable citizen stood up and gave him a seat. The room was buzzing and no one was smiling. This was a coroner's inquest being carried out on the fly.

As soon as his brother's remains had been found, Simp Francis had called attorneys Vernon and Mayfield. They in turn contacted Sid Roach at Linn Creek. Young Prosecuting Attorney Austin Ivon Lodge completed the foursome who had arrived in Stoutland by noon and set up shop at the Odd Fellows Hall. Sheriff Hufft, Sam Paxton, and Constable Charlie Manes were on hand to keep order and corral witnesses. The group had spent three hours interviewing those who had come forward with information they thought useful. Other parties of interest, including Charlie Blackburn, Minnie Blackburn, and Virgil Evans, needed a summons. Prosecutor Lodge was signing subpoenas faster than Hufft, Paxton, and Manes could serve them. The presence of witnesses was demanded "immediately and without delay."

Witnesses, peaceable citizens, and a few hotheads filled the hall and stairwell. Another 100 congregated outside the building. Fully one-half of Stoutland's population had turned out. Sensing anger and indignation building among the throngs, Roach had wished to let the citizenry cool down overnight and convene the coroner's trial the following day. However, with rumors running rampant amid ominous "mutterings" among citizens on the street,[7] Roach had taken the advice of a few respected citizens and decided to proceed immediately.

Ivon Lodge was Sid Roach's junior by twelve years, but a century of maturity separated the two. Lodge was enormously relieved that such "good help" was on hand. Nothing can stunt a budding legal career like a botched murder case, and young Mr. Lodge was as eager to please as a puppy dog. "Yes sir, no sir, and I'll get right to it, Mr. Roach," were the watchwords of the day. Vernon and Mayfield, considerably senior to Roach, were properly deferential and helpful. Subscribing to the "lead, follow, or get out of the way" maxim, they had chosen to be happy followers. Privileged to be on the Francis family's payroll with the meter running, they would prove their worth a few days later.

By 4:00, Roach could wait no longer and asked the Coroner, J.L. Jackson, to call the proceedings to order and swear in the coroner's jury. The appointed jurors were Marvin Calkin, W.L. Martin, Lynn Partlow, L.F. Fulbright, E. Arnold, and R.T. "Rolla" Smith.[8] The interests of the People's Bank were well represented on the jury by Calkin (President) and Smith (Assistant Cashier). Since Virgil Evans would be speaking for the bank, it was not thought necessary to call the two as witnesses. Jurors testifying as witnesses would have been something of a novelty.

State law required that the inquest be carried out "over the body." The jury, amid great tumult, pushing and shoving, was marched by Sam Paxton down the steps and up the street to Palmer's Dry Goods (and undertaking parlor) to view the remains. When all were convened in the presence of the deceased, Roach hastily advised the Coroner that it would be perfectly acceptable and advisable to adjourn the proceeding and reconvene back at the Odd Fellows Hall. Having witnessed that the good man was in fact dead, the jurors escaped to the street, considerably sobered and dedicated to the task at hand. Sometimes, legal niceties do have their place. The corpse remained in the custody of Constable Manes, standing just outside the door with a shotgun at order arms.

The inquest then got going in earnest, with each witness sworn and every utterance taken down in Gregg shorthand by court stenographers Mrs. D.D. McDonald and Fern Hufft, a relative of the Sheriff. They would be paid a total of $41.10 for their efforts.[9] Nothing if not thorough, Sid Roach began questioning the various medical doctors who had examined the body of Jasper Francis. It took more than an hour.

Although Doctors Pool and Carlton had carefully examined the body, other members of the medical establishment had felt compelled to make a call on the unresisting Jasper Francis. Not about to be banished to the second team, Doctors William Schlicht (pronounced "Slick") and Edward Claiborn found excuses to make examinations of the body Tuesday morning.[10]

Facing medical purgatory, Claiborn arrived, puffing and blustering, all the way from Decaturville to weigh in on the cause of Jap Francis's demise. His presence put local civic pride in severe jeopardy. After all, weren't *Stoutland's* excellent physicians competent to ascertain the cause of death of one of *Stoutland's* own leading citizens? The "think so's" of a Decaturville doctor, considered by some to be a quack, were deemed not only extraneous but downright unwelcome. However, Claiborn's hometown patients were hugely impressed. The expertise of Decaturville's only physician had been required to bring resolution to the "difficult" Stoutland autopsy. Decaturville didn't swell with such civic pride again until uranium was discovered and then undiscovered there in the 1950s.

Ultimately, the testimonies of Doctors Pool and Carlton were the only things that really mattered. Questioned by Roach, they described the location and position of the body where it was found and then gave the clinical details of what caused Jap Francis's death. Pool led off:

"[I] was called to see the dead body where it was found in the woods; it was lying face down, the back of the coat up over the side of his head and neck; his body upon his hands, and leaves and stuff upon his back.

"[I found] a gunshot wound along the right mastoid process, one and a half inches below the right ear, [which] came out through the [left] jaw [near the chin] badly tearing it; his hair was singed near where the bullet entered and the skin was hardened at that place; the skull was crushed and the nasal bones were broken and the frontal bone was caved in. The skin was not broken—only where the bullet entered and where it came out. Death was caused from the gunshot and the crushing of the head. We found his neck was broken. There was no evidence of a struggle."

Q: "Could the crushing of the skull have been caused by the gunshot wound?"

A: "No, but I found no abrasions or lacerations of the skull. We didn't find very much blood, none upon the flesh or skin."

Q: "In your opinion, about how long had Mr. Francis been dead?"

A: "I would say that death had come to the body five to ten days before it was found."[11]

Carlton was more technical:

"[I] examined the body where found and after its removal assisted in [a] postmortem examination; [I] dissected the scalp and found fractures of the skull and face; one fracture extended from the orbit on each side up to the top of the head and one extended from each orbit down to the superior maxillary, the inferior maxillary was fractured on both sides and a fracture near each ear; and also the occipital, or the back of the head was fractured."

Q: "Regarding the gunshot wound, could you tell what kind of gun was used?"

A: "[I'm] not for sure, but it was caused by a single slug with an entrance wound about one-half inch in diameter. It could have been a large caliber pistol or rifle or a slug-loaded shotgun."

Q: "In your opinion, in what position was Mr. Francis, in relation to the killer, when he was shot?"

A: "It's difficult to say, but I would judge that the gunshot wound was made by somebody on a level with him; possibly by a left-handed person using a pistol."

Q: "In your opinion, which came first, the gunshot wound or the blows that crushed the skull?"

A: "It's impossible to know. The gunshot wound would have likely caused death from severe loss of blood, but not immediately; but the blows which produced the fractures were sure to cause death in a very short time."[12]

Only the killer would ever know the answers to the last two questions. Was Francis shot while he was standing upright as he desperately turned away to avoid the muzzle of a gun and then, while hemorrhaging massively, beaten until moribund and silent? Or was he knocked to the ground with a leather- or cloth-wrapped club, beaten about the head, and then, to silence his muted cries, given a poorly aimed *coup de grace* gunshot with the gun's muzzle pressed against his flesh?

The crowd may not have understood all the anatomical terms, but they "got it." Jap Francis had been beaten unrelentingly and without mercy, with his head crushed, nose broken, and neck fractured. He had been shot under his right ear with a large caliber bullet tearing off a portion of his left jaw as it exited. The jurors had witnessed the havoc wrought on Jap's body and were sickened. The atmosphere in the room was abuzz. Coroner Jackson gaveled the crowd silent.

As Simp Francis took the witness chair, the sun had gone down, extinguishing the dim light coming from the tall front windows facing the street. A helpful Odd Fellow, standing on a chair, set about lighting the coal-oil lamps mounted high on the walls. Reflected by concave mirrors, the yellow flames sent shafts of light at odd angles throughout the hall. Light and shadow created surreal patterns on the walls and ceilings. With fumes of burning kerosene tainting the air, flickering flames awash on the walls and talk of death and murder on a multitude of tongues, a wandering innocent might have supposed he had stumbled into the lower reaches of hell. Stoutland had become Paradise Lost. Billy Reed, glued in his seat and taking notes in the poor light, was feeling more than a little warm. Simp, with gentle but persistent urging from Sid Roach, told the whole story as he knew it.

He began with the last time he saw his brother alive early Tuesday morning, November 9, and continued until his identification of the remains shortly before noon the day before. Hearing much of the testimony for the first time, Roach probed every nook and cranny, including:

Q: "Why were you not at first concerned about your brother's disappearance?"

A: "I was used to Jap goin' on cattle-buyin' trips. He had told me that he had just sold his entire herd, except for a couple of milk cows and calves, to Charlie Blackburn. I thought he might have gone down to Conway or Marionville or someplace else to buy some young cattle."

Q: "When did you begin to look for your brother in earnest?"

A: "A week ago, Sunday."

Q: "Why had you become concerned?"

A: "He had never been gone that long. I reckoned he would have come home or let me know where he was. Somethin' had to be wrong."

Q: "What did you do first?"

A: "I called Virgil Evans at the bank. Jap is—or was—on the board of directors. I knew that Jap had sold his cattle to Charlie Blackburn, and I thought Virgil might have seen Jap or know somethin' about his business."

Q: "What did Mr. Evans tell you?"

A: "He told me that Jap had been to town Tuesday, the 9th. He said that Jap had mailed in Charlie Blackburn's $1,200 check for the cattle at the bank for payment a few days before. He said that Charlie had shipped the cattle to St. Louis, but the returns had not come into the bank for payment of the check. He said that Jap had said he was comin' back the next day to look into it, but he never showed up."

Q: "Is that all Mr. Evans had to say?"

A: "Yessir, that's about it. He recommended that I give Charlie Blackburn a call to see what he knew."

Q: "Did you do that?"

A: "Yessir, Charlie told me that my brother hadn't sold him his cattle at all, but they were put in on a trade for my brother to buy Charlie's farm and that he had expected Jap to meet him at Leb'non to get a mortgage paid off and draw up some papers, but he didn't show. The next day, Charlie came by my place. He said he was on his way to Linn Creek to meet Jap to finish the farm sale if Jap showed up."[13]

Q: "Mr. Francis, did your brother ever say anything to you about buying Charlie Blackburn's farm?"

A: "No sir, he did not!"[14]

Q: "Mr. Francis, do you believe that your brother would have negotiated and entered into an agreement to buy Mr. Charles Blackburn's farm without telling you about it in advance?"

A: "No sir, no sir, I do not. I absolutely do not! And he for danged sure would not have paid any $11,500 for that old Craddock place!"

Simp Francis's last statement caused pandemonium in the hall. Half the crowd stood up, turned, and glared at Charlie and Minnie Blackburn, along with Miz Mary Craddock, sitting quietly in the back row. If they had any thoughts of remaining inconspicuous, their cover had been blown.

"Charlie Blackburn, what d'ya know about the killin' of Jap Francis!" angrily yelled one hardy citizen.

"Yeah, Charlie, maybe you'd best be tellin' us all about it!" chimed in another.

More ominously, another intoned, "I reckon you'd better have a purty durned good story too, Charlie—around these here parts we know how to get us some justice pretty danged quick-like!"

Having said his peace, the last speaker, Jesse, shouldered his way through the crowd to the door, down through the packed crowd in the stairwell and out the doors. Rumors were already spreading, epidemic fashion, on the street. Jesse helped clarify matters as he went. Outside, unrestrained by the decorum of the judicial proceedings, he loudly opined, "Sounds to me like that damned Charlie Blackburn had sumpin' to do with Jap Francis's killin'—why he may a done hit hisself!"

Inside, Coroner Jackson, gaveling loudly, shouted, "Order! Order! If I have to clear this hall, I'll sure do it! Order! Order!" Jackson's entreaties had little effect.

Deputy Sam Paxton, height, poundage, and all, arose from his seat at the lawyer's table and turned around. Sam was an intimidating figure anytime. This time, he was holding his double-barreled shotgun at port arms, just ahead of the large silver star pinned to his vest. Forgetting the exact nature of the proceedings, Sam, with resonant bass voice, bellowed, "The jedge says order! We will have order in this here court!" The crowd silenced as quickly as the roar of a Frisco caboose clearing a road crossing.

Sheriff Hufft quietly unbuttoned his coat, displaying his holstered .38 revolver, and positioned himself within an arm's length of the Blackburns. Nobody knew if he was there to protect Charlie or prevent his hasty departure.

A hurried conference at the Prosecutor's table suggested that the crowd had been subdued enough that the inquest could be continued but completed with dispatch. It didn't happen.

Chapter 28

> . . . he [Charles Blackburn] was summoned as a witness and sworn, put under the duress of an oath, was not represented by counsel, was suspected of the crime and not advised thereof, nor of his right to refuse to testify, was examined, cross-examined, browbeaten, threatened, treated with contempt and disrespected, surrounded by a mob, and statements made under such conditions are inadmissible against him.[1]
>
> —Defense Brief, Missouri Supreme Court

Volumes have been written about the psychology of mob violence, but a common element is the acquiescence of otherwise "good" people who should know better. The ringleaders are almost never the leading citizens. Most often, they are on the fringe of the social order, the rougher elements in the community. Although they would never admit their inferiority, they "look up" to those they perceive as their betters. If given an opportunity to please them, they will go to almost any lengths.

Plied with generous volumes of liquid courage, one or two vocal hotheads, along with a small pack of reinforcing followers, can morph an otherwise law-abiding crowd into a murderous mob. Without immediate and stern reprimand or overwhelming counterforce, such "pot lickers" become convinced that they are actually pleasing their betters by taking the law into their own hands. In their warped view, they're just doing their "civic duty." Just doing the dirty work for which their betters haven't the stomach. A kind of higher calling, pursued on a sturdy oak limb with a few yards of Manila hemp rope. Silence is perceived as consent. Inaction is seen as "a wink and a nod." Once triggered, mobs are hard to stop. No one who has ever seen one in action wishes to see another. Charlie Blackburn, subpoenaed and cornered on the second floor of Stoutland's Odd Fellows Hall, was in jeopardy.

Just after 6:00 P.M., Sid Roach resumed questioning witnesses. The sun had disappeared an hour earlier, and an evening chill settled on the throngs of people milling about on Main Street. By morning, a low of 32 degrees would create thin skims of ice on ponds and animal watering troughs.[2] A nearly full moon was peaking over the eastern horizon.[3] The burning of soft Illinois coal in St. Louis, some 150 miles eastward, dirtied the atmosphere and, while magnifying the moon's size, turned it a deep reddish orange. A few alarmists at first proclaimed it to be a terrible fire, perhaps leveling the nearby city of Rolla. Others gave it a theological twist, decreeing it a sign of the impending wrath of God upon whomever shed the blood of the late Jasper Francis.

Among the first served with subpoenas, the Blackburns had been biding their time in the Odd Fellows Hall for several hours. Earlier in the afternoon, Minnie nervously chattered at some length with Edna Kissinger, confiding that she was "just so nervous and unstrung" by the whole thing. She mentioned Charlie's intent to sell their farm to Jap Francis. When the boy had delivered the telegram concerning the sale of the cattle, Minnie said, "I thought I would fall dead! I didn't know what in the name of God they wanted to send us a telegram for. Why, we didn't tell them to do any such thing!"[4]

If the cattle sale was on the up and up and merely a liquidation of property put up by Jap Francis on the farm purchase, why was Minnie so nervous? Was she fearful that a clandestine plan to keep the sale secret and send the proceeds to Lebanon had been uncovered? She did use the plural pronoun "we."

With the crowd in the hall settled but uneasy, Roach called Sheriff Hufft and Deputy Paxton. Hufft detailed the several day search, including the finding of a sorrel horse belonging to Francis, "alive, but in terrible shape."[5] As Hufft described the way the horse had been carefully tied in such a way that it could never escape,[6] the audience again became unruly. Some would speculate that Stoutland residents were nearly as upset about the brutal mistreatment of Sam as they were the murder itself.[7]

Paxton explained the location, the disposition of the body, and the singular lack of eyewitnesses:

"We've only found one person who claims to have seen or heard anything suspicious over there on Rouse Hill—that is, until we found the body. She's a-settin' right there [pointing to Mrs. Henry Kissinger]. I reckon she'll speak for herself, but we're a-hopin' that some more people around here is gonna come forward with a little more evee-dence."

It was Edna Kissinger's turn in the witness chair. She testified that she lived about three-quarters of a mile north of Stoutland, in a hollow below Rouse Hill where Francis was killed. She said that she was up getting a fire going in the cookstove at about 5:00 A.M., Wednesday, November 10, when she heard a gunshot in a southwest direction, "about the Oliver place," which was on line with Rouse Hill and between the Kissinger home and the murder scene.[8] Her husband was just getting out of bed and did not recall hearing the shot.

Q: "What made you remember hearing the gunshot?"

A: "Well, it just seemed odd, just before daylight like it was. I reckoned that it weren't no squirrel or rabbit hunters, and all the possum and coon hunters would a' already been in by that time of the mornin'."

Charles Winfrey and John Frey related their conversations with Jap Francis Tuesday afternoon and evening, November 9. Frey confirmed Jap's stated intent to return to Stoutland the next morning to learn where the returns for his cattle had been sent. He sensed the volatility of the crowd and the effects of his words. Ever the diplomat, Frey testified truthfully but with a certain reservation. Few people are anxious to finger a neighbor, even one not especially liked, with the suspicion of murder. The stakes were much too high. And there was Charlie Blackburn glaring coldly at him from the back of the room. It was downright awkward.

The words of John Frey and Charlie Winfrey were not lost on the crowd, who took turns shifting in their seats and rubber necking Charlie and Minnie. Hard of hearing, poor old Miz Mary Craddock kept asking Minnie to repeat the witnesses' increasingly incriminating testimony about her son-in-law. Minnie, starched, trussed, corseted, hatted, and perfumed, appeared as nervous as a prostitute yanked into a revival meeting.

Virgil Evans then took the stand, and for once he was tight-lipped. Under urging, he confirmed all the earlier witness testimony, including that he had informed Jap Francis at the Peters sale that Charlie Blackburn had shipped Francis's cattle and that the returns had not come in, that the bank was holding for payment a $1,200 check from Blackburn to Francis for the cattle, that he had spoken twice with Francis that evening, and that Francis intended to return the next morning to make further inquiry about the cattle returns. And, "Oh yes," Rollie Smith had told him that Jap Francis had been in several days earlier and said that Charlie Blackburn was selling his farm to Joe Givens and to be sure and collect the bank's outstanding loan.[9]

Sid Roach then put Virgil Evans exactly where Virgil did not wish to be—on the spot. The reputation of the People's Bank was at stake. Banks live or die on their reputation for security and integrity. Virgil could not afford to give an inch.

Q: "Mr. Evans, didn't you think it was unusual that Mr. Jasper Francis, a member of your bank's board of directors, who had told you *personally* he would be returning on the morning of November 10 to learn more about the cattle returns, did not show up?"

A: "Well, it really didn't cross my mind at the time one way or the other. I'm a busy man—I guess I just plumb forgot it."

Q: "When Mr. Charles Blackburn came into your bank on Thursday, November 11, and told you he was selling his farm to Jasper Francis, did that seem odd to you, given what Mr. Francis had told your Assistant, Mr. Smith, only a week or so earlier?"

A: "I did wonder a little. Why, I even asked Charlie about it. I told him that I had heard he was selling his farm to Joe Givens, but he denied it."[10]

Q: "So, Mr. Evans, did it not concern you that Mr. Blackburn, while telling you that he was selling his farm to Mr. Francis, came into the bank and cashed checks and notes that completely emptied Mr. Francis's account—and Mr. Francis had not reappeared since you saw him only two days before?"

A: (shifting in his seat) "No, I can't say I was concerned. I've known Charlie Blackburn for a long time, and in these parts, a man's word is his bond. I had no reason then and I don't have any reason now to figure anything was wrong."

Q: "It not only emptied Mr. Francis's account but it even overdrew it. Didn't it, Mr. Evans?"

A: (testily) "That's right. But as I say, we at the People's Bank trust our customers, and when they present paper that appears bona fide, we're always going to give good service."

Q: "So, in giving good service to your customers, did you carefully compare the signatures on that paper with known authentic signatures of Jasper Francis, a member of your bank's board of directors?"

A: (exchanges glances with Rolla Smith at the jury table—hesitates) "Yes, yes, I did. I sure did." (indignant) "Besides, I know Jap Francis's signature when I see it!"

Q: "Mr. Evans, as the bank's cashier, were you and the board of directors worried about whether Mr. Blackburn's $3,311 loan, outstanding for some time, would ever be repaid?"

A: "Well, the loan was considerably in arrears and the board had discussed it a few times. But I couldn't say we were terribly worried about it—Charlie has always managed to pay off his loans with the bank."

Q: (sarcastically) "Isn't it true, Mr. Evans, that you breathed a great big sigh of relief when you were able to move all that money out of

Mr. Francis's account over into the bank's account with the repayment of every nickel of that $3,311 loan?"

A: (angrily) "I don't know what you're a-gettin' at, Mr. Roach. We're always happy when folks can pay off their honest debts to the bank!"

Roach: (curtly) "You're excused, Mr. Evans."

Disgusted with the People's Bank's indifference to the interests of Jasper Francis, Sid Roach had publicly called the bank's business practices into question. At the jury table, the bank's president, Marvin Calkin, glared at Roach. Assistant Cashier Rollie Smith smiled weakly and re-crossed his legs.

Virgil Evans did not volunteer that the last time he saw Francis alive he had urged him not to go by Blackburn's place and confront Charlie about the missing cattle returns for fear he might "get away that night."[11] It had hardly been a ringing endorsement of Charlie Blackburn's character.

Rube Winfrey was an old man, retired and well-off financially. He did not share John Frey's reluctance to "tell it like it is." Unlike Virgil Evans, he had no interest in protecting the bank's reputation. He minced no words. After Winfrey related his conversation with Jap Francis as he left Stoutland, Roach asked Winfrey:

Q: "Did Mr. Francis tell you what he intended to do if the cattle returns had not come in by the morning of Wednesday, November 10?"

A: "Yessir, yessir, he shore 'nough did."

Q: "What did Mr. Francis say?"

A: "He said that by the end of the day he was gonna garnishee ever' single thing that Charlie Blackburn had!"[12]

Chaos reigned again. In many minds, the motive and the identity of the murderer of Jap Francis had become "plain as the nose on your face." Most of the crowd were on their feet. Everyone had something to say and none of it was pleasant.

"Lock him up right now, Sheriff—looks like you've got your man!" shouted one opinion leader.

Another offered sage advice: "Yeah, Sheriff, you'd better lock Charlie Blackburn up, alright—for his own protection."

For once, even Charlie Blackburn was cowed. Pale and shaken, he stood up, seemingly weighing the advisability of fight or flight. Charlie looked like a man staring into the blinding carbon-filament headlight of the Frisco's onrushing Meteor.

A few observers had heard enough and rushed from the hall. One, as he crashed out the double doors onto the street, became the town crier: "Sid Roach has got his man sure 'nough! Charlie Blackburn was a-cheatin' Jap Francis on a cattle deal and Jap was gonna lower the boom, so old Charlie killed him! Why, it's as clear as day to ever'body settin' up there."

A small band of men, including Jesse, had been lounging on a flatbed hay wagon across the street, taking turns sipping from an ironstone jug. Energized by such interesting and definitive news from the hall of justice, they slid off their perches and had a hurried and noisy confab. Passing the jug around one more time, they mounted their horses and rode away together. They would be back.

Order was restored in the hall only after Sheriff Hufft and Deputy Paxton again threatened the crowd with expulsion. Sid Roach delivered a little speech:

"Ladies and Gentlemen, I must remind you that what we're doing here this evening is not a court of law. No one is on trial here. There is no judge and the rules of evidence, including hearsay, do not apply. A coroner's inquest is nothing more than a formal inquiry, seeking to determine the cause of a suspicious death and any relevant facts surrounding that death. You must be cautioned that interfering with public officials doing their duty is a felony in the State of Missouri, and the County Prosecutor, Mr. Lodge, sitting here, and the Deputy Sheriff, Mr. Paxton, standing there, are fully empowered to arrest and charge anyone who further disrupts these proceedings."

In future months and years, Sid Roach would hear a lot about hearsay evidence and the questioning of witnesses suspected of a crime, under oath, without advising them of their rights. For now, bowing to the authority of the State, the crowd returned to their seats and shut their mouths—for a while. Charlie Blackburn had heard plenty of hearsay evidence about his cattle deal with Jap Francis and insinuations by Sid Roach. He had a story to tell and was anxious to talk. Suddenly arising, he moved toward the prosecutor's table. Hufft, sitting nearby, stood upright and slid his hand toward his holstered revolver.

Charlie had decided the best defense was to go on offense:

"I reckon it's about time I got to say my piece, Mr. Roach. My wife here is in delicate condition, sufferin' from nerves and terrible headaches, and my poor old mother-in-law could hardly get up them steps. We've been dragged in here, cooped up for I don't know how long, and we've been a-threatened, and these here people a-starin' at us like we wuz some kind of a damned freak show. I don't think it's fair what's a-bein' done. Just when is it that we get to talk?"

The penetrating gaze of Sid Roach met the flat, emotionless blue-eyed glare of Blackburn. The staredown lasted a few seconds. Observers swore it was a full minute. Roach broke the dead silence. With a frozen smile, he icily replied, "Have a seat, Mr. Blackburn."

Roach began his questioning in a friendly, almost helpful manner, sort of a "good guy" approach. Charlie Blackburn would prove not as big a rube and bumpkin as Roach assumed. Charlie's story was simple and straightforward. Told with an air of haughty confidence, it made a perfect liar out of the dead Jasper Francis.

He said he had been negotiating the sale of his farm to Jasper Francis from late September or early October. They had agreed upon the price of $11,500, consisting of the following:

$1,200 worth of cattle (net of two mules that Charlie had delivered to Francis)
1,500 check
3,000 note
3,000 mortgage on the farm to be paid by Francis
2,000 second mortgage given by Francis to Blackburn
800 cash money
$11,500[13]

The mules were transferred to Francis Saturday, October 30 and cattle received by Blackburn, Sunday, October 31. The cattle were then shipped to market a week later with the returns sent to The State Bank of Lebanon. The $1,500 check and the $3,000 note had been written and signed by Francis on November 2. Charlie had last seen Jap Francis the morning of the 9th at the Francis Farm. At that time he had asked Jap to go with him to the bank in Stoutland to exchange the "papers" and pay off his loan to the People's Bank. They would then take the train to Lebanon to pay off a second mortgage on the Blackburn farm held by W.I. Wallace. Francis declined, saying he was going to a sale, and if he bought some calves, he would be getting back late.

Charlie said, "Jap tol' me, 'If I don't come to your place tomorrow in time to go to Stoutland with you, or on Thursday in time to catch the train, I will go through the country Thursday and meet you in Leb'non.'" Jap didn't show in Stoutland on Thursday, so Charlie cashed the check and note and then went on to Lebanon. Likewise, Jap didn't show up in Lebanon, where Charlie paid W.I. Wallace $2,223.80, coming from $1,014.35 in proceeds from the cattle shipped on the 7th, along with a $1,209.45 check on the newly deposited money in his account at the People's Bank of Stoutland. Charlie had then traveled to Linn Creek on Tuesday, the 16th, as agreed with Jap. Jap did not show for that meeting either. The next thing he heard about Jap Francis, his dead body had been found on Rouse Hill.[14]

It was all very pat, but the devil is in the details, and Sid Roach spent the next two hours seeking to expose Charlie Blackburn as a perjurer. He reexamined Charlie's version. Over and over.

At times, Blackburn, under siege and knowing every word was being recorded, refused to answer immediately. He sat mute for long periods of time before answering.[15] Catcalls from the audience had no effect. A casual observer might have suspected he was making it up as he went along. For all his early bravado, Charlie Blackburn hardly acted like a man armed with the God's truth. Early on, he made a statement that would dog him for a very long time:

Q: "Mr. Blackburn, I'm holding in my hand a check, signed by you, in favor of Mr. Jasper Francis for $1,200, dated November 6, 1915. Now then, what was this check for?"

A: (hesitating) "Well, Mr. Roach, that was my check to pay for the cattle."[16]

Q: "Mr. Blackburn, you told us earlier that you and Mr. Francis had been discussing sale of your farm for at least a month and that you had agreed on a price of $11,500. You've testified, sir, that Mr. Francis's cattle, valued at $1,200 was being given by Jasper Francis as partial payment upon the purchase of your farm. Now then, sir, can you explain to me and this jury why this check, deposited for payment at the Bank of Stoutland by Mr. Francis, was written in the first place?"

A: (hesitating) "Well now, it's all kinda runnin' together just exactly how that all went. I reckon I just don't recall right now."

Q: (scathing) "Isn't it really true, Mr. Blackburn, that this farm sale you've testified to is just an invention? It's just a falsehood, isn't it?"

A: "No sir, it's not! It's a fair deal and we both agreed to it!"

Q: "There was never any farm deal, was there, Mr. Blackburn? This check [holding it up] represents the only agreement that you ever made with Mr. Francis—$1,200 cash and two mules for his herd of cattle. And isn't it true, Mr. Blackburn, that there was no money in your account to cover this check when you wrote it, and you still have not, to this very day, deposited the money from the sale of Jap Francis's cattle in the People's Bank of Stoutland to cover this check?"

A: (hotly) "There ain't a word of truth to that! We had a deal, alright, for the farm and the cattle were considered in—if you'll give me a little time to recollect it—I figger I can explain the whole thing and just exactly how it all was."

Roach agreed:

"Fine, Mr. Blackburn, I'm a fair man. Why don't we just give you a little more time. We'll move on with a few more witnesses, and when you think you've got your story straight, just let me know and we'll get you back up here so that you can testify for the record. Oh, yes, Mr. Blackburn, while you're thinking, would you please try to recall why the late Mr. Francis wrote you this [holding up] check for $1,200, dated the very same day that you had written him this [holding up] check for exactly the same amount?"

Roach continued his questioning of several witnesses who saw and spoke with Francis on the Linn Creek Road the evening of November 9. After each was dismissed, Roach, as if reproaching a schoolboy, asked, "Mr. Blackburn, have you focused your mind—are you ready to explain these checks?"

Finally, some one and a half hours later, Blackburn responded. His face red with anger, Blackburn was seething. "Yes, Mr. Roach—I reckon I remember ever' bit of it now."

Q: "Well, now then, you've had plenty of time to think about it, Mr. Blackburn, why is it that you wrote this $1,200 check, dated November 6, 1915, to Mr. Jasper Francis?"

A: "That there check was really just meant to be a bonus back to Jap Francis on the sale of my farm to him.[17] He reckoned that we had somehow misfiggered it all, and he thought he had put in too much with the $3,000 note and $1,500 check and assumin' the mortgage and so forth. It was just easier for me to write a check for the diff'rence as kind of a bonus back to him, than redo the other paper all over ag'in."

Q: "What! Do you mean to tell these people [motioning to the jury] that after all these weeks of discussions, at the last minute, there was doubt about how it all added up? First you say your check was for the cattle, and now you say it was a "bonus" back to him on the farm sale?"[18]

A: "That's right."

Q: "Well, then, Mr. Blackburn, what about this check for $1,200? You would have us believe that Mr. Francis wrote this to you on the very same date that you wrote this *bonus* check, for exactly the same amount, to him to remedy a miscalculation of the price of the farm? Are you trying to tell us that Jasper Francis, a good businessman and director of the bank, was just sitting there trading checks back and forth with you, unable to figure out how much he owed you for your farm and how it would be paid?"

Blackburn was silent for several moments, shaking his head.

Q: (quietly) "Mr. Blackburn, any reasonable person would understand that if what you say is true about selling your farm to Jasper Francis, neither one of these $1,200 checks were necessary. What you are saying is at odds with all reason. How do you explain this?"

A: (more silence) "It's just real tangled up—I reckon I didn't understand it all just right at the time myself. I was just doin' what Jap asked me to do!"

Roach proceeded to bombard the witness with leading questions based upon the utterances of Jasper Francis as related by others:

Q: "Mr. Blackburn, didn't you tell Jasper Francis that you were selling your farm to Joe Givens and you would make this check [holding up Blackburn's $1,200 check to Francis] for the cattle good as soon as the sale of your farm was completed to Mr. Givens?"

A: "No sir, I did not. I was never plannin' on sellin' to Joe Givens and I never told Jap Francis any such a thing."[19]

Q: "Are you saying that all these people [motioning], Mr. Evans, Mr. Winfrey, Mr. Rolla Smith, Mr Frey, and uh, uh, Mr. Rube Winfrey, sitting right here [pats him on the shoulder]—that these people that you have known for years are all lying when they say Jasper Francis told them you said you were selling your farm to Joe Givens?"

Q: "No, I ain't sayin' that, but if Jap Francis did tell 'em that, I don't know why he said it."

A: "Mr. Blackburn, isn't it true that you asked Jap Francis to help you write that $3,000 note and that $1,500 check, with him expecting that those papers were being prepared for Joe Givens to sign for the purchase of your farm?"

Q: "No, I just told you. . . . "

A: "And didn't you cash that note and that check, *supposedly* signed by Jasper Francis, along with this [waving] $1,200 check *supposedly* signed by Jasper Francis at the People's Bank of Stoutland on the morning of November 11, the day after Miz Edna Kissinger, [pointing] sitting back there, heard a gunshot over there on Rouse Hill where the mortal remains of Jasper Francis were finally found?"

Q: "No sir, that is not true! That is not true! Jasper Francis signed them papers intendin' to buy my farm. It was a deal he agreed to, fair and square."

Q: "Mr. Blackburn, would you really have us believe that a respected businessman and cattle farmer like Jasper Francis would have lied to all these people whom he had known for many, many years? Why, Mr. Francis was on the board of directors of the People's Bank of Stoutland—do you think he would have lied to employees of the bank? And not only that, would he have withheld the fact that he was about to buy your farm from his own brothers?
(pause)

"His brothers, Mr. Blackburn, are sitting right here at this table. He farmed with his brother, Simpson Francis and corresponded with Ben Francis—who is still in shock at hearing, only today, the terrible news about his late brother. You're saying he would have lied to all these people [gesturing] and not told his own brothers? Do you really expect us to believe that, Mr. Blackburn?"

A: (bristling) "You can danged well believe it or not, as far as I'm concerned. But I'm a-tellin' you it's the God's truth. And to tell you real straight, I'm tired of bein' run over by you and all these big-shot lawyers you've got there with you that yore a-conferrin' with ever' whipstitch. I ain't done nuthin' wrong, and as far as I know, I ain't on trial here, am I?"

It was a wonderful question and very timely. It brought Roach and all the attorneys there assembled to a screeching halt. Roach had answered the question earlier in his little civics lesson to quiet the crowd. Indeed, no one was on trial. It was time for a huddled conference of lawyers and coroner in the corner of the room.

Should Blackburn be advised that he was, in fact, a suspect and had the right not to answer any further questions and to have an attorney present? When does it become incumbent upon a prosecutor to advise a person that they are suspected of a crime? When does a person become a "suspect"? Is it only when a prosecutor says he is?

It would be 51 years until the U.S. Supreme Court mandated "Miranda warnings" to those suspected of a crime:

> You have the right to remain silent. Anything you say can and will be used against you in a court of law. You have the right to speak to an attorney and to have an attorney present during any questioning. If you cannot afford a lawyer, one will be provided to you at government expense.[20]

The phrase has now been drilled into the consciousness of policemen, prosecutors, and fans of *Law and Order* everywhere. In 1915, it was murky legal water. Miranda warnings were certainly not required, but Sid Roach would learn that the testimony of a suspected party, subpoenaed before a coroner's jury, without counsel and subjected to adverse interrogation, would prove to be a problem—a big problem.

Sid Roach and company concluded they shouldn't swim in these waters much longer without putting Charlie Blackburn on notice that he was suspected of the crime of murder. Still, much like a quarterback seeking encroachment on the defense, Roach believed he still had a "free play" with Charlie. He couldn't resist throwing the ball long and ending with a flourish:

Q: "Just a couple more questions, Mr. Blackburn, and then we'll be done with you for now. Did Jasper Francis ever sign a written contract to buy your farm?"

A: "Well, I reckon not—there were no papers signed by either one of us except for the checks and the note that he wrote up. That was what we wuz intendin' to go to Leb'non and Linn Creek for, was to get the papers all drawed up."

Q: "Do you mean to say that when you left the People's Bank of Stoutland Thursday morning, November 11, 1915, you had gotten $5,700 of Jasper Francis's money and cattle, and he had absolutely nothing from you to show for it? [shouting] Is that what you mean to say? Is that what you mean to say? That you had gotten $5,700 of Jasper Francis's money and property, and he had nothing from you to show for it!"

A: (shaken) How is it?

Q: (leaning forward in Blackburn's face) "Mr. Jasper Francis had nothing in writing from you to show for the $3,000 note, the $1,500 check, and the $1,200 check, did he?"

A: "No, nothing to show for it—nothing signed in a contract."[21]

Q: (lowered voice and pointing accusingly) "Mr. Charles Blackburn, did you have anything to do with the killing of Jasper Francis?"

A: (surprised) "No! No sir, I did not!"

Q: (pausing for effect) "Mr. Charles Blackburn, are you aware that you are a suspect in the killing of Jasper Jacob Francis?"[22]

A. "I reckon not."

Roach's startling question echoed down the stairs and reverberated to the crowd waiting outside. Both Hufft and Paxton stepped within protective distance of Charlie Blackburn. Mary Craddock and Minnie Blackburn glanced fearfully at each other, wondering what was going to happen next.

Claude Mayfield stepped to Coroner Jackson's table and urgently implored, "Mr. Jackson, we need to adjourn this session right away—you'll need to convene it again tomorrow sometime, but we need to clear this hall. We've only got two officers of the law here and this thing could get out of hand."

Jackson, a mild-mannered functionary, agreed. Hammering his gavel down several times, he shouted, "This coroner's court for the County of Camden, State of Missouri, is hereby adjourned until tomorrow afternoon at 2:00 P.M.!"

Chapter 29

Billy Reed, engineer turned reporter, had become sickened from the kerosene-fouled air and body heat in the coroner's jury room. Midway through the two hours of relentless questioning of Charlie Blackburn, he had given up his seat and, squeezing his way down the stairs, found himself in the crisp fresh air on Stoutland's Main Street. The bloody Hunter's Moon[1] that had at first puzzled and even frightened some had arisen high in the northeastern sky. Now shining through a clear and pristine atmosphere, it was as brilliant as a freshly minted Double Eagle gold piece. The town was illuminated in its soft, lustrous light. Somewhere, bundled lovers may have been encouraged to take a walk in the moonglow. In Stoutland, it was not a night for romance. "Taking a little air," Reed didn't like what he was seeing and hearing.

It seemed that nearly every household in Stoutland possessed a contraband railroad lantern with the name "Frisco" stamped into the base. Used by conductors and brakemen to signal the train's engineer at night or during bad weather, its flickering yellow flame was enclosed in a windproof circular globe. As excited people moved from place to place, the swinging lanterns appeared as fireflies flitting about on a summer evening. But it wasn't summer. It was also well past the bedtime of most Stoutlanders. The lanterns were signaling danger—trouble was afoot.

Billy moved in the direction of a large cluster of lanterns that had collected across the street in front of the City Restaurant. Remaining in the shadows, he heard the impassioned voices, both male and female, of an assembly getting larger by the minute. A wide variety of views were being expressed, some sober, some not so sober, about the murder of Jasper Francis and what ought to be done about it. Most were simple expressions of hardworking poor people who had lost a friend:

> "Poor old Jap Francis, he was as fine a man as ever lived."
> "He was a gentleman if there ever was one!"
> "You betcha."

"Yeah, I'll miss old Jap—if you were down and out, you could always find a payin' job out at his place to get you through hard times!"

"You'd better believe it—he helped me out a' many a time. And when things got really rough, he'd advance you a little money to get food back on the table for the wife and kids and help pay the store bill."

"Why, there'll never be anothern like 'im! And don'sha ever wonder? Why is it that it's always the good ones that have to die? When some ornery cuss that'd never do a damn thing for nobody—hell, he'll live forever."

"Ain't that the truth! I reckon some folks are just too durned mean to die—they want to hang around, a-raisin' Cain and aggravatin' their neighbors."

"Yeah, or chisel you out of what little you got if you wuz to scrape together a couple a' nickels—and you won't haf'ta walk too fur to find one or two a' them kind right around here clost!" (nodding toward the People's Bank)

Others were repeating rumors:

"I ain't been up there [coroner's inquest] but Jesse was and he says that Simp Francis told Sid Roach that Charlie Blackburn claimed to be sellin' his place to Jap for $11,500. Shoot, that's unheard of—there ain't no way that Jap would a' paid that much for that old place."

"Especially the way Charlie has let it go down—nobody does much work around there but Skip Archer, and Charlie don't hardly pay him nuthin'—he mainly just gets his room and board."

"I wonder where old Skip is? I ain't seen a thing of 'im."

"I hear that Charlie let him go and he's movin' back in with his mom and dad. In fact, I'm told that Charlie and the old lady moved back in with Minnie, and they're sellin' off their stock and gettin' out of farmin' altogether."

"Seems mighty funny that Jap is killed at the same time he had this queer land deal a-goin' with Charlie Blackburn. I wonder if maybe he did it?"

"Well, Luther come down awhile ago, and he'd for shore made up his mind about hit. He says that Charlie was tryin' to cheat Jap on a cattle deal and Jap foun' out about hit and Charlie kilt him jest to shet 'im up! Him and Jesse and a few more boys rode off awhile ago. Nobody knows what thar up to, but by gum, I rikken they'll be back!"

Then the subject got around to law and order around Stoutland. Some had long memories:

"For all his downright arragunt ways, it's hard to believe Charlie'd do somethin' like that. But then a' course I never thought Bobby Partlow would a' killed anybody neither, but he killed the Prices, just as sure as I'm a-standin' here. Think about it! He killed two people over a few pigs and never served a day in prison!"

"That ain't the half of it. Why, I could quote you chapter and verse on a haffa dozen killin's around here, includin' Tom Bohannon a-shootin' Merritt Fulbright away back there. They say he shot old Merritt down like a dog right in front of twenty people at a meetin', and even with all them eye witnesses, Bohannon still got off scot-free! My daddy said when he was young, Merritt got wounded and nearly killed at Wilson's Creek. Think of it! I don't care if he was a danged rebel, he was a-fightin' for what he believed in—and then that's what had to become of him!"

"The trouble is, we ain't got much law here in Camden County and what little we got don't seem to reach all the way over here to Stoutland. Why look at just t'night! We got the Sheriff of Lay-clede County here just as big as you please. And all we got is one deputy from Linn Creek. Nobody's seen hide nor hair a' that sheriff of our'n, that fella Salsman. You'd think that on a murder case, he could find his way to Stoutland."

"Hell, he'd prob'ly need hisself a map to find his way over here."

"And did you see that young dandy of a prosecutin' attorney? He don't look to me like he could argey his way out of a tow sack! I hear the Francis boys hired Sid Roach and them other lawyers to help out—I figger they think the same thing—that nobody'll pay for killin' thur brother."

"Yessir, 'pears to me like the law in this here county might could use a little extry hep!"

As the evening waned on, the idea took hold that the party who killed Jasper Francis would never "get what's a-comin' to 'im." The talk was getting louder and the crowd impatient. Expectations were high and unrealistic. They not only wanted to know who did it but wanted to see justice done—and the sooner the better. A mob needs a leader with charisma and simple ideas. And about that time, both arrived.

Jesse had indeed returned with obedient "yes men" Luther and Orville, along with several other ready volunteers. All had consumed a lot of Wade Brumley's finest clear moonshine whisky.[2] A supply line extending all the way from adjoining Miller County assured a plentiful supply of the 120-proof hooch. It was said to be the finest unstamped whiskey this side of Hazard, Kentucky.

Jesse and company had come prepared for the task at hand. They were well armed with pistols stuck in their belts and a small arsenal of rifles and shotguns, all locked and loaded. They had brought a little something else to the party. Thirty feet of ¾-inch hemp rope and the skills to tie a clean hangman's noose. Without delay, they put their craftsmanship to work and had a presentable article prepared within minutes.

As soon as the crowd saw the rope, a majority cheered and yelled encouraging words. Luther volunteered his neck to test the proper "fit and finish" of the noose. Pulling the knot tight under his Adam's apple and stretching the rope's length heavenward, he kinked his head at an angle and did a little dance. Recalling the old abolitionist's fate, Orville sang a verse or two of "John Brown's Body," but forgot some of the words. The appreciative crowd cheered wildly. Luther then delivered his considered opinion that "It'd snap a neck before nary a person could blink his eyeballs."

Some in the crowd were instinctively repulsed at the thought of what might happen. But they lacked the courage to step forward and take issue with the rough-hewn and obviously drunk ringleaders. Others were ambivalent and neutralized by the now oft-repeated belief that the only justice for Jap Francis would have to come in Stoutland and not at distant Linn Creek. They were willing to stand back and watch. Finally, there were the thrill seekers. They had heard about distant lynchings of "uppity" negroes who had not "learned their place" or were unlucky enough to have been accused of "ruinin'" a white woman. These were the same people who would walk five miles to gawk as shattered bodies were extracted from a Frisco train wreck. The excitement of impending death drew them near and held them like ferrous iron to a magnet.

When the rope was launched up and over a limb of the big chinkapin tree near the barbershop, a shout went up that carried all the way to Rouse Hill. The cry was heard inside the Odd Fellows Hall, but no one wished to break protocol by walking around the coroner's table and gazing out the window. The source of such pleasureful hysteria went undiscovered.

Having ventilated his lungs, Billy Reed was feeling even worse. Having seen and heard enough, he ran toward the big double doors leading up to the hall. He had barely squeezed inside and started to mount the steps when he was met with a wall of people leaving the hall. One name was on everyone's lips. It was "Charlie Blackburn" and it was prefixed with "murderin'."

Swimming against the human tide and not without a couple of bruises, Reed found his way back into the nearly empty meeting room. Seeking out Sid Roach, his breathless greeting held the words that no believer in the rule of law ever wants to hear: "Mr. Roach, there's a lynch mob with a rope waitin' outside! There's a bunch of 'em, and they're good and drunk. Every one of them is armed to the teeth, and I think they mean business!"

Roach knew in a second that this well-dressed stranger was telling the truth. "Mr. Paxton! Mr. Hufft! Would you please step up here." The two lawmen standing protectively beside Charlie, Minnie, and Miz Craddock did as they were bid.

"I ain't a bit surprised" was Paxton's response to the shocking situation as it was revealed. "Mr. Roach, you let this thing go on way too long and now we may be in a hell of a mess. I'm goin' down there with this here shotgun along with my old hogleg [touching the Navy Colt 45 on his hip] and put a stop to it!"

"Don't you do it, Mr. Paxton!" replied Roach. "We don't know who they are or what they intend, but we don't want to incite a mob with a show of force—not just yet! If they're serious, you won't stand a chance, and a whole bunch of people could get killed or hurt. Mr. Lodge and I will go down there and talk to them. We'll see if we can get them settled down." Mr. Lodge turned a little pale.

It had not been a good day for Charlie and Minnie Blackburn, and it was threatening to get a lot worse. Both had overheard the exchange between Roach and Paxton. Pulling the window curtains back, they saw what appeared to be 150 people standing outside shouting threats:

"Come on down, Charlie; we got us a little surprise here fur yuh!"

"Yeah, Charlie, we're gonna have us a little play party and yore the guest of honor!"

"Shore, come on down and meet yore neighbors. Why, you don't even need to dress up! We done got you a real nice necktie—you're gonna look real purty!"

Releasing his lips from his pursed whistle, Charlie blurted, "Now listen here, Mr. Roach, you've set a mob on an innocent man and his family, and we're in need of protection here!" Judging others by himself, Charlie figured that Roach, Paxton, and Hufft would likely turn him over to his tormentors before risking a shoot-out. It would not be a desirable outcome.

"Nobody is going to get hurt here as long as I have anything to do with it," grimly replied Roach. Outmanned and outgunned, Roach delivered his final instructions:

"Mr. Paxton and Mr. Hufft, if they're beyond reason and should get past us and come up those stairs, you must warn them twice, and if they keep coming, fire a shot over their heads. After that, you are authorized to take any action that you see fit, including the use of lethal force, to defend yourselves and the people in this room."

Roach and Lodge, followed by the Francis brothers, descended the steps. It seemed odd that the stairway was empty. The door latches consisted of a pair of brass hand grasps, each with a thumb latch release. Roach was chilled by the fact that neither door would open. The two outside door handles had been tied together with a section of rope. To strengthen the barrier, the simple expedient of an iron window weight, pushed through the handles, had firmly secured the doors. They wouldn't budge. The entire Camden and Laclede County law contingents, along with the Blackburns and the Francis brothers, were now trapped inside the Odd Fellows Hall. Constable Manes had not left his post guarding Jap Francis's body. Orders were orders.

"This is Austin Ivon Lodge, Prosecuting Attorney for Camden County. I demand that whoever is out there open these doors immediately! You are breaking the law by hindering law-enforcement officials in carrying out their official duties!" Lodge's thin adolescent voice didn't get any respect.

Drunken laughter came from just outside the door. "That's what we're here for too, *Mr. Austin Ibon* [sic]*Lodge,"* someone roared derisively. "We're law enforcement officers too, by God! Some of the best, I reckon, in these parts, and we're just here to lend a little assistance."

"We're good citizens of this here town, and we'd like to ask you, *very, very respectfully, sir,* and with the *most honorable intentions, sir,* to send Mr. Charlie Blackburn out here. We just want to parley with him awhile. We promise, *Mr. Austin Ibon* [sic] *Lodge,* that we won't hurt a single hair on old Charlie's pretty head!" (uproarious laughter)

Shouting through the door, Sid Roach spelled out the consequences of the mob's actions.

Unlawful restraint and interfering with law officers in the performance of their duties were mentioned prominently. He specified the statutes, the citations, and the likely length of prison terms. He didn't get as far as murder by hanging of an untried suspect. Roach sweetened the deal with:

"Whoever you people are, I know it's been a long day and tempers are short. You all knew and respected Jasper Francis, and I can understand you wanting to see justice done—and I promise you, justice is going to be done. Mr. Lodge and I have no interest in placing you under arrest—providing that you release this door and then get away from here just as quickly as you can. If you do that, we're willing to take no further actions."

Jesse was unimpressed:

"Well now, Mr. Roach, that's a *very gen'rus offer*, but there's a lot of us out here believin' that there ain't never gonna be no justice done for Jap Francis. People in Stoutland cain't seem to git no justice from all the way over there in Linn Creek and we aim to git it right here tonight! We got the *men* and we got the *method,* Mr. Roach. [more laughter] Now then, you just need to sashay Mr. Blackburn down here, and we'll open up these here doors and take proper cus-tuh-dee of that fine gentleman."

Luther weighed in: "Say, if you and the fellers in there with you behave yourselves, we promise not to arrest *you*! Now, how's that sound? Why, you'll be nice and safe right in there with the Odd Fellers, while we hold us a little court right out here on the street!" Laughter and shouts of approval rewarded this bit of daring bravado.

Another voice chimed, "Hell yes, I reckon you and Jesse can arrest 'im as good as old Wild Bill Hickok hisself." The crowd roared its appreciation of such clever wit.

Jesse continued with lowered voice and an ugly tone, "Now, if that don't suit you, Mr. Prosecutor, we'll be a-comin' in to get that killin' dog, Charlie Blackburn, whether you like it or not, and the first person that gets in the way is gonna be a dead man! Yuh hear me, Mr. Roach?"

It was a standoff moving toward a fateful conclusion.

Simpson and Ben Francis then stood as tall as any men have ever stood in Stoutland, Missouri. Without conferring with Roach, Lodge, or anyone else, they took charge. They moved to stop the lynching of the man they firmly believed to be their brother's murderer.[3]

Simp led off, shouting through the door, "Jesse——, is that you? And Luther ——, I know you too. Orville ——, I can't believe you've cast your lot with this bunch! I want you boys to open these doors and let me and my brother Ben through. You all know both of us. Nobody gets harmed and everyone stays just where they are. Jesse, you know it's me and Ben's brother that's a-layin' dead down there at Palmer's. You know danged good and well we've got a stake in what's a-goin' on here. Now, you let me and Ben out of here and let us say our piece!"

After several moments of silence and some muttering outside, a fumbling with the door handles was heard. The ropes were cut and the iron window weight slid free. "No funny business now, Mr. Roach, we got a lot of artillery trained right on this door," warned a voice outside.

Feeling things moving in the right direction, Roach confirmed, "We'll take no action whatsoever. Go ahead and let these gentlemen out."

The crowd respectfully parted for the Francis brothers as they stepped off the sidewalk and crossed the street. Ben climbed on the back of an old buckboard and stood up. The crowd hushed. With the nearly full moon rising over his right shoulder and illuminated with the light of a hundred lanterns, he said what was on both their minds:

"Listen folks, this is a good town, made up of mainly good people—a lot of good people! I just got back here today to find out that my brother [voice choking] has been killed. Me and my wife and boys have lived in two different states since we left here, but we decided to come back home to our farm. And it's because Stoutland is home to us. You people have always been honest and good to ever' one of us all these years, includin' my mom and dad. Some of you standin' right here set up with 'em all night when they were old and ailin' and about to die. I reckon Doc Carlton's out tendin' the sick right now or he'd be here. I know good and well that if he was, he would not be approvin' of what's a-goin' on here."

Simp Francis then sought to close the deal with the unruly crowd:

"If my little brother Jap could be a-standin' right here, I know that he would tell all of you to go on home and let the law handle this![4] He wouldn't a' wanted anything to happen to anybody without a fair trial. He was that kind of a man. [pause] So, if you want to do somethin' for Jap, don't be out here on the street breakin' the law. It's not right and you know it—every one of you knows it. So, we're asking you to just go on home. That's the way Jap would a' felt about it, and that's the way me and Simp wants it! Mr. Roach has said that he's willing to let this all go and we'll just forget about it. Now then, what do you say?"

After a long silence, "He's right," said one of the fence-sitters. "Jesse, I know you and Orville and Luther are tryin' to do what you think we all want done—but just as Ben says, Jap wouldn't a wanted it this a-way. I, for one, am goin' home."

The dam was broken. As others voiced agreement, the crowd dissolved quietly into the night. Ben Francis's heartfelt words had brought the best of humanity out in some folks who had temporarily lost their way. The men who were anxious to take the life of Charlie Blackburn with a rope slung over a chinkapin tree under a Hunters Moon mounted their horses and rode out of town.

Walking home, Charlie and Minnie got a good look at the rope and noose abandoned by the mob. It waved gently in the night breeze, a symbol that can always help focus the mind. Charlie Blackburn would never forget it. In a daily nightmare, he would fight its placement over his neck for the rest of his life.[5]

Hufft and Paxton, joined by Charlie Manes who had never left his post, escorted the Blackburns to their home just down the street. Hunkered under macintoshes and slickers in their Model-T Ford cars, they kept a protective vigil all night outside the Blackburn house.

Just in case.

Chapter 30

The inquest into the circumstances of Jap Francis's death resumed at just after 3:00 P.M. Wednesday, November 24. Ben Francis's impassioned plea to the would-be lynch mob had taken hold. The size of the crowd was halved. The blood of the townsfolk had cooled and reason would prevail. Sometime before sunrise a shadowy form had claimed the hangman's noose from the big chinkapin oak. Either a scavenger decided a "nickel a foot" rope had salvage value or maybe Jesse decided his well-bucket needed its companion. Cold limestone well-water, gargled in a dry, cottony mouth and sloshed over an aching head, can do wonders for a bad moonshine hangover.

Missing the night train back to Springfield, Billy Reed had found a bed in Harriet Davis's rooming house close to the depot. He ate an early breakfast at the "City" and caught the Southwest Special and arrived in Springfield in the early afternoon. He knew his wife and family would be worried—maybe frantic. Nevertheless, Billy detoured to the office of the *Springfield Republican*, the city's leading newspaper. There, he awakened a nodding city editor and spilled the news. Sensationalism, especially murder, sells newspapers, and the scribe recognized in a second that this volunteer stringer had a good story. He jotted notes furiously. Published daily, the *Republican* would scoop by 24 hours the *Laclede County Republican*, published at Lebanon, as well as the weeklies *Stoutland News* and *Linn Creek Reveille*.

The Springfield newspaper's Thursday, November 25 headline shouted:

> MURDER OF CAMDEN COUNTY FARMER IS CAUSE FOR THREATS
>
> Body of J. J. Francis, Who Resided Near Stoutland, Found In Woods Thirteen Days After Victim's Disappearance

HORSE TIED NEARBY FOUND TO BE WEAK FROM HUNGER

Bullet Hole Is Found In Head And Skull Is Crushed—Expect Verdict Of Coroner's Inquest Thursday

What followed was a surprisingly accurate account of what was known about the demise of Jasper Francis. Maybe more engineers should dabble in journalism. Having left Stoutland in the morning, Billy Reed still feared mob violence. The article continued:

"The jury's verdict, Mr. Reed said, is being anxiously awaited and fear is being entertained how those interested in this case may receive the information, which will probably be revealed by the conclusion."

He need not have been concerned. When Charlie Blackburn resumed testimony Wednesday afternoon, the sight of that swinging rope had indeed focused his mind. The two $1,200 checks, dated the same date, were very troublesome. One was definitely filled out in Francis's handwriting and Blackburn had not denied signing it. The other was filled out in Blackburn's handwriting and was ostensibly signed by Francis. Francis's words, as repeated by several witnesses, seemed to ring true. He had spoken of a cattle deal going bad between Blackburn and himself and Charlie's bum $1,200 check. Charlie's characterization of that check as a "bonus" to Jasper Francis on the sale of his farm to Francis had been singularly unconvincing. Backing away from that claim and "needing to study on it" seemed very suspicious. To many, it appeared that the $1,200 check from Francis was likely a forgery and nothing more than a clumsy attempt by Blackburn, post-mortem Jasper Francis, to cancel out his own $1,200 check to Francis.

As Sid Roach renewed his interrogation, Charlie Blackburn had been warned that he was a suspect but still had not been informed of his rights to remain silent and be represented by counsel. Roach immediately bored in on the matter of the $1,200 checks. Charlie needed an explanation and he needed it fast. He spun a remarkably good story and stuck with it.

Q: "Mr. Blackburn, if you don't mind, could we just get back to these two $1,200 checks? [holding them up] You first stated that one of these checks was payment by you for a herd of cattle you purchased from Mr. Francis. That of course, is exactly what Mr. Francis said it was for when he sent it in to the People's Bank of Stoutland to be held for payment. But then, Mr. Blackburn, you said [looking at notes] that this check was really a 'bonus' check, written by you to correct a miscalculation on the sale of your farm to the late Mr. Francis. [pause]

"Now then, I've got this other $1,200 check here [holding up] dated the very same day, supposedly signed by Mr. Francis and made payable to you. This is the check that you presented to the People's Bank of Stoutland on the day after it appears Mr. Francis was killed. This check from Mr. Francis [holding up] cancelled out this check [holding up] from you—I think Mr. Evans said the two checks 'butted up against each other.' Yesterday evening, sir, you said that you couldn't recall why the two of you exchanged these checks. Is that right?"

A: "Yes, sir."

Q: "Mr. Blackburn, as you put it, have you had a chance to 'study on it' for a while?"

A: "Yes, sir."

Q: "Well, Mr. Blackburn, why don't you just tell us all about it? The jury is sitting right here. Mr. Lodge and Mr. Jackson and all these folks [wide gesture] are all ears—just go right ahead—take your time!"

A: "Alright, Mr. Roach, I will. You see, me and Jap Francis had been on this farm deal for quite a while just like I explained yesterday. We'd agreed on a price of $11,500, and I was allowin' his cattle in at about $38 a head or $1,200 even, which we agreed to. Now then, he said he could use a couple of mules so I threw them into the deal 'to boot,' kind of a bonus—like I was a-talkin' about before. I [had] taken the mules to him on a Saturday and then we drove his cattle over to my farm the next day, on a Sunday—I believe it was the last day of October."[1] [hesitates]

Q: "We're listening—the lady there [stenographer] is hanging on every word. Go on."

A: "Well then, I went over to Jap's place on the second of November and he drew up the papers and he wrote me the check for $1,500 and he drew up the note for $3,000 and dated 'em both back to Saturday when he got the mules—so it'd draw interest from the reg'lar start of the deal, you might say. Then Jap says to me, 'I'd 'preciate it if you would let me hold these papers a few days and not take 'em to the bank—I'm a-makin' some arrangements to sell my farm and don't want the word gettin' around that I've already bought yore place. Besides, I may need to get some of that money in to make yore's all good.' Yeah, I think that was just about what he said. I said that would be just fine. I was in no partik'lar hurry, and I wanted to be accommodatin' about it. Jap told me not to say a word to the neighbors about our deal one way or the other and I told him I wouldn't.[2]

"After a few days—I think it was the next Saturday, me and Jap got together, and I asked him if he was ready to exchange the papers at the bank so I could pay off another loan I had on the farm and the place in town and he handed me the papers but he says, 'I hear there's talk around town that I've bought your farm and I'm afraid it's gonna knock me out of the sale of my place. Now here's what I'd like for you to do—why don't you give me a check for $1,200 for the cattle and I'll take it to the bank and turn it over to Virgil Evans to hold. So's if anybody comes in there a-askin' any questions, Virgil can show 'em this check, which would show that I've sold you the cattle and not put 'em in on no land deal.[3]

"I said to Jap, 'I reckon that'll be alright—I don't see nuthin' wrong with it.' And then I got to thinkin' that maybe since my $1,200 check wasn't supposed to amount to nuthin' anyway, that to kind of protect myself, so to speak, I asked Jap, 'How would it be if you was to write me a check for $1,200? That way, we'll just be holdin' each others paper.' He said that would be fine, and I wrote it out and he signed it. We dated 'em both that day, November the 6th. So that's how that all happened.[4]

"So, then, like I said before, the last time I saw Jap Francis was Tuesday morning, on the 9th when he was a-wantin' to go to that sale and he said he couldn't go with me that day and he would meet me in either Stoutland or Leb'non to finish up the deal on Thursday."[5]

Charlie's new and improved version had a certain logic to it. The chronology seemed to make sense and followed the known facts. The premise that someone both seeking to buy and sell at the same time might wish to create an innocent subterfuge to preserve a negotiating position wasn't so farfetched. Except no person could be found who could corroborate that Francis was seeking to sell his farm. No one, except the dead Jap Francis, had ever mentioned that Charlie was selling his farm to anyone. Jap had said Charlie had sold it to Joe Givens of Decaturville. Mr. Givens had not yet been found. Later, when he was located, he claimed no knowledge of purchasing Blackburn's farm and was immensely puzzled by the whole matter.

Jap Francis had mailed the $1,200 "cattle check" to the bank for payment. He had not enlisted Virgil Evans in any disinformation plan. For Charlie's story to be true, Jap Francis had engaged in an elaborate ruse from his first conversation with Rollie Smith to his last-known utterances to Rube Winfrey. The deception would have extended to his friends, his family, John Frey, and his associates at the bank. All to create and sustain a pretense that he was not buying Charlie Blackburn's farm?

Charlie's narrative had libeled Jasper Francis as a crafty liar and a manipulator. It positioned Charlie as a naïve soul, trying only to accommodate Francis in seeking top dollar for his own farm. Those who knew Francis scoffed at the very idea, but the clever tale would bumfuzzle more than one jury. It illuminated the dark and damning trail of circumstances leading to Charlie Blackburn with one gleaming and indispensable ray of hope called "*reasonable doubt.*"

Sid Roach pounded upon Charlie Blackburn for almost two hours until the cows literally came home and the sun set. Charlie stubbornly stuck to his story.

Interest had ebbed among observers in the Odd Fellows Hall—many slipped away down the steps and disappeared into the gloom. Life goes on and it was nearly suppertime. Only the evening before, the same people had turned their thumbs down and demanded the lynching of a long-time acquaintance and neighbor. Now, boredom and indifference had set in. Perhaps the law should handle such matters after all. Determining guilt or innocence is such a tedious and tiresome process. States of high indignation are hard to sustain. Art Linkletter was right when he said, "People are funny."

At about 5:30 P.M., Minnie Blackburn was sworn as a witness and "stood by her man." She verified that she had been aware for some time of the planned sale of the farm to Jap Francis:

"I knew what the business was; I knew that he was going to get the money on the farm deal; he had told me all about it; they had been figuring on the deal for six weeks; he [Charlie] said they wanted Kellerman [lawyer at Lebanon] to draw the deed."[6]

Minnie said that Charlie had walked into town "a little bit after noon" to read a telegram on November 9, the day before Francis was likely killed. He remained only "about 20 minutes" and then he started back to the farm. Her husband was not in Stoutland in the early morning of the 10th, but she had ridden out to the farm at 8:00 A.M. and found her husband and Skip Archer "throwing out a load of corn."[7] Nothing unusual going on here—just the wearisome humdrum of life on the farm that Minnie so abhorred.

Miz Mary Craddock, sturdy pioneer, wasn't "buffaloed" in the slightest by the squad of hired-gun attorneys, ranked and filed at the table before her. She "stood by her daughter's man." She gave Charlie Blackburn a perfectly detailed alibi for his whereabouts at 5:00 A.M. the likely day and time of the murder. Inexplicably, her account of Charlie's walking trip to Stoutland the day before varied significantly from her daughter's, but no one seemed to notice:

"I knew that Jap Francis and Charlie were on a deal for his farm and had known it for quite awhile; maybe a month or six weeks. . . .

"Charlie left the field about 4:00 to go to Stoutland. It was after dark and about suppertime when he came back. He stayed there all night and was there the next morning. He did not leave the house that night and no one called for him. I heard nobody leave the house.

"I heard no noise nor shooting of any kind on Tuesday night, the 9th of November or in the morning of Wednesday, the 10th. Me and Charlie usually got up at about the same time between 4 and 5 o'clock. Charlie ate an early breakfast, and he and Skip [Archer] gathered corn in the morning."[8]

Unable to find either Skip Archer or Joe Givens and without knowledge of the available testimony of Wes Scrivner and other important witnesses, Sid Roach and coroner J.J. Jackson brought the inquest to a close. After an hour of deliberations, Foreman Lem Fulbright reported the verdict. The *Springfield Republican* gave this account:

> UNKNOWN PARTIES KILLED FRANCIS
>
> Coroner's Jury Fails to Place Responsibility for Murder Near Stoutland
>
> An open verdict, finding that J.J. Francis, whose body was found near Stoutland Monday afternoon, came to his death at the hands of unknown parties was returned by the coroner's jury investigating his death, according to advices to the *Republican* Thursday.
>
> As a result, it is believed that Camden County authorities will be unable to place the blame upon anyone, it was stated, as they have no clues to work on.
>
> The inquest was held in the Odd Fellows Hall at Stoutland and was attended by almost the entire populace of the little town. The high feeling which was said to have prevailed Monday night and Tuesday, has now subsided, according to the reports received here.

> Charles Blackburn, the farmer with whom Francis was negotiating at the time of his death for the purchase of his farm, was the principal witness. He testified in detail as to the deal.
>
> Funeral services for the slain man will be held today.

The *Stoutland News* put it a little differently:

> The Jury rendered their verdict after carefully considering the evidence and decided that J.J. Francis had come to his death by the hands of an assassin, name unknown. This is all the jury could do, honorably, but we sincerely hope that the perpetrators of this murder, planned and premeditated, will promptly be brought to justice.

After 14 days, it was time to lay Jasper Francis to rest.

Chapter 31

> Stoutland
> The funeral of the late J.J. Francis was held by the I.O.O.F. lodge of this place, at Liberty Church, in Laclede County, Thursday, November 25. A large number attended the burial. Several went from here, both Odd Fellows and Rebekahs. He was a member of the Odd Fellows lodge here, and well respected by a large circle of friends, both in the lodge and out. Two brothers, and their families, besides many friends, mourn his death, to whom we extend our heartfelt sympathy in their sorrow.
>
> —*Linn Creek Reveille*
> December 3, 1915

As they say in small town Missouri, "Jap was put away real nice." It was a chilly and rainy day[1] when his unvarnished oak casket was carried into the church by his Brothers of the Stoutland Odd Fellows Lodge. The funeral bier was covered with a cascade of lovely late-autumn chrysanthemums. A photograph of Jap, astride his beloved horse Sam, was placed atop the coffin, along with his Odd Fellows jewel of ruby and gold, signifying 25 years of membership. It was said that the casket was lined with a "Lone Star" quilt handmade for him by his mother a long time ago.

People came from far and near to the funeral. Most were friends, neighbors, and acquaintances wishing to show their respects. Some hardly knew the deceased and a few were complete strangers. Fascinated with the morbid and sensational nature of his death, they came out of curiosity. The crowd totaled as many as 300. It overflowed the little white, gable-roofed Liberty Christian Church and spread outside upon the grounds. Many stood in the steady drizzle under parasols. Groups of three and four held weatherproof slickers aloft to stay dry.

Ministers of mainstream Christian denominations have railed at fraternal organizations like the Masons, Odd Fellows, and Elks for centuries. Their secretive and exclusive nature is downright suspect. Might they be practicing outright paganism? The quasi-religious rituals performed by their members are thought to encroach upon matters deemed the sacred province of the Church. Of particular concern are allusions to "God," "Divine Master," and "Creator" only in a generic sense. In seeking a universal brotherhood of man, such organizations are reluctant to exclude Jews and Muslims by mentioning Jesus Christ by name, hence, the unpopularity of fraternal lodges with Christian clerics. Catholics are prohibited from membership.

Today, there would be no such conflict. The division of labor was clear-cut. The Christian Church (Disciples of Christ) would conduct the funeral inside its church. The Odd Fellows would hold their rites at the graveside. Besides, in deference to criticism, the "Fellows" had adopted a funeral ceremony in 1902 that acknowledged the saving power of Jesus Christ.[2]

Accompanied on an old Hammond organ, a little choir began the service. They chose to sing the last hymn that Jasper Francis ever heard in life, "Softly and Tenderly." The great evangelist, D.L. Moody, who preached to multitudes on two continents, gave the ultimate homage to his friend, W.L. Thompson, the song's lyricist and composer. On his deathbed, the man who ministered to both Abraham Lincoln and Ulysses S. Grant[3] motioned for Thompson to draw near. He feebly whispered, "Will, I would have rather written 'Softly and Tenderly' than anything I have been able to do in my whole life."[4]

Thompson's masterpiece summoned Jasper Francis home to glory:

> Softly and tenderly Jesus is calling,
> Calling for you and for me;
> See, on the portals He's waiting and watching,
> Watching for you and for me.
>
> Come home, come home,
> You who are weary, come home;

Earnestly, tenderly, Jesus is calling,
Calling, O sinner, come home!

Following an opening prayer, Brother Frank Moneymaker spoke of the "tragic and untimely death" of the lately departed Mr. Francis. His message of salvation and hope was replete with some of the most inspiring scriptures in the Holy Bible [King James Version]:

"Our friend and brother, Jasper Jacob Francis, having believed and having confessed and repented his sins, was baptized at an early age into the hope of everlasting life. In John, Chapter 11, verses 25 and 26, Jesus said, '*I am the resurrection and the life: he that believeth in me, though he were dead, yet shall he live: And whosoever liveth and believeth in me shall never die.*'

"To the family, I say it is very natural that your hearts be troubled. It's only to be expected that you should be saddened by the sudden loss of your dear brother—your brother-in-law—and your dear uncle. We mourn his passing and our sympathy is without bounds. Surely, your minds have wandered back in time only a few short years ago. Then, we stood at this very place, along with Jap and said goodbye to your loving parents, Bill and Lucy. More recently, we have remembered the tragic passing of your devoted sister, Murtie. [Pause] But when you think of them and are burdened with grief, be comforted that the great Jehovah, in the final days '. . . *shall wipe away all tears from their eyes; and there shall be no more death, neither sorrow, nor crying, neither shall there be any more pain: for the former things are passed away.*' [Rev. 21:4]

"Be consoled and cheered by the promise of Jesus's words! I read to you from the book of John, Chapter 14, verses one through six. No words uttered by man have ever been so complete and so sublime as those uttered by Christ to his Apostles at the Last Supper: '*Let not your heart be troubled: ye believe in God, believe also in Me. In My Father's house are many mansions: If it were not so, I would not have told you. I go to prepare a place for you. And if I go and prepare a place for you, I will come again, and receive you unto myself; that where I am, there ye may be also. And whither I go ye know, and the way ye know.*'

"Thomas, a doubter, said, '*Lord, we know not whither thou goest; and how can we know the way?*'

"Jesus's answer was the answer for all mankind's questions down through the ages. He turned to Thomas and said, '*I am the way, the truth, and the life: no man cometh unto the Father but by me.*'"

No preacher worth his salt misses the opportunity at a funeral to do a little admonishing of the faithful, as well as the not so faithful, whose appearances at church are reserved only for end-of-life events. Frank Moneymaker had a full house and a captive audience. He sought to gather a few strays back to the flock:

"Ladies and gentlemen, brothers and sisters, as we come here to pay a final tribute to our friend and brother, Jasper Francis, let us look within ourselves. Let us examine our hearts and minds. Let us contemplate upon the hereafter. Are you prepared to meet your maker? There is none among us today who is without sin. There is none among us who, like Jap Francis, will not someday '*walk though the valley of the shadow of death.*' Friends, none of us will escape the cold clutch of death. There is not one of us whose mortal remains will not be returned to the dust from which we came. [pause]

"Hebrews Chapter 9, verse 27 says, '*And as it is appointed unto men once to die, but after this the judgment.*' The judgment, friends!

"I quote from the Apostle Paul's second letter of Timothy, '*I charge thee therefore before God, and the Lord Jesus Christ, who shall judge the quick and the dead at his appearing and his kingdom.*'

"On that great day when, '. . . *the Lord himself shall descend from heaven with a shout, with the voice of the archangel.*' [1 Thess. 4:16]

"No, brothers and sisters, there is not one among us who doesn't need Christ's saving grace. There is not one among us who has not been corrupted by the evils of this world and temptations of the flesh. I beseech you to believe and trust in the Lord. Confess your sins! If you do, Jesus will forgive them and welcome you with his mercy. [pause]

"The prophet Isaiah foretold the coming of a Savior who would say, '. . . *though your sins be scarlet, they shall be as white as snow.*' And folks, I said that in order to say this: Never forget Jesus's words to the thief, hanging in agony next to him on a cross, who said, '*Lord, remember me when thou comest into thy kingdom.*' And Jesus said, '*Verily I say unto thee, Today shalt thou be with me in paradise.*' [Luke 23: 42, 43].

"Do as the Lord has commanded! And if you do, you will surely find your place among those many mansions that Jesus has prepared you! And with open and loving arms, He will welcome *you* into paradise as '*thou good and faithful servant . . . enter thou into the joy of thy Lord.*' [Matthew 25: 21]

"In closing, as we remember and bid farewell to our friend Jasper Francis, a righteous man, a generous man, and a kindly man who left this world a better place than he found it—let me read to you from the book of Psalms. David, the King of Judah, more than 2,000 years ago, spoke of God's goodness and God's grace. Now, as we commend our dear brother Jasper to his Creator and to his eternal reward, let us reflect on the words of David:

'*I will lift up mine eyes unto the hills, from whence cometh my help. My help cometh from the Lord, which made heaven and earth. He will not suffer thy foot to be moved; he that keepeth me will not slumber. Behold, he that keepeth Israel shall neither slumber nor sleep . . .*

'*The LORD is thy keeper; the LORD is the shade upon thy right hand.*

'*The sun shall not smite thee by day, nor the moon by night.*

'*The LORD shall preserve thee from all evil: He shall preserve thy soul.*

'*The LORD shall preserve thy going out and thy coming in from this time forth, and even forever more.*' [Psalm 121: 1–8]

"Amen and Amen."

The choir then broke into Dr. Jeremiah Rankin's "God Be With You,"[5] a hymn of parting often used as a funeral benediction. They chose to sing it a cappella:

"God be with you till we meet again;
By His counsels guide, uphold you,
With His sheep securely fold you;
God be with you till we meet again.

Till we meet, till we meet,
Till we meet at Jesus' feet;
Till we meet, till we meet,
God be with you till we meet again."

With pews emptying in sequence and including all those standing outside, the crowd filed silently by the coffin. A few, moved by the finality of the hymn's words and its haunting melody, brushed tears from their eyes. The choir never broke stride, slowly singing all four verses and chorus three times over to accommodate the number of mourners.

Then came the Odd Fellows. Dressed in dark suits, they stepped forward and faced the casket. Slowly and solemnly, they reached with their right hands to their hearts, where red Odd Fellow parade ribbons were pinned. Each reversed his ribbon, turning the black side out, revealing IN MEMORIAM inscribed in silver. Six Brothers then hoisted the coffin onto their shoulders.

Led by the Noble Grand Master and trailed by the Vice Grand Master and Chaplain, Jap Francis and his mourners proceeded to the grave.

The Odd Fellows ceremony was carried out to the letter as prescribed in "Funeral Ceremony for the Use of the Lodges of the Grand United Order of Odd Fellows in America." The Brothers stood circling the grave into which the coffin had been lowered, the Noble Grand Master at the head, the Vice Grand Master at the foot, and the Chaplain on the side. The Chaplain read a brief oration, interspersed by responses from the brethren assembled. They all stood in a meditative posture with sprigs of evergreen pressed to their lips. Upon pronouncement of "Amen," each stretched their arms out full-length, then brought them back in a "graceful manner."

After numerous allusions to "Friendship, Love, and Truth," the Chaplain finished with:

"Now to God who doeth all things well, do we commit the spirit of our deceased brother, trusting when the Savior cometh to make up His jewels, we all may be found acceptable and to the earth do we commit his body, for 'Naked we came into this world and naked we return out of it. The Lord gave and the Lord hath taken away; blessed be the name of the Lord.'"

With hands clasped close to their hearts, the Brethren responded, "Blessed be the name of the Lord."

Main Street, looking west—Stoutland, Missouri, circa early 1900s.
—*Courtesy of Frances Shepherd Metzger*

Main Street, looking west—Stoutland, Missouri, 2002.

Top of Rouse Hill with dark depression (center) where Jasper Francis's decomposed body was found, circa December 1915.
—*Courtesy of Lucille (Alexander) Gregory*

Jasper Francis's prized Fox-trotter "Sam" at the site of his starvation ordeal. Photo likely taken in December 1915, while being led home to the Francis farm.
—*Courtesy of Jasper J. Francis*

Sam, from another angle, with Jap Francis's empty saddle aboard. Only Sam knew who killed his doting owner.
—*Courtesy of Lucille (Alexander) Gregory*

Sam as an old horse, with Jap Francis's great-nephews, James and Jasper J. "Jap" Francis (the murdered man's namesake) aboard.
—*Courtesy of Jasper J. Francis*

Recreation of Jasper "Jap" Francis by Donna (Bloomer) Crim.

Jasper Francis' older brother, Thomas Benjamin "Ben" Francis, circa 1930.

—Courtesy of Jasper J. Francis

Jasper Francis's nephews; left to right: Silas, Ward, Ray, and Leonard, sons of Ben and Lucy Francis

—Courtesy of Jasper J. Francis

Silas Francis Family, circa 1943. Silas, Opal (Sweatt), and son, Jasper Francis, namesake of his murdered great-uncle.

—Courtesy of Jasper J. Francis

Modern-day Jasper Jacob "Jap" Francis. Francis still lives on the original Francis farm in Camden County where "Uncle Jap and Uncle Simp" lived in 1915.

The author's Uncle Tunney Allee (named for world heavyweight champion Gene Tunney) stands where the Frisco Railway Station once stood in Stoutland, Missouri.

Ruby (Allee) Wright at the intersection of the old Fulbright and Linn Creek Roads. Hail fell and winds blew only on Rouse Hill, July 2, 2000.

Recreation of Charlie Blackburn by Donna (Bloomer) Crim.

Gladys "Purg" Blackburn, Charlie's brother.

—Courtesy of Robert Blackburn

"Purg" Blackburn and Lynn Blackburn, Charlie Blackburn's brothers.

—Courtesy of Robert Blackburn

Easter Sunday, April 17, 1938.
Seated: Charlie Blackburn's mother, Dolly Blackburn.
Standing: Charlie's siblings: Maude, Mattie, Purg, and Imogene.

—Courtesy of Robert Blackburn

Lynn Blackburn, wife Edith, and son Robert Blackburn.

—Courtesy of Robert Blackburn

Robert "Bob" Blackburn, nephew of Charlie Blackburn, and his good friend, Sunny DeManche—Citrus Heights, California.

Donna (Bloomer) Crim, great-niece of Charlie Blackburn. A portrait artist with a firm memory of Charlie's likeness, only Donna could bring both Charlie and Jasper "Jap" Francis "back to life."
—*Courtesy of Donna (Bloomer) Crim*

Sixteen-year-old Donna Bloomer sits on her 1949 Plymouth—Chino, California, 1959. When the car broke down, Charlie lent her $200 to buy the '52 Mercury across the street.
—*Courtesy of Donna (Bloomer) Crim*

Left to right: Robert "Bob" Blackburn, Donna (Bloomer) Crim, and author Alan Wright—Shingle Springs, California, 2003. Both Bob and Donna knew Charlie Blackburn well during their teenage years.
—*Courtesy of Donna (Bloomer) Crim*

Tombstones of Charlie and Minnie Blackburn's infant sons, Clyde and Floyd, along with the marker of Minnie (Craddock) Blackburn-Lankford—Hillhouse Cemetery, near Stoutland, Missouri.

Stoutland Cemetery marker of the financial magnate of Stoutland, Virgil M. Evans and his wife, May.

Dr. William Oscar Pool, who assisted in the examination of Jasper Francis's body.
—*Courtesy of Frances Shepherd Metzger*

Beloved Stoutland physician Dr. C.E. Carlton and his wife, Minnie, in 1951. Doc Carlton performed a detailed dissection of Jasper Francis's body.
—*Courtesy of Ernest Carlton*

Key prosecution witness farmhand Harrison Fernando "Skip" Archer, rear, with his parents, Marian and Matilda
—*Courtesy of Della Sage*

Left to right: Rolla Smith, Assistant Cashier, and Virgil Evans, Cashier, in front of the People's Bank of Stoutland, circa 1915.
—*Courtesy of Frances Shepherd Metzger*

The People's Bank of Stoutland (now City Hall) where Charlie Blackburn passed suspicious checks and note the day after the killing of Jasper "Jap" Francis in 1915.

Stoutland historian Bob Barr stands behind marble People's Bank teller's window where Cashier Virgil Evans accepted checks and note submitted by Charlie Blackburn in 1915.

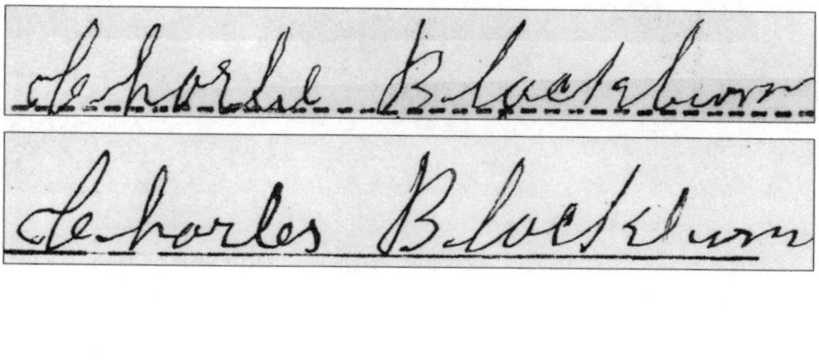

Samples of Charlie Blackburn's shaky and irregular handwriting. Is this the writing of a clever forger?

Sidney Crain "Sid" Roach, relentless chief prosecutor of Charlie Blackburn, circa 1922.

—Courtesy of Camden County Museum and Historical Archives

Jackson King "Jack" Roach II, sales executive and grandson of Blackburn prosecutor Sidney Crain "Sid" Roach. Jack Roach is now deceased.

W.C. "Waldo" Mayfield and his father I.W. "Irwin" Mayfield in their Lebanon, Missouri, office, circa 1915. Mack and Smith Blackburn undoubtedly sat in this room and engaged the Mayfields to defend their son and nephew.

—Courtesy of Gene Mayfield

Camden County Courthouse at "Old" Linn Creek where Charlie Blackburn was tried and sentenced to life imprisonment in 1916.
—*Courtesy of Camden County Museum and Historical Archives*

Old Camden County courtroom (reconstructed in Camden County Museum) where Charlie Blackburn was tried for the murder of Jasper Francis.

Judge Cornelius Skinker, Missouri 18th Judicial Circuit, 1935.
—*Courtesy of Missouri State Archives*

William T. Salsman, Sheriff of Camden County, who, along with Deputy Sam Paxton, arrested Charlie Blackburn on the charge of first-degree murder.
—*Courtesy of Camden County Museum and Historical Archives*

Old Camden County jail at Linn Creek where Charlie Blackburn spent December through February 1915–1916.
—*Courtesy of Camden County Museum and Historical Archives*

Steamboat *Homer C. Wright*. The "*Homer C.*" or another Osage River steamer took Charlie Blackburn to Missouri's state penitentiary at Jefferson City.

Senator Frank H. Farris, lead defense counsel for Charlie Blackburn, circa 1910. The "Boy Orator of the Ozarks" was often compared with William Jennings Bryan.

—*Courtesy of Mary Susan (Farris) Goodwin-Tubbesing*

Senator Frank H. Farris, seated at his desk in the Senate chamber, circa 1906. The "Boodle Scandals" are past.

—*Courtesy of Mary Susan (Farris) Goodwin-Tubbesing*

The Farris family together at their Rolla, Missouri home, circa 1925. Back to front: Senator Frank H. Farris, Bertha (Dent) Farris holding Mary Susan. Frank Farris would be dead by September of 1926.

—*Courtesy of Mary Susan (Farris) Goodwin-Tubbesing*

Retired attorney, Mary Susan (Farris) Goodwin-Tubbesing, daughter of Senator Frank Hiram Farris—St. Louis Club, July 2002.

Phil M. Donnelly, Charlie Blackburn defense counsel and future Governor of Missouri, circa 1924.
—*Official Manual of the State of Missouri*

Governor Phil M. Donnelly, 1946.
—*Courtesy of Missouri State Archives*

Phillip David "Dave" Donnelly, Lebanon, Missouri, attorney; son of Missouri Governor Phil M. Donnelly and wife Juanita (McFadden) Donnelly. The governor's oil portrait is in the background.

Ruby (Allee) Wright communes with Jasper "Jap" Francis, whose spirit she believed she encountered as a child in 1928 at the murder scene. Old Liberty Cemetery, July 2, 2000.

Author kneels at the grave of Charlie Blackburn, Fairhaven Memorial Park, Santa Ana, California.

Author is lowered by hoist into Civil War-era dug well on the old Craddock farm, looking for long-disposed-of evidence.

Author's son, James Wright, and a canine assistant take a break from "archeological dig." James's Eagle Scout knots likely saved his dad from serious injury.

Author gazes skyward from the bottom of the old Craddock well.

Stoutland High School students Amanda Hill and Kaylah Domer, along with young Joseph Rogers, before they get filthy dirty sifting through the mud in Charlie Blackburn's well.

Long-time Stoutland residents Joe Rogers (left), Bob Barr (rear), and Jasper Francis (seated) await the results of well dig.

After a closing prayer, which did indeed seek the blessings of God "through Jesus Christ, our Lord" and a closing hymn, the Lodge Brethren performed the final Rite of Benediction. In single file, they passed around the grave three times, each dropping their evergreen sprig into the grave. They then bowed and gave "honors three times three." The Noble Grand and Vice Grand Masters then threw three shovels of dirt into the grave. The remaining Brothers did likewise. In reverse order they then marched away. The thing was done.

And so Jasper Francis was laid to rest. Most everyone who witnessed the graveside rites agreed that they were grandly done, but it all seemed, well—just a little odd.

Jasper Francis's final resting place would go unmarked for 10 years. When Ben Francis's wife, Lucy, died in 1925, he buried her close by Jap's grave at the Old Liberty cemetery and erected a lovely gray/rose marble stone in her memory. At the same time, he and Simp had a virtually identical stone placed for their late brother. There is no mention of the violent and premature circumstances of Jap's death. A reserved man who never sought the limelight, that's probably the way he would have wanted it. The inscription is simple and brief:

JASPER J. FRANCIS
MAY 4, 1870—NOV 9, 1915

Jap Francis almost assuredly died near onto five o'clock in the morning, Wednesday, *November 10*, 1915. The reason for the monument's incorrect date is as unknowable as the precise circumstances of the man's death. Maybe Ben and Simp Francis had "just plumb forgot." The Odd Fellow's three linked chains symbolizing "Friendship," "Love," and "Truth" were never engraved.

Chapter 32

Before the inquest's second day of questioning began, lawyers Claude Mayfield and Don Vernon had spent some time earning their keep. In the morning, they moseyed over to the People's Bank of Stoutland and had a little session with Messieurs Rollie Smith, Virgil Evans, and Marvin Calkin, along with bank directors H.D. Evans, Jas. H. Smith, and Dr. C.E. Carlton.

The conversation centered upon the "careless and reckless" way that the "help" had handled the very substantial bank account of one of the bank's directors and chief depositors, the late Jasper Francis. Words like "fiduciary responsibility," "negligence," and "failure to take reasonable care" were part of the lively discussion. "If you didn't have a policy in place to prevent the looting of a man's bank account, you should have!" pronounced Mayfield. He continued:

"Mr. Francis's account was not only plundered, but a $1,200 check that he had placed with you for payment was crossed with another one of very questionable authenticity. And even worse, *gentlemen*, the man was burdened with a $3,000 note! All of these actions were taken in his absence, without question, and with no attempt whatsoever to contact him—then or later!

"Mr. Evans [pointing to Virgil], you had every reason to be suspicious of these transactions. Everything about them shouted of a nefarious plot," growled Mayfield with his deep bass voice. "They directly contradicted the spoken words and intentions of Jasper Francis, an honest man and a director of this very bank."

In spite of Virgil Evans's hot denials, the Board members were considerably sobered. Unspoken was the possibility of Jap Francis's estate suing the bank and these matters being aired in the newspapers. Worse, there might be a sensational public trial. A few forward thinkers even pondered the possibility that key investors might withdraw their capital. Panicked depositors could create a run on the bank's assets. The voice of reason began to sink in on these pillars of civic virtue.

Unlike the others, Dr. Carlton wasn't worried about the value of his bank stock. He just wanted to do the right thing:

"I'm one of the people who talked Jap into moving his account over here before the other bank closed, and I think we need to set this thing straight. If there wasn't any contract between Jap and Charlie Blackburn, and if Ben and Simp Francis don't want to go through with this farm sale, then the bank needs to cooperate."

Without disagreement from the others, Carlton summed up: "Marv, you and Virgil and Rollie need to do whatever it takes to get this deal disentangled and put the money back where it belongs! Gosh durn it, we at least owe Jap Francis that much!"

The "help" had gotten their marching orders.

As Vernon and Mayfield walked back to the Odd Fellows Hall, Claude chuckled and remarked under his breath, "Hot damn, Don, I think maybe we put the fear of God into these Stoutland boys!"

After Jap Francis's funeral on Thursday, November 25, things moved at warp speed—by 1915 standards.

Wednesday afternoon, December 1, 1915

Ben and Simp Francis met lawyers Mayfield and Vernon at Linn Creek. Amid the requisite "whereases and therefores," the brothers signed a contract engaging the attorneys to ". . . recover the balance due on said cattle and also the $1,500 being the amount of the check which the said Charlie Blackburn claims to have received from the said J.J. Francis and also to prevent the collection of said $3,000 note. . . ." It was agreed that the lawyers would be entitled to 30 percent of whatever was recovered, whether "accomplished by suit or compromise or whether the same be settled in or out of court."[1]

The group immediately found Probate Judge J.W. Williams at the courthouse and filled out an Application for Letters of Administration of Jasper Francis's property. The good judge immediately signed the document giving the Francis brothers "full power and authority to secure and dispose of said property according to law, and collect all moneys due said-deceased. . . ."[2]

Armed with the lawful charge of their dead brother's estate, Ben and Simp stepped across the hall to see the clerk of the circuit court. Vernon and Mayfield had already prepared a neatly typed petition seeking an Attachment Writ on the farm and town properties of Charles and Minnie Blackburn and any other property and effects of the defendants. The amount claimed for recovery was only $1,200, the agreed upon net price of the cattle. Apparently the attorneys thought it inadvisable to claim the $1,500 check and $3,000 notes as forgeries. Not just yet. One plain-language phrase laid out their complaint:

". . . plaintiffs state they have good reasons to believe and do believe that the said defendants never intended to pay for said cattle at the time the said contract was made and entered into and that the *same was made in fraud on their part with a view to cheat the said J.J. Francis. . . .*" (emphasis added).[3]

The Francis brothers signed a surety bond for twice the amount claimed, or $2,400. The Camden County Circuit Clerk, W.O. Esther, swung into action. He immediately issued a Writ to the Sheriff to attach:

"Charles Blackburn and Minnie Blackburn by all and singular their lands and tenements, goods, chattels, moneys, credits, evidences of debt and effects, or so much thereof as shall be sufficient to secure the sum of *$1,014.35* . . ." (emphasis added).[4]

Twenty-three days after Jasper Francis had threatened to "garnishee everything that Charlie Blackburn's got," his brothers had made good on his threat. For reasons unexplained, Esther issued the writ only for the actual proceeds of the cattle and not the agreed upon value of $1,200.

Esther commanded the Sheriff to deliver certified copies of the Petition and the Attachment Writ to Charlie and Minnie Blackburn and summon them to the next term of the circuit court to "answer the petition."[5] Deputy Paxton never served it. Francis and his attorneys asked Paxton to hold off until they could arrange a meeting with Charlie Blackburn and officers of The People's Bank of Stoutland.

Friday, December 3, 1915

Simp and Ben Francis paid a call on Charlie Blackburn. They found him at Minnie's house in Stoutland. Charlie had returned from spending some time with his brother, Robert, who lived at Buckner in the Kansas City area. Minnie Blackburn had packed her hats, her starched petticoats, black satin dresses, kid gloves, spoiled child Robert Ray, and had caught a train. She moved in with relatives at Lee's Summit, another town near Kansas City. Charlie, Minnie, and Ray would never return as permanent residents of Stoutland. With death threats on his life, Charlie was presumed to be armed. When seen in Stoutland, he was shunned.

The conversation was brief and to the point. Ben and Simp informed Charlie that they were empowered to represent their brother's estate and that since there was no written contract for the purchase of the Blackburn farm, they did not wish to complete any such transaction. They further informed Charlie that they had obtained an attachment writ on all of his properties, effectively prohibiting him from selling them without their permission and repayment of "monies owed the estate." However, they were willing to withhold service of the writ and the summons to see if the dispute could be resolved. They proposed that they all meet the next day at the People's Bank of Stoutland and try to settle the matter. If that happened, they would drop the suit.

Charlie Blackburn was in a box. He put up weak objections, but having little choice in the matter, he caved: "I reckon you don't think so, but the trade I was on with your brother was as fair as anything ever made—but, if that's the way you want it, I just wanna try and do what's right."[6] Charlie agreed to be at the bank the next day at 1:00 P.M. The Francises didn't tell him they would have their attorneys with them.

Saturday, December 4, 1915

The meeting convened in the boardroom of The People's Bank. A cheery fire burned in the corner fireplace, but as the group settled into comfortable, green leatherbound chairs, the conversation was hardly lighthearted chatter.

Don Vernon, representing the Francis brothers, laid out a plan: "We demand that our client, the estate of the deceased Jasper Jacob Francis, be made whole. There are many facts in this matter that are in dispute, but one fact is not. No evidence of any contract between the deceased and Mr. Blackburn for the purchase of Mr. Blackburn's farm exists. Therefore, we insist upon the following:

- That Mr. Blackburn make good the $1,200 check which, along with the mules previously delivered, would settle the transfer of cattle from Francis to Blackburn.
- That the $1,500 check, purportedly signed by the deceased, be forfeited and a like amount returned to the estate. Since it left the deceased's account as cash, it should be returned as cash. Any overdrawn funds shall be returned to the bank.
- That the $3,000 note, purportedly signed by the deceased, be cancelled and held to no effect."

With surprisingly little wrangling from Blackburn or the bank, the Francis brothers got nearly everything they wanted. It was agreed that[7]:

- Charlie Blackburn would reimburse the Francis estate the $1,014.35 proceeds of the sale of the cattle. Since Charlie had only a few dollars in his account, the remainder would be taken by the estate as a second lien on Charlie and Minnie's farm and town properties.
- The $3,000 note would be canceled by the bank and the bank's loan to the Blackburns reinstated and called immediately, secured by new liens on the Blackburn properties junior to the first mortgage and the Francis estate liens. Virgil Evans's face was pinched and grimacing.

- $1,500 of the bank's funds, less the small overdraw, would be deposited in the Francis estate account. The bank would be given an additional $1,500 junior lien on the Blackburn properties.
- Those infernal wild and undersized mules, grazing unattended for more than a month, would revert to Charlie Blackburn. That is, if he would come and get them.

The prospects of the bank ever recovering all of its $3,311 were poor. The State Savings Bank of Springfield's mortgage of $4,000, plus considerable outstanding interest, must be paid first. With the Francis estate claim of $1,014.35 standing ahead of the bank's unsecured loan, Virgil Evans's worries of a major blow to the balance sheet had become an unpleasant reality. Judge W.I. Wallace had his money and smelled like a rose.

Charlie Blackburn had proven to be a pussycat, repeating his determination to "do the right thing." Perhaps he entertained the delusion that if he fully cooperated, the Francis brothers, Sid Roach, Sam Paxton, and the State of Missouri would "let bygones be bygones." He was badly mistaken. As soon as the new liens were filed, the Francises dropped the attachment writ and swore out a complaint for a State warrant against Charlie Blackburn.

The charge was murder in the 1st degree.

Chapter 33

Sam was feeling as spry as a spring colt. The ministrations of Chase Mooney at Stoutland's livery stable had brought the 5-year-old fox trotter back to health. A regimen of warmed bran mash, a little molasses, and limited amounts of water for the first 24 hours was followed by extra water and short rations of sweet prairie hay and oats. Within 72 hours, Sam was back to eating like, well—a horse. Knowing very well how Jasper Francis had spoiled the creature, Mooney even fed him an apple every evening. Sam munched appreciatively. The big sorrel got exercised twice a day, led around a large paddock behind the stable. Sam was getting to like this man Mooney. Nevertheless, he was envious of other horses passing so free and easy on the Linn Creek Road.

Sam got a lot of visitors during his recuperation. Every kid in town and half the adults came to see him and that was fine with Sam—he loved being a celebrity. Teenaged boys were especially enthralled, as curious as a future generation of juveniles would be of the restoration of a '60s muscle car. Everyone petted him and offered words of encouragement. Ben Francis and his sons had walked down the hill to see him on the wrenching day they had arrived by train from California. Simp had stopped by a couple of times to check on him, but the Francis brothers had a lot on their minds and knew that Sam was in good hands.

By Tuesday, November 30, eight days after Sam was found, Chase Mooney called Simp and pronounced Sam well enough to be taken home. He had gained weight and although noticeably thin, especially in the haunches, was lively and on his way to recovery. Simp and Ben were going to Linn Creek the next day to take care of legal matters. A neighbor, Neal Alexander, volunteered to ride to Stoutland and bring Sam back to the farm. Neal had been a close friend of Jap and felt honored to bring his horse home where he belonged.

Neal's wife, Carrie, had bought a little Kodak box-camera with some extra butter and egg money. She urged her husband to take the camera and photograph the place on Rouse Hill where

Jap Francis's body was found. "Be sure and get a picture of Jap's horse right where he was tied," she advised. "Why, you never know, someone might want to write a story about it sometime." Anxious to please and wanting to preserve something of Jap's memory, Neal agreed.

Light snowfall began Tuesday evening and partially covered the ground by morning. As Alexander rode north over Rouse Hill leading Sam, the horse exhibited a behavior that he would repeat for the rest of his life. As they approached the murder scene, he became agitated and shied to the opposite side of the road while turning his head and looking warily into the woods. Without the heart to take Sam to the site of the shallow grave, Neal tied him a little distance away and snapped a quick picture.

Fully excavated when the body was moved, the grave stands out in the picture as a darkened area in the blanket of snow. Alexander took a fallen tree branch and swept the snow out of the depression. "Otherwise, nobody will know where he was," he counseled himself.

Not about to lead the skittish and recovering horse all the way down the steep ravine to the place of his ordeal, Alexander thought, "Shoot, these old scrubby woods all look alike anyway, I'll just take Sam's picture up here where it's handy." Leading Sam among the trees, he tied him at a suitable location and stepped away. Sam didn't like it a bit. Was his misery to begin all over again? Neal snapped pictures of Sam from two different angles, quickly loosened the reins and led him away. As far as anyone knows, Neal Alexander's photos, shared with the Francis family, are the only photographic record of the murder on Rouse Hill.

After spending a few weeks in Simp Francis's good care, Sam would be taken to Ben's farm nearer to Lebanon. Within a few years, Ben and Lucy Francis had moved their family to Jap's farm in Camden County and returned Sam to familiar territory. There, he would spend the rest of his life with Ben, Ben's son Silas, and Silas's sons James and Jasper (namesake of his murdered great-uncle). Sam still had a lot of living to do.

> Nothing has ever stirred this community like the brutal murder of Jap Francis.
>
> —Wet Glaize News
> *Linn Creek Reveille*
> December 10, 1915

> Deputy Sheriff Paxton has been away most of the week, looking after his official duties.
>
> —Courthouse Notes
> *Linn Creek Reveille*
> December 10, 1915

Sam Paxton spent most of the time after the inquest scouring Stoutland and the surrounding countryside for witnesses in the Jasper Francis murder case. Wes Scrivner, urged by his "whittlin' and spittin'" buddies at the general store, came forward with his conversations with Charlie Blackburn before the body was found. Paxton was most anxious to talk to Skip Archer, and he found him at his parents' house just off the Fulbright Road. Skip had made himself very scarce since the discovery of the body. In fact, when he arrived at the Archer farm, Paxton spied Skip hightailing it for the woods. The deputy was well accustomed to dealing with reluctant witnesses:

"Harrison Archer, this is the Law—you come out from behind that tree!" did the trick. Use of his Christian name had brought Skip up short. It probably reminded him of another authority figure—his mother.

Skip's memory was alternately poor, then excellent, then poor again. First, he said he had no recollection of the whereabouts of Charlie Blackburn the night of November 9 and the morning of November 10. Under Paxton's persistent questioning, he then reckoned that, "Charlie leff the house that night, 'long about midnight, and as far as I could tell, he was gone pert' near all night."[1]

"When did you see him again?"

"I never see'd him ag'in until after sun-up," drawled Skip. sounding for all the world like Festus Hagan of *Gunsmoke*, "He was out by the way-ell pump beside the house a-washin' hisself off—it 'peared to me like he was a-washin' blood off his hands."[2]

"Are you for sure which morning it was?"

"Yay-ess, I 'member it well 'cause the next day Charlie went off to Stoutland and Leb'non, seein' 'bout some bizness and leff me tuh do all the work."

After several more questions, Paxton tested the reliability of what might be the prosecution's star witness. "Skip, I'm gonna need you to testify in a court of law. It could be very important. Can I count on yuh to get on the witness stand and tell the truth—just like you just told me?"

Skip's memory faded fast. Hesitating and clearing his throat, he replied, "Way-ell, now then, if I had tuh swar to it, maybe I ain't sa shore—mebbe I wuz miss-taken. Well, now, come to think of hit, all that may a' happened the week a'fore and mebbe not that week a-tall."

Disgusted, Paxton wrote down several notes and prepared to leave. "Skip Archer, you are a material witness in a murder case—don't you leave this county without lettin' me know—do you understand?"

"I reckon I won't, Mr. Paxton—I reckon I won't."

Don Vernon and Claude Mayfield worked overtime in their office Friday, December 10, drafting an important document. It was the Francis brothers' "Complaint of State's Warrant" seeking the arrest of Charley [sic] Blackburn *and* Skip [sic] Archer for the crime of murder. In addition to accusing Charlie Blackburn of killing their brother, the complaint claimed that Skip Archer "did . . . move, procure, aid, counsel, hire and command him, the said Charley [sic] Blackburn . . . [to commit] the said felony and murder."[3]

Accusing Archer of not only being implicated but "hiring and commanding" Blackburn to do this monstrous crime went way over the top. Backed by no evidence whatsoever, it was a ploy designed to improve Skip's memory. And it worked. Skip was arrested and jailed for a time in the Laclede County Jail at Lebanon.[4]

Fearful that his might be the next body found bludgeoned and shot, Archer had at first been reluctant to testify against his former employer. The thought of a long prison sentence, or maybe a scaffold and rope, changed his mind. He would testify. The charge was dropped and he was promptly released.[5] Properly chastened, Skip hitched a ride back to Stoutland and then trudged the two miles home. His aged mother and father threw their arms around him and bawled like babies. Skip got his favorite supper of pinto beans with ham hocks, corn bread, fried potatoes, and blackberry cobbler.

Saturday, December 11, 1915

Wasting no time, the Francises and their lawyers arrived in Linn Creek Saturday morning and filed their complaint with Prosecutor Lodge and A.J. Estes, Justice of the Peace for Osage Township. As the J.P. for the township that included the county seat, Estes was often called upon to handle matters that could not wait for the next semiannual session of the circuit court. The Honorable Cornelius Skinker, Judge of Missouri's Eighteenth Judicial Circuit, would not arrive in Linn Creek until the third Monday in February. This was clearly urgent business. Murder in the first degree demands attention. It is, after all, an affront "against the peace and dignity of the state," not to mention the dignity of the aggrieved victim.

Prosecutor Ivon Lodge would use language lifted right out of the Francises' complaint to formally charge Charlie Blackburn with murder in the first degree. The wording is so quaint that a portion bears repeating. No redundant phrase was left unturned:

"Simpson Francis and T.B. Francis, being duly sworn, upon their oaths states [sic], that on or about the tenth day of November, A.D. 1915, at the County of Camden and State of Missouri, one Charley [sic] Blackburn, in and upon one Jasper Francis, then and there being feloniously, willfully, deliberately, premeditately [sic], on purpose and of his malice aforethought, did make an assault and [sic] a dangerous and deadly weapon, to wit, a pistol the nature and kind being unknown, then and there leaded [sic] with gunpowder and a leaden ball, which he, the said Charley [sic] Blackburn, in his hands had and held, at and against him, the said Jasper Francis, then and there feloniously, on purpose, willfully, deliberately, premeditately [sic], and of his malice aforethought, did shoot and strike him, the said Jasper Francis, in and upon the back of the neck and head of him the said Jasper Francis, giving to him, the said Jasper Francis, then and there with the deadly and dangerous weapon, to wit the gun and the gunpowder and leaden ball aforesaid, in and upon the back and neck of him, the said Jasper Francis, one mortal wound of the breadth of one half inch and the depth of six inches of which mortal wound the said Jasper Francis, then and there instantly died. . . .[6]

A second count, in equally tortured language, referred to death resulting from being "beat in upon the head" with "heavy instrument or weapon to this Prosecuting Attorney unknown..."[7]

Justice Estes promptly issued a warrant for Charlie Blackburn's arrest ". . . directed to the Sheriff of Camden County, Missouri, commanding him to *have the body* [emphasis added] of the said Charley [sic] Blackburn forthwith before said justice to be dealt with according to law . . ."[8]

Apparently "forthwith" didn't include Sunday because Deputy Sam Paxton and his boss, Sheriff William T. "Bill" Salsman, waited until Monday to "go see about" arresting Charlie Blackburn.[9] If Charlie had wanted to run, he would have had a two-day headstart. It was leisurely law enforcement, but it didn't matter. Charlie hadn't gone anywhere.

Contrary to popular belief in Stoutland, Sheriff Salsman had not been reluctant to involve himself in the investigation of the Francis murder. In fact, he had offered his assistance to Sam Paxton several times. Paxton, a loner and a "man's man," had brushed polite offers aside, and Salsman had chosen not to press the matter. It seems that Paxton was determined to ". . . handle this job all by myself." Paxton's soon-to-be-announced plan to run for Salsman's job at the next election might have had something to do with his rugged display of individualism.[10]

But Salsman put his foot down when it came to the arrest of Charlie Blackburn. He insisted on participating and for good reasons. A car was needed to transport Charlie to the jail at Linn Creek, and Sam Paxton had declined to learn how to drive the Sheriff's battered Model-T Ford. It was also a prudent thing to do. People being arrested for murder can get downright squirrelly, and Salsman did not want any slipups. His absence during the "incident" at the inquest had not burnished Salsman's professional reputation around Stoutland. A "perp walk" down Stoutland's Main Street could be a career-redeeming experience.

Monday morning, Salsman and Paxton chugged into Stoutland shortly before noon and parked in front of Burhams Drug Store. Without fanfare, the two quickly walked the 200 yards to the Blackburn house on the east end of Main Street. Paxton covered the rear entrance while Salsman pounded on the front door. Charlie stepped onto the front porch and Salsman read him the arrest warrant. Charlie seemed unsurprised and put up no fuss. He only asked for the privilege of collecting some clean clothes in a small carpet bag. Arriving from the rear, Paxton followed Charlie inside to watch his preparations for departure. With Minnie and Ray long gone, Charlie locked the house. He would not be coming back.

Salsman handcuffed the prisoner with his hands in front of him and the three took the long walk up past the Odd Fellows Hall, Evans's Store, and The People's Bank. It was a busy Monday morning in Stoutland, and numerous people observed Camden County's finest taking Charlie Blackburn to jail. One interested observer was Wes Scrivner. Appearing from nowhere, he trailed the group to the car. As Charlie was placed in the rear passenger seat, Wes could not resist one more dig. "Charlie, I reckon they're still a-lookin' for that contract, all wrote up and put in Jap's little red book—nice and pretty? Do yuh think they'll find it pretty quick now, Charlie?" Charlie ignored the taunt. He had weightier things on his mind than troublesome old men.

Before leaving for Linn Creek, Charlie asked Salsman to take him by Smith Blackburn's house. Smith was summoned to the car and Charlie told him:

"Uncle Smith, they think that I killed Jap Francis and are a-takin' me to jail. Here are the keys to both houses—would you try to see that the bank don't skin me too much when they sell 'em? And would you write to Minnie and Ray and let 'em know what's happened? The last thing is, you gotta tell Daddy and Bob what kind of trouble I'm in. I'm for sure gonna need me a lawyer and I hope you'll all see to it! Uncle Smith, it's the God's truth that I had nuthin' to do with Jap Francis's killin'." Charlie pursed his lips and asked, "You believe me don't yuh?"

Smith Blackburn, long-time and well-respected resident of Stoutland, could hardly reply otherwise. "Yes, Charlie, I believe you. Don't worry, we'll be gettin' you a lawyer."

The backfiring car then chugged down the hill and out of town.

Charlie would get four lawyers—the best representation that money could buy. The legal fees would bankrupt nearly the entire Blackburn family and change their lives forever.[11]

> Charles Blackburn Arrested on Murder Charge
>
> Charles Blackburn, of Stoutland, was arrested last Monday, charged with the murder of J.J. Francis, whose body was found near Stoutland several days ago. Blackburn was lodged in jail here Monday evening. A preliminary examination is set for Wednesday, December 29, before Squire Andrew Estes. Blackburn seems self possessed and calm, betraying no uneasiness, but says very little about the case.
>
> —*Linn Creek Reveille*
> December 17, 1915

At least Charlie had the good sense not to talk to the press while he was combating bedbugs in the cold and dank Camden County jail.

Chapter 34

Compared to the shamelessly solicitous ads of today, Mayfield and Son's weekly ad in the *Linn Creek Reveille* was quite modest. Wedged between ads for "Parker's Hair Balsam" and "L.A. Lackey's Marble and Granite Works," it read:

> I.W. Mayfield & Son
> Will attend to and look after any
> legal business in Camden County,
> Mo. Address all communications to
> Mayfield & Son, Lebanon, Mo.

Nevertheless, the few attorneys with offices at Camden County's seat of government resented the ad, believing that it reflected poorly on the quality and availability of local legal representation. Insulting or not, it was very effective. Name recognition is a good first step in gaining a customer. McGary "Mack" Blackburn and his brother, Smith, thought immediately of the Mayfields when it came time to defend Mack's son, Charlie, charged with first-degree murder. If convicted, a jury would choose between death by hanging or life imprisonment. Neither seemed especially tempting.

Interestingly, Irwin "I.W." Mayfield was attorney Leander Claudius "L.C." Mayfield's older brother. Claude was already gainfully employed representing the Francis estate in recovering the alleged ill-gotten gains of Charlie Blackburn's alleged fraud upon Jasper Francis. In addition, Claude and his partner, Don Vernon, continued to serve as private counsel in the prosecution of Mr. Blackburn for murder. Irwin Mayfield's 29-year-old son, Waldo "W.C." Mayfield, was his father's understudy and helpmate. If you hired "I.W.," "W.C." came with the bargain. After the Blackburns engaged the Mayfields to defend Charlie Blackburn, three Mayfield attorneys were working the case; two determined to set him free and one working industriously to either hang or send him "down river" for the rest of his natural life. Literally.

Camden County felons were usually put aboard Osage River steamers for their trip downstream to prison. Those convicted of serious crimes like murder wore both handcuffs and leg irons and prayed that the boat did not sink. The manacled prisoners were then transported the few miles overland to Missouri's ancient limestone-walled prison at Jefferson City.

Waldo Mayfield's son, Gene, is a retired attorney living in Hilton Head, South Carolina. He reflected with some humor upon his father, grandfather, and great uncle serving as both defenders and prosecutor of Charlie Blackburn: "On different sides of the same case? In a small town, one didn't turn down a chance for a fee."[1] Irwin and Claude Mayfield's good reputations apparently allayed any Blackburn family fears of conflicts of interest.

Irwin W. and Claudius Mayfield were the sons of William and Sarah Mayfield, who emigrated from Kentucky to Missouri sometime between 1850 and 1860. In 1880, William was a farmer living in the northeastern corner of Laclede County just south of the growing railroad town of Stoutland. William and Sarah's brood, along with related Mayfield families, grew so numerous that Laclede County's "Mayfield Township" still carries the family name. Irwin and Claude's formal legal training is unknown, although it was common for young men ambitious in the law to "read" with established attorneys for a number of years before being examined for admission to the Missouri Bar.

Gene Mayfield provided a wonderful photo of his dad and grandfather in their Lebanon law office about the time of the Blackburn trial. Undoubtedly, Mack and Smith Blackburn sat in this very office to discuss Charlie's case, including how the legal bills would be paid. Irwin may have done a little "discovery" work in his brother's office down the street seeking details of the prosecution's evidence against his client.

Charlie's case seemed weak but hardly hopeless. It might boil down to whether a jury could be deprived from hearing the words of the dead Jasper Francis, as repeated by several witnesses. These consistent utterings of a respected businessman, known for his truthfulness, established a compelling motive for the murder. A capable defense would seek to make those words inadmissible under the rules for hearsay evidence. After all, a dead man can hardly arise and speak for himself—or can he? If Francis's account of his deal with Blackburn could be silenced—things looked rosy. Charlie

Blackburn had his own reasonably plausible account, backed up by an alibi from his mother-in-law, a respected old-line resident of Camden County. If Francis's words were "let in" by the judge, things looked bleak.

The Mayfields' first order of business was to bring 24-year-old Philip Matthew Donnelly aboard the defense team. Young Phil M. Donnelly (always known only by that name) had graduated from the St. Louis University Law Department in 1913 after having been admitted to the practice of law a year earlier in 1912. A Jesuit school, St. Louis University contested with the law schools of the University of Missouri and the elite Washington University of St. Louis as the major trainers of lawyers in the state. Although never partnering, Donnelly and the Mayfields worked closely together, sharing cases and referring clients to one another when it made sense. Donnelly brought a sharp intellect to the team as well as a recent law-school education with exposure to "cutting-edge" case discussions. If the case were appealed, he would be the primary researcher of applicable case law. Donnelly had another asset. His name wasn't Mayfield.

Phil M. Donnelly's father, also named Phil, was at various times the postmaster of Lebanon and proprietor of a meat market and general store. Born in Ireland, the son of Matthew "Big Matt" Donnelly, he had been a professional jockey as a young man. With a knack for "seeing the field" and plotting a course through the pack, the older Donnelly had a reputation for bringing home winners with ruthless abandon. A gregarious charmer in the paddock, Phil became a warrior at the crack of the starter's pistol. He also served for some time as Laclede County's Democratic Chairman.[2] His keen observation, opportunism, and abiding interest in politics would serve his son's future very well.

Phil M. Donnelly was a tall, black-haired young man with flashing dark eyes and a firm set to his jaw.[3] Although genuinely friendly, he was far from a booming extrovert. His quiet reserve and dignified demeanor were inherited mainly from his mother, Margaret "Maggie" (Halloran) Donnelly. As a boy, Phil was seldom one of the gang that "went fishing or peeled down for a swim in the 'crick' with the other boys. He did play baseball and football and, for years after his graduation from St. Louis University in 1913, umpired baseball games in the little towns up and down the Frisco line."[4] Phil's reputation for scrupulous truthfulness and ability to keep a confidence inspired trust, invaluable for a young attorney building a practice. No blabbermouth, he chose his words carefully, preferring gravitas over flights of fancy or bombast. From an early age, when Phil spoke, people usually listened. He took pains to be a man of his word and was conscientious to a fault.

Phil M. Donnelly also believed in paying his dues, joining all the expected fraternal lodges, including the Masons, Shriners, and Odd Fellows; as well as business, professional, civic, and church organizations. As straight an arrow as ever produced by Laclede County, Donnelly had no known vices. In a lifetime, he neither smoked nor drank.[5] By his mid twenties, Phil Donnelly was recognized by many as a political "comer" and they would be right.

The Mayfields, along with Donnelly, constituted a credible defense team, yet more was needed. First, they were still outnumbered. If there were to be four prosecutors, shouldn't the defense be equally weighty? A matter of symmetry, it would just look better to the jury. More importantly, they needed star power. The killing of Jasper Francis was sufficiently brutal and bloody to rank as both heinous and ghastly. The use of two different weapons and the violence wrought on poor Francis's body described the work of a determined fiend. A very ugly picture indeed. A picture that would be indelibly etched upon the jurors' minds by Sid Roach, Don Vernon, Claude Mayfield, and, if he made it into the game, Prosecutor Ivon Lodge. Undoubtedly, Roach's summation would be an impassioned work of art capable of goading even a reluctant jury to a guilty verdict.

The prospects of a jury reluctant to convict were rather poor. Circuit Judge Cornelius "Neil" Skinker, known as a "prosecutor's judge," had a principled dislike for requests for changes of venue. He took literally the precept that juries should be "peers" of the accused. It was also costly. Transporting and housing witnesses "all over God's creation" cost money, and Skinker took pride in an efficient and economical circuit. No, the defense must assume that its client would be tried before a Camden County jury in a courtroom filled with Stoutlanders seeking Charlie Blackburn's scalp.

Yes, more was required for Charlie's defense. What was needed was a lawyer with instant name recognition. A lawyer renowned for his oratorical skills, who could turn juror's heads (and minds) with grandiloquent phrases. Phrases delivered with a deep bass voice, pear-shaped tones and every syllable perfectly enunciated. Phrases tempered to appeal to the common sense and inherent "goodness" and "Godliness" of all those of Ozarkian birth. A man whose charisma could silence a room when he entered, whether that room was the bar at the old Madison Hotel in Jefferson City or the marbled floor of a packed Missouri Senate chamber. Most importantly, what if Charlie Blackburn's life and freedom must ultimately rest at the door of the Missouri Supreme Court? He would need a lawyer whose power and influence would command "extreme courtesy and respect."[6] Although the good jurists' judgments might not ultimately be swayed, such a lawyer's arguments would get full and rigorous consideration. An expedited hearing might even be forthcoming. And if the call was a close one? Well, were umpires more deferential to Stan Musial or Solly Hemus? Ted Williams or Billy Consolo? Judges are humans too.

The lawyer that fit the bill was Senator Frank Hiram Farris, a practicing attorney in Rolla, Missouri, some 71 miles up the Frisco Line from Lebanon. Someday, a historian may write a book about the life of Frank Farris. It would read like a novel and be hugely entertaining. Sadly, like many who led fascinating lives, wielded immense power in their times, and received the accolades of thousands at their deaths, Frank Farris is now but a footnote in Missouri history. His name, mostly forgotten, stirs only the most dedicated of Missouri historians, including John F. Bradbury Jr. and Lynn Morrow.[7]

Actually, in 1915, "Senator" Frank Farris, a Democrat, wasn't a senator at all. He was the state representative from Phelps County in Missouri's Legislature. From 1899 to 1907, he had been a state senator from the 24th District, made up of Crawford, Washington, Dent, Iron, Reynolds, and Madison Counties. He would become a senator again in 1922, elected to represent the 24th District which now included Phelps County.[8] It was and remains customary to address legislators by the highest office that they have held. In 1915, Farris proudly answered to the title "Senator."

Frank Farris was well known in Lebanon. He was born there in "Old Town," August 8, 1867. His father, John W. Farris, had been both a state senator and representative and was, for a time, speaker of the Missouri House of Representatives. As a schoolboy, Frank had served as a page boy in the General Assembly.[9] He learned every nook and cranny of the old capitol building which burned in 1911. He also soaked up the courtesies, folkways, and mores of the legislature. He quickly learned the vote trading, the compromises, the cajolery, the flattery and insincerities, the deals, and if necessary, the brute exercises of power that make the machinery of government work. He watched and listened carefully, honing his knowledge of parliamentary procedures. Quite simply, he was a child of the legislature. He spoke its language.

By the time Farris completed his education in the public schools of Lebanon and at Marionville Institute, where he graduated in 1884, he could easily have taught classes in civics and government. He may have. While studying law, he taught school for three or four years in Lebanon, becoming a school principal. One of the teachers who served under Farris was Phil Donnelly's mother, Maggie.[10] Although enjoying education, Farris was inevitably drawn back to the legislature. Through the good offices of his father, he was appointed to various functionary posts, including assistant secretary and reading clerk of the senate. By 1898, he was probably the most prepared person to ever run for Missouri's upper chamber. By then a practicing lawyer in Steelville, Missouri, Frank Farris ran and won, assuming office in January of 1899. Amazingly, within two years, he was elected to the senate's highest office, that of president pro tem.[11] He was only 33 years old. Yes, Farris had mastered it all in the State capitol. A capitol infected with blatant and pervasive corruption.

Kenneth H. Winn, Missouri's State Archivist, authored a fascinating essay about political corruption and reform in Missouri. In it, Winn quoted Henry S. Priest, an attorney representing a wealthy businessman who sought to create a streetcar monopoly by bribing members of the St. Louis Municipal Assembly. Priest said, "There are worse things than bribery; bribery is, after all, not such a serious crime. It is a criminal offense . . . [but] a trifling offense, a mere perversion of justice."[12] Such criminality was not confined to ward politics in the City of St. Louis.

At the turn of the century, bribery had become business as usual in the marbled halls of the State Capitol at Jefferson City. If a special interest wanted a bill passed, they talked to key members of the "combine" or the "lobby" and shot them a figure. If accepted, the fix was in. Small-town lawyers with modest practices and frame bungalows traded up to the elm-shaded "old money" streets. Magically, they could now afford brick Victorian ramblers with turrets, bay windows, decorative iron, and lots of lightning rods. Plush carpeting, the latest "mission oak" furniture, and grand pianos (including lessons for their young prodigies) signaled a new affluence. Maybe even a nice farm with lots of quail for the shooting and a limpid stream full of bass, perch, and sunfish could be afforded by the newly arrived squires. Constituents shook their heads in wonder. But then, weren't the roads getting a lot better? And wasn't there the promise of a new state mental hospital or blind school or sanitarium in the district?

Missouri's Legislature had become a safe harbor for the unprincipled, the unscrupulous, and the unlawful. Then, riding to the rescue of public morals and integrity, came Joseph Folk. A reform-minded circuit attorney in the City of St. Louis, Folk first went after local bosses and scoundrels and then launched a successful campaign for the governorship in 1904 with a flood of subpoenas and indictments of state legislators. He dubbed these crooks "Boodlers" and the "Boodle Scandals" were born.[13]

Senator Frank H. Farris, recently elected for his first full term, came immediately into Folk's gunsights. Missouri Attorney General Edward Crow, working with a Cole County grand jury at Jefferson City, also believed that Mr. Farris deserved scrutiny. Even the briefest discussion of the life and times of Frank Farris must mention the biggest scandal of the "Boodle" era. Of all things, it was about that lowly staple in every bakery and kitchen, common baking powder.

In 1899, the Legislature passed a bill forbidding the use of alum in food products. Former Governor William J. Stone, acting as an attorney and lobbyist for the "Baking Powder Trust,"[14] advocated passage of the "Pure Food" law in order to "protect the people from adulterated foods." Alum was classified with "arsenic and rat killers" as a toxin.[15] Alum (either sodium or potassium aluminum sulphate) was, and remains to this day, a common ingredient in baking powder, hardly a public-health hazard. Some formulations of baking powder use cream of tartar as a substitute for alum. Exactly why the "Trust" wished to ban the use of alum in its own product remains cloaked in mystery. Contemporary accounts suggest it was part of a scheme to drive independent baking powder producers out of business and establish a baking-powder monopoly in Missouri.[16] City slickers and country rubes alike supported the "Pure Food" bill, believing it was in the interests of public health. A few of the people's representatives had less altruistic motives.

Later, during Senate debate on a bill to repeal the Pure Food law, Farris spoke against the bill and piously defended himself. "No man can impugn my motives. I am alone answerable to my conscience and my God. The most precious heritage which I will leave to my family is a record of performances well done."[17] It was a great performance. However, a skeptical reporter wrote:

> As the chief orator of the combination which lacked many members of forensical powers, his professions of fairness and high-mindedness were particularly well adapted to holding the clique together. It was after one of his bursts of eloquence—Frank is the best speaker in the Senate—that a St. Louis senator remarked: "Wouldn't we look like dubs without him to explain our feelings?"[18]

Lieutenant Governor John A. Lee, who had acted as a conduit for "boodle" delivered to the "Combine" by New York-based baking-powder operative D.J. Kelly, got cold feet. Lee turned state's evidence and was a willing witness before Crow and Folk's grand juries. He implicated Farris, who was thought to be the "paymaster" of the "Combine" of key Senators.[19] The denomination of choice for the alum boodlers was $1,000 bills. A witness claimed to have observed a man matching Farris's description attempt to "change" a $1,000 bill (a huge sum in 1903) in Parle's Saloon in St. Louis. This reckless indiscretion occurred just the day after the General Assembly adjourned. Shortly thereafter, unnamed persons in Farris's hometown of Steelville claimed to have seen Farris exhibit two $500 bills, an extreme rarity in that tiny Ozark town.[20] These revelations were very unhelpful to Farris's protests of innocence.

Summoned before Folk's grand jury in St. Louis, Senator Frank Farris could not at first be found. Although present in that fair city, he was reported to be suffering from a "state of nervous collapse" and had been spirited to a private sanitarium by friends. Sheriff's deputies continued the search for him.[21] When finally appearing before the grand jury Friday, April 10, 1903, Farris was at first as sanctimonious as he was bellicose. A newspaper account said: "He asserted that he knew nothing about boodling, but that he did not wish to appear unwilling to testify, so he came to St. Louis. But he added that, even if he did know anything about boodling, he would be willing to rot in jail rather than tell on any of his associates. . . . Farris denied he was the man [who changed a $1,000 bill]."[22]

First news accounts were deceiving, because the Kansas City Star, in its Saturday edition, April 11, reported that Farris had confessed that he had, indeed, received a $1,000 bill from people interested in legislation and had changed it in a St. Louis saloon. The article continued:

> "Members of the Senate and some members of the House knew him [Farris] better than they knew Lee, they had confidence in his nerve, his swaggering declaration that he would stay in jail forever before he would tell what happened in legislative circles that involved his friends was believed by everybody. Farris was looked upon as the sort of man he claimed to be. Nobody expected a damaging admission from Farris.
>
> "'Boodling is very common in Jefferson City. A good many members, I don't know but what most of them, take boodle in one way or another.' These words are quoted by excellent authority as the exact

> language of Frank H. Farris, head of the 'alum combine' in the Missouri Senate, who testified before the St. Louis grand jury yesterday afternoon."[23]

Chronicles of Missouri's "Boodle Scandals" must be left to others, but not surprisingly, Senator Frank Farris was indicted by the grand jury. Just as relatives of Charlie Blackburn employed the best counsel available to defend their relative in 1915, Frank Farris employed two excellent attorneys to represent him on the charge of having accepted a bribe. He chose James A. Reed of Kansas City, who would later be elected to the U.S. Senate. The other was Morton Jourdan, Esq., of St. Louis. Obtaining nonjury trials, Senator Farris was tried twice. His first trial, before Judge W.W. Graves at Jefferson City, ended in a mistrial. In the second, before Judge Sam Davis at Marshall, he was acquitted.[24]

The presumption of innocence must apply to Frank Farris, never convicted of a crime. Undoubtedly, his very serious "dust up" with the law served to wizen and mature the man. Even if he never touched the hot stove of corruption, he certainly felt the heat. If he had dabbled in 'boodling," he likely never engaged in such practices again. With one exception, his constituents elected him to every office for which he ever chose to run. Whatever dents were hammered into his reputation were ignored by the voters, and he remained beloved by the common folk in his Senate and House districts until his death in 1926.

Americans are renowned for their willingness to forgive. Redemption is part of the national character. The home of the brave is the home of the second chance. By the time of Charlie Blackburn's trial in 1916, the boodle scandals were long in the past. Frank Farris's reputation had been fully restored and he was one of the most respected leaders of the Democratic Party in Missouri.

When Sid Roach learned that Frank Farris had been employed to lead Charlie Blackburn's defense, even his ample reservoir of self-confidence must have been shaken. Roach, a Republican, had served with Farris in the Legislature from 1909 to 1913. He had observed, first hand, Farris's skills in "running debate," as well as his famous speeches to a hushed and full House chamber.

Colonel James H. Higgs, an old newspaper reporter, made a sentimental journey back to Jefferson City in 1976. Higgs covered the Missouri Legislature for the *St. Louis Globe-Democrat* from 1919 to 1937. During WWII, he had been the public relations advisor to General Henry H. "Hap" Arnold, Commandant of the U.S. Army Air Corps. Colonel Higgs reminisced:

"As we took seats to listen to the floor debate and enjoy the beauty of the magnificent chamber, with its inspiring murals, my mind's eye brought into focus the figure of a tall stately gentleman, his white hair long in the style of today's youth and curled over the collar of his tan frock coat. He sat on the center aisle near the rear of the chamber. He was rising, seeking recognition from the presiding officer. He was the representative from Phelps County, Frank Farris. A bill designed to protect the bobwhite quail is being debated.

"Frank Farris needed no electric amplifiers to carry his voice. It was power itself. His sonorous bass notes, ringing the four corners of the chamber, demanded the complete attention of his audience and got it. On this particular occasion in 1913, for 40 minutes he delivered an address with such care and in such tones that it has survived 64 years in at least one memory."[25]

By 1915, Frank Farris had become chairman of the House Judiciary Committee with power over budgets for state courts, including the Missouri Supreme Court. Perhaps more importantly, at a time when supreme-court justices were subject to direct election by the people, the support of a powerful Democratic Party leader like Frank Farris could mean the difference between success or failure at the polls.[26] Fascinatingly, Waller Washington (W.W.) Graves, who presided over Farris's first boodle trial, ending in a mistrial, was now the Chief Justice of the Missouri Supreme Court.[27]

The addition of Senator Frank Farris to the defense team confronted Sid Roach and company with a worthy adversary. Not only did he know his way around a courtroom, but he had wielded power in Jefferson City for many years. He knew every skeleton in every closet, and every chit given and owed. Inclusion of Frank Farris would guarantee a long and hard fight. Neither Farris nor Roach could have imagined just how long and how hard that fight would be.

Chapter 35

The town of Linn Creek was platted in 1845 on the banks of the Osage River near its confluence with the smaller Niangua River.[1] It undoubtedly took its name from Lewis Fields Linn, a U.S. Senator from Missouri who served from 1833 until his death in 1843. Linn was caught up in the "Oregon Question" in which the U.S. and Britain disputed, and finally settled, the northern boundary of much of the United States. It was a time when common folk revered their elected representatives in Congress and named things after them. In rapidly developing "western" states like Missouri, lots of new things needed names. Now a small asterisk in history, Lewis F. Linn lives on. Two Missouri towns and a county still bear his name.

No one would have imagined in December of 1915 that Linn Creek's days were numbered. But Thomas Edison's inventions were creating an insatiable thirst for electric power. George Westinghouse's alternating current permitted the transmission of electricity through copper wires over long distances. By August of 1929, the Union Electric Light and Power Company of St. Louis had begun construction of a huge hydroelectric dam on the Osage River. One hundred and twenty-six air miles from St. Louis,[2] the site was just upstream from the little steamboat landing of Bagnell and only a few miles downstream from Linn Creek. Earth had hardly been turned when the stock market crashed. "Black Monday," October 28, 1929, signaled the beginning of the Great Depression. Unemployed workers from all over the U.S. flocked to the instantly created town of "Dam Site," seeking a job. Any kind of job.[3] Three thousand men (1,000 per shift) worked 24 hours a day and completed the project in only 21 months. The lowest-paid made 35 cents per hour and received three square meals each day.[4] Times were hard and those fortunate enough to be hired rejoiced.

When Bagnell Dam was finished in 1931, at a then-astronomical cost of $30 million, it created the beautiful Lake of the Ozarks. The "Lake" would cover 95 square miles, have a length of 129 miles, a shoreline of 1,300 miles, and would impound 650 billion gallons of water.[5] By the spring of 1931, the town of Linn Creek had been leveled. Some structures were torn down and others were moved to higher ground. The rest were burned where they stood.[6] A "new" Linn Creek would be built 3 or 4 miles away, but as an important center of commerce, the town was finished. The county seat was moved to Camdenton, a spanking new town constructed on a hill some 8 miles distant. At full reservoir, the "Lake" would cover "old" Linn Creek to a depth of 40 feet.[7] The town's giver of life, the mighty Osage, had buried the town forever in a watery tomb.

Charlie Blackburn wasn't interested in Linn Creek's future. He just wanted out of the county jail. It was an ugly, two-storied, cut-limestone structure located a few paces down the street from the courthouse. The buildings were separated by a little grassy courtyard with a single large shade tree and a couple of lounging benches. Built "shotgun" style, the jail's only windows were on the narrow front. Two were for the Sheriff's office and quarters on the ground floor and two barred versions provided a little light for the prisoners housed on the second floor. As an accused murderer, Charlie didn't merit exposure to natural light. His maximum security 8' x 8' steel cage was located in the rear.[8]

After Blackburn's arrest, Justice of the Peace Estes scheduled a preliminary hearing for Wednesday, the 22nd of December. A preliminary hearing is a judicial proceeding to determine whether there is "probable cause" to believe an accused has committed a felony.

At the appointed day and hour, all 8 attorneys, some 50 witnesses and "quite a number" of interested parties from Stoutland[9] appeared before Estes. The *Stoutland News* noted that "All the automobiles and 'hurry up machines' were pressed into service to carry to Camden County's capitol over fifty witnesses. . . ." Longtime observers could not remember so many attorneys present for a single case. It might be a record that still stands. Word quickly spread that the famous Senator Frank Farris was among the aerie of legal eagles preparing for pitched battle. All empty seats in the circuit courtroom on the second floor were quickly filled. These proceedings would be standing-room only.

The hearing took the better part of the day. Notable among the State's witnesses were Skip Archer, Joe Givens, Rolla Smith, Edna Kissinger, Charles Winfrey, Virgil Evans, Rube Winfrey, John Frey, Doctors Pool and Carlton, 74-year-old Judge Washington Irving "W.I." Wallace, and Simp and Ben Francis.

Sid Roach and the prosecution team first proved, with the testimonies of Pool and Carlton, that Jasper Francis had died as a result of a homicide in the manner described in the murder warrant. With Wallace, Evans, and Smith, it was established that the defendant was desperately in debt with liabilities exceeding any reasonable estimate of assets. With Wallace, it was proved that Blackburn's properties in both town and country were threatened with foreclosure and that money from the cattle sale had been sent to Lebanon to repay a portion of Wallace's loans to Blackburn.

With the Winfreys, Frey, Evans, and Smith, the prosecutors proved that Jasper Francis, prior to his death, had stated that Charles Blackburn was selling his farm to Joe Givens in order to make good on a cattle debt to Francis. Later, with Blackburn selling the cattle without his permission and with no "returns" coming into The People's Bank of Stoutland, Francis had come to believe that Blackburn might be seeking to cheat him on the cattle deal. Francis had intended to come into Stoutland early November 10 to determine where the cattle returns had been sent. If unable to get satisfaction of his debt, Francis had made threats to "garnishee everything that Charlie Blackburn has got." Edna Kissinger testified that she had heard a gunshot from the direction of where Francis's body was found at about 5:00 A.M., November 10.

Roach sought to prove that Givens was an unsuspecting party to a lie told to Francis to delay payment on the cattle and "keep him on the string" until the crimes of murder and forgery could complete the plot. Joe Givens told the judge that he had never expressed any intention of buying Charlie Blackburn's farm. Most dramatically, Skip Archer testified that Charlie Blackburn had been "gone all night" the evening of November 9 and the early morning of the 10th, returning only after daylight and after Miz Craddock had fixed and served the two of them breakfast. He said they had both wondered aloud about Charlie's absence. Archer then startled the crowd by saying that upon Charlie's return, he had observed him washing "what 'peared to me like blood off his hands by the way-ell on the west side a' the house."[10] The courtroom buzzed, and Estes had to use his gavel for the only time during the proceedings.

With the Francis Brothers, Sid Roach sought to establish that the two checks and note presented to the bank the day after the killing were "clever forgeries" by Charlie Blackburn as the final act in an evil plot to defraud the late Jasper Francis not only of his cattle but all his liquid assets. "In addition, with a forged note Blackburn sought to obtain $3,000 against Mr. Francis's good name and credit—all with murderous, premeditated intent."

It then became the defense's turn.

Charlie Blackburn took the stand and told the same story that he had honed at the coroner's inquest. If believed, it explained everything. If disbelieved, it was a clever lie. All his actions were the reasonable and logical actions of a man who had agreed to sell his farm to Jasper Francis. The checks, the note, and the cattle shipment were all a part of a transaction that Francis wished to conceal for a while in order to improve the prospects of selling his own farm. Charlie had never planned to sell his farm to Joe Givens and had never told Francis such a story! Yes, Skip had seen him washing blood off his hand. He had gotten up early and accidentally cut it on some barbed wire. No, Skip was mistaken, he had trouble sleeping and had gone outside for some air around midnight. He had returned and gone back to bed, arising before Archer awakened. Archer was wrong—both of them had eaten breakfast with his mother-in-law, Mary Craddock, and she would so testify. No, he had no written contract for the farm sale to Francis, but the signed checks and note in Francis's hand were proof enough. He had absolutely nothing to do with the death of Jasper Francis and should be freed immediately.

Miz Craddock, unable to attend because of ill health, entered a sworn deposition confirming Charlie's story. Minnie Blackburn took the stand and affirmed that the farm deal with Jasper Francis had been known to her for several weeks prior to his death.

Evans and Smith were recalled by Farris and testified that the signatures to both checks and the note were in the hand of Jasper

Francis, although Rolla Smith admitted that neither he nor Evans had compared the signatures with authentic ones when Blackburn came into the bank.

It was time for closing statements. Roach summed the prosecution's case with phrases that gave Frank Farris and the other defense lawyers a sample of what was to come:

"Your Honor, Charlie Blackburn was not a man pushed to the edge by his creditors who acted impulsively out of fear or panic. That would have been bad enough. No, Your Honor, the man who sits before you [pointing to Blackburn] acted with murderous intentions from his first offer to buy Mr. Francis's cattle. It was not a matter of *whether* he would kill the innocent and naïve Mr. Francis, but simply a matter of *when*. He had to know that he could never consummate his vile and duplicitous plan while Jasper Francis lived! No sir! He acted coolly and with calculation. He acted with malicious intent and, like a predator stalking his prey, he carried out this shockingly brutal crime.

"When he appeared at Mr. Francis's farm on the morning before the murder, he undoubtedly had every intention of killing that good man then! But his hand was stayed by the creaking wheels of an approaching wagon. That wagon was driven by Mr. Simpson Francis, sitting there. [quietly and sadly] Oh, but if we could always be our brother's keeper. [voice rising] When Charlie Blackburn next got his chance—before dawn—on a public road—he beat Mr. Francis's head in with a rain of blows; crushing the poor man's skull in four places, breaking his nose, and even his very neck! Then, [waggling his finger and shaking his head] not satisfied that his victim was dead, he placed the muzzle of a large caliber gun at the back of that good man's head and pulled the trigger. [pause, pacing] Your Honor, the gaping wound so inflicted drained the entirety of Mr. Francis life's blood onto the rocky soil—right there by the side of the road.

"Your Honor, there is more than sufficient evidence to establish that the actions of the defendant, Charles Blackburn, were the probable cause of the death of Mr. Jasper J. Francis. We ask that the defendant be bound over for trial before the Eighteenth Circuit for the crime of murder in the first degree!

For a grand orator, Frank Farris's closing statement was surprisingly brief and reserved. By not extending or dramatizing the proceedings, he sought to emphasize his argument that the prosecution had not come close to establishing the "probable cause" necessary to hold his client. Those expecting to be entertained by the great orator were generally disappointed. First thanking the judge for his service and "diligent attention to the evidence presented," Farris spoke slowly, quietly, and even patiently. He first complimented his opponents:

"Your Honor, I have, along with these fine gentlemen [pointing to Donnelly and the Mayfields], listened to the State's witnesses ably questioned by Mr. Sid Roach. I might add that I have the highest respect for Mr. Roach. I had the pleasure and honor of serving in the Missouri Legislature with this fine man for several years. The citizens of Camden County were lucky to have such a distinguished and conscientious citizen represent them in the General Assembly. And, [patronizingly] although we may have differed on matters of policy from time to time, I can tell you that Mr. Roach's integrity and his desire to perfectly serve his constituents were always without question. My compliments to Mr. Roach and the other lawyers at the State's table.

[long pause, pacing and sadly shaking his head] "Nevertheless, I must state to you in the strongest possible terms that in the matter before this court, Mr. Roach and his good counsel have come up very short. Very short indeed. Simply put, they have failed the test! My client, an innocent man, sits here wrongly imprisoned. There has been *nothing* [stretching the word] presented here today that comes *remotely* [stretching the word] to the level of establishing "probable cause" of Mr. Charles Blackburn's guilt in the unfortunate death of Mr. Jasper Francis.

"All the testimony presented is circumstantial in nature and presumes that my client killed Mr. Francis because he was in debt and owed money at the bank. May I remind the court that not one smidgen of evidence was presented that shows that Charles Blackburn has ever been anything other than an honest and honorable man and a good citizen of Camden County. His record is as pure as the driven snow! Yet the prosecution would have you believe that this good man, a man of mature years, in the fifth decade of his life, would suddenly commit this murderous act? And for what reason? Are we to believe that just because a person owes money at the bank, he goes out and kills his neighbors? My heavens, sir, if that were true, all my neighbors would be in severe jeopardy! [laughter in the courtroom] Why, every neighbor in this state would be looking over their shoulder while fearing for their very lives. *Every man* would need an armed bodyguard. *No man* could feel secure in his bed at night.

"Your Honor, my client has fully explained his business dealings with Mr. Francis. He was selling the man his farm. The truth of the matter is that this innocent man [putting his hand on Blackburn's shoulder] not only had nothing to do with Mr. Francis's death but he had every reason in the world for Mr. Francis to live! He had every reason to wish and believe that the farm sale would go forward just as planned. It was an honest transaction, fully agreed to by both parties.

"In closing, let me emphasize that the state has found *no one* who witnessed this crime. *No one* saw this happen. Missus Kissinger, that dear lady, claims she heard a shot—but she doesn't know who fired that gun. The state hasn't found one tiny piece of physical evidence placing my client at the scene of the crime. Not only that, the state has produced a string of witnesses who gave tainted hearsay testimony, to which my fellow counsel and I have fully objected, that Jasper Francis said he was coming to Stoutland the morning he was allegedly killed. But they have not produced a single witness who claims to have told my client of Mr. Francis's plan. My client not only had no motive to kill Mr. Francis but neither did he have the opportunity!

"Your Honor, we all know the test that must be met at a hearing of this kind; that a reasonable person, after hearing the evidence, could find probable cause to believe that the accused committed the crime. Here, sir, there is simply no such probable cause, and I ask that my client, Mr. Charles Blackburn, be freed! Return him to his home and his family where he can seek to restore his good reputation sullied by these completely unfounded charges.

"Thank you for your patience, Your Honor."

Young Phil Donnelly, sitting at the defense table, glanced sharply at Farris when the older attorney, out of the blue, broached the question of opportunity. It was true that Roach had not produced any witness who had told Blackburn of Francis's travel plans, but it didn't mean that no such person existed. With the defense having raised the subject, the testimony of such a witness would be doubly damaging. It would not be the last time that Farris would move into uncharted waters, violating the lawyer's maxim of: "Don't ever ask or raise a question to which you don't know the answer." Years later, Donnelly would speak of Farris's unorthodox courtroom questioning and deem it a virtue:

"Many times I have seen him draw facts from witnesses which looked detrimental to the side which Senator Farris represented, and to the ordinary lawyer would have been detrimental, but, on account of his fairness in the trial of cases, and because the jury knew that he wanted to be fair and get all the information before them, it won for him the respect of the jury and the court, and enabled him many times to obtain verdicts from juries when others would fail."[11]

Phil Donnelly need not have worried. If anyone told Blackburn of Francis's intentions and travel plans for the morning he was killed, they never came forward.

Squire Estes didn't buy Charlie's story nor his family's alibi and confirming testimony. After pondering the evidence overnight, Estes ordered that Charlie Blackburn be held without bail and bound over for trial on the charges of first-degree murder. The next circuit court session in Linn Creek would not convene until the third Monday in February, nearly two months away. Blackburn's lawyers pleaded in vain for the setting of a "reasonable bond" for their client. The request was denied. Charlie was taken back to his cell. His Christmas would be entirely ruined.

The *Stoutland News* reported the proceedings this way:

> We are glad to see our county authorities so prompt and active in efforts to maintain the fair name of our county and bring the guilty parties to justice *and hope and trust that no mistakes will be made.* [emphasis added]

Frank Farris, Phil Donnelly, and the Mayfields believed that the circumstantial case against their client was unconvincing. Optimistic that they could get Judge Estes to dismiss the charges, they had been wrong. They now knew they were in for a fight. The immediate problem was to get their client released on bond. Who could imagine that the Missouri Supreme Court could be persuaded to reach down into a circuit-court bond hearing and set Charlie Blackburn free? Frank Farris could, and he was determined to see to it.

Chapter 36

Sometime during the first week of February 1916, Charlie Blackburn walked briskly out of the Camden County jail a free man. A $10,000 surety bond had been posted by his brother, Robert Blackburn; his uncle, S.H. "Smith" Blackburn; and one Caleb Odell.[1] In 2004 dollars, the bond was the equivalent of $173,500, a not-insignificant sum.[2] Charlie had resided in the calaboose at the taxpayer's expense for some 50 days. Noticeably pale and tired of beans, salt pork, biscuits, and boredom, Charlie was in a rare jocular mood. He quipped to Deputy Sam Paxton, "I reckon I'll be seein' you way too soon."

"Charlie, you know I'm lookin' forward to it—maybe you'll be comin' back here to see us for good," was Paxton's cynical reply.

In the company of his brother and his lawyers, Charlie Blackburn disappeared into the frigid late-afternoon gloom. The jolting automobile ride back to Lebanon would take three hours and Model T's didn't have heaters.

If it had been up to Justice of the Peace Estes, Circuit Judge Cornelius Skinker, and Prosecutors Sid Roach and Ivon Lodge, Charlie Blackburn wouldn't have been going anywhere. They considered him a serious threat to jump bail. Charlie faced a mountain of debt, a less-than-ideal marriage, and, most vexing, a first-degree murder charge that could send him to the hangman. He seemed a fair bet to "make tracks." At the prompting of Charlie's celebrity counsel, Senator Frank Farris, higher judicial authorities had decided otherwise.

The steps in Charlie Blackburn's fight for freedom are sketchy, but it appears an immediate application for a writ of habeas corpus was made to Missouri's Southern District Court of Appeals at Springfield.[3] That court rejected the application and required the matter first be put before Eighteenth Circuit Court Judge Cornelius Skinker at Bolivar, Missouri. Perhaps miffed that Blackburn's lawyers had sought to bypass his jurisdiction, Skinker confirmed the J.P. court's decision, keeping Charlie safe and secure in jail. Unfazed and determined, the defense was granted permission to appeal the decision directly to the Missouri Supreme Court. Overruling a circuit's decision in bail and bond matters would be unusual for the court. Matters of prisoner safekeeping and bail risk were usually left to local authorities. But not in the case of Charlie Blackburn. Some 30 days after Skinker's decision, the Supreme Court granted Blackburn's application and specified the bail at $10,000.[4]

Phil Donnelly's son, David Donnelly, a former circuit judge and retired principal of an "old line" law firm in Lebanon, has said, "I suspect the supreme court judges treated Mr. Farris with extreme courtesy and respect, but that their decisions in his cases were based only on the law and only on the evidence as they saw it. . . ." Undoubtedly the court did pay extreme courtesy to the Chairman of the House Judiciary Committee. The matter before them was a subjective one. Did Charlie Blackburn pose a serious risk of forfeiting bond? And if so, did he pose a clear and present danger to the citizenry at large? They listened to Farris's impassioned plea and decided to cut the renowned lawmaker and his client some slack. The decision hardly seems capricious, but one wonders what the outcome might have been had a lesser attorney brought the application?

Less than two weeks after his release on bond, Charlie and his lawyers appeared before Judge Skinker at Linn Creek and requested a continuance of the case in order to better prepare their defense. Sid Roach and the prosecution team made no objection. Skinker then decreed that Blackburn's murder case would be tried at an adjourned session of the Eighteenth Circuit to be reconvened at Linn Creek, June 26, 1916.[5]

The stage was set for a battle royal amid a carnival atmosphere in the normally sleepy steamboat town. It would pit accomplished politicians versus aspiring "wanna-be's." Lackluster lawyers mixed it up with some of the sharpest legal minds in Missouri. With legal meters running, the first steps in the bankrupting of the Blackburn clan would be taken. The family's rural Missouri world would be forever shattered. The Francis family wanted justice for their bludgeoned brother and were willing to put up every cent of Jasper Francis's money to get it. For one brief week, in a doomed town with only 15 years to live, the drama of the murder on Rouse Hill would be played out.

Chapter 37

"Please Rise! Oyez, oyez, oyez! The Missouri Eighteenth Circuit Court, Camden County, Missouri, is now in session! The Honorable Cornelius Skinker presiding," intoned Sheriff William T. Salsman. The dignity and power of the court having been declared, Judge Skinker seated himself on the bench and the murder trial of Charles "Charlie" Blackburn began.

Unanxious to travel to the distant reaches of the county to investigate murders, Salsman managed always to be present for "law days" in Linn Creek. The good Sheriff relished the opportunity to meet and greet potential voters. It was an opportunity to see and be seen by large numbers of the citizenry, including lawyers, clients, jurors, witnesses, happy merchants, unwary country rubes, and a pickpocket or two.

It was eight o'clock A.M., Wednesday, June 28, 1916,[1] and the tobacco spitters on the bench at the side of the courthouse allowed as how it would be a "hot one." They were right. The morning's low temperature had been a cool 60 degrees, creating a dense fog over the river. But the cloudless sky and broiling sun would burn the mist away and push the afternoon high to 89. It would get a lot worse.

Voir dire of the jury pool had begun on Monday and taken the better part of two days. The stakes were high, and both sides used their full allotment of peremptory strikes of incompetent or otherwise unsuitable jurors. Predictably, prosecution lawyers plumbed jurors' willingness to convict on circumstantial evidence alone. The defense pounded upon the prosecution's necessity to prove guilt beyond a "reasonable doubt." They questioned each juror's willingness to "stick with their convictions" even if a majority believed the reasonable-doubt test had been met. Other questions centered on: "Have you ever borrowed money at a bank?" "Do you believe that just because law enforcement officers arrest someone, they are most likely guilty?" "Have you or a relative ever served as a law-enforcement officer?" and, "Have you or someone you know ever been the victim of a violent crime?" Both sides pressed and impressed upon the jurors their essential duty: "Can you keep an open mind, listen to all the evidence, and make a fair and impartial decision?" Most said they could.

After eliminating the fools, felons, and openly biased, a jury of 12 "good and lawful men" was picked.[2] Their names are listed below:

George Edwards	George Thomas	Henry Mauss
George Green	W.S. Osborn	Jim Whitworth
William Varner	Charles Martin	Julius Smith
Grant Eldred	John Edwards	Elijah Trease

Notably absent were family names closely associated with the town of Stoutland. There would be no "jury lynching" of Charlie Blackburn.

This court session was very special. The population of the town had more than doubled. More than 75 witnesses had been summoned from the Stoutland area and transported to Linn Creek by every motorcar that could be hired.[3] They came by horseback and wagon as well. Fifty potential jurors had been summoned for duty.[4] Added were eight lawyers, the judge, and his stenographer, F.L. Templeton. A multitude of the curious from all over Camden County swelled the town's usual compliment of 250 souls to over 500. The sensational "Blackburn trial" nearly brought the making of moonshine whiskey in the county to a halt—nobody was left in the hills and hollows to distill it. Any shortage of the precious liquid went unnoticed. Full flasks were observed in the hip pockets of the town drunks as well as rowdy young louts testing their mettle for that prestigious title.

Purveyors of street foods popularized a decade earlier on the "Pike" at the St. Louis World's Fair had magically materialized. Hot dogs, iced tea, lemonade, and fish sandwiches made from fillets of catfish, carp, buffalo, and blue gill seined right out of the river assured anyone with a dime or a quarter that they would go neither hungry nor thirsty. The two restaurants in town had geared up with extra help. The baking of pies and cakes had continued throughout the night. Fried-chicken or roast-beef plates with plenty of new red potatoes, early sweet corn, yeast rolls and butter, along with fresh white and red radishes, leaf lettuce, and green onions satisfied even the most vigorous eaters. And yes, those wonderful ice-cream cones, popularized at "The Fair" were available for 3 cents. Ice cut from the river in January and stored in mountains of sawdust produced the cooling power. America had developed a serious appetite for the delectable marriage of freshly churned ice cream with crisp, sugared waffles.

Players in the drama that would reveal whether Charlie Blackburn would live or die were certainly well fed. The problem was they didn't have anyplace to sleep. One small hotel and a rooming house could provide only about 20 extra beds. Lawyers, jurors, and witnesses were forced to seek haven in private homes. Many Linn Creek citizens, greedy for the windfall fruits of justice, posted handwritten "bed available" signs in their front yards. The going rate was a half-dollar with breakfast thrown in. "Doubling up" was a necessary but risky business. Frighteningly, a person might go blissfully to sleep and find that a lawyer had moved into his bed during the night!

Still, after every bedroom and sleeping porch in every home on every street was occupied, it was not enough. The *Springfield Republican* noted:

> The community is greatly stirred over the commission of the crime and Linn Creek is filled to overflowing. Many people here for the (Blackburn) trial have been forced to go into the country to find lodging.[5]

Some slept in their cars or on straw pallets in wagon beds. A few pitched tents and camped on the lawn of the plain but stately courthouse.

Cornelius H. Skinker was of the old school. His white starched collars, dark vested wool suits worn year-round, and hair parted high on the forehead signified a man of regularity and substance. He suffered no fools lightly, but assumed a quizzically bemused expression while seeking to divine particularly abstruse arguments from upstart young attorneys. Known to his friends and acquaintances as "Neil," he was an amiable man, well liked in his home town of Bolivar. In the courtroom he was a no-nonsense arbiter of justice who demanded strict decorum. Although scrupulously fair, like many of his era, Skinker was a "prosecutor's judge." Relevant evidence was rarely excluded because of the claimed rights of the accused. Skinker abhorred the notion of the guilty being set free on technicalities. Had Judge Skinker been soured on the case by Frank Farris's victory in the Missouri Supreme Court freeing Blackburn on bail? The judge had been overruled before the trial even began. It's safe to say that Charlie would get a fair trial but not be catching any breaks.

Cornelius Hite Skinker was born during the Civil War in Stafford County, Virginia, September 20, 1863, shortly after the Confederate Army's catastrophic defeat at Gettysburg. Only a year earlier, Robert E. Lee's victories at Fredericksburg and Chancellorsville had been fought near the Skinker family home. Skinker had been educated at the Middleburg Academy in Virginia and then Missouri's State University at Columbia. Admitted to the Bar at Bolivar, Missouri, in 1885, he had married Miss Minnie Gravely, sister of his law partner's wife. After serving several years as Polk County's prosecuting attorney, Skinker was appointed a circuit judge by the governor in 1909. Elected in his own right in 1910, Neil Skinker would not relinquish the job until his retirement in 1941 at the age of 77.[6] Skinker classified his politics as Republican, a comfort to Sid Roach and a worry for Frank Farris.

Skinker retained a soft, cultured drawl from his native Virginia, and was a gentleman in every respect, foreswearing swearing and seldom raising his voice. Nevertheless, he was a man of iron will and keen knowledge of the law. Both sets of lawyers would tread carefully in his presence. It was time for the titans to clash.

Chapter 38

Sid Roach's strategy was clear. It's every prosecutor's game plan in a case anchored only with circumstantial evidence. Put a lot of telling facts before the jury. None unto themselves would put a noose around Charlie Blackburn's neck, but when the tiles of the myopic mosaic were all in place, a closing argument would lead the jurors onto a high hill from which to view the masterpiece with 20/20 vision. From there, the mural of truth would become vividly clear. The close would be everything. Win or lose, go for broke. The final picture must exclude deviant conclusions and leave no reasonable doubts nagging a reluctant juror's psyche.

The State's job was to intercede for the murdered Jasper Francis. Only the State could deliver that ephemeral thing called justice. Absolutely convinced of his guilt, Sid Roach didn't have the power to condemn Charlie Blackburn to hell. He could deal only with Charlie's life on earth. As the prosecutor in a first-degree murder case, he could deliver Charlie to the hangman and let God "sort it out" immediately. Or he could send Charlie to the "Big House" for his natural life and give the Creator more time for consideration.

Frank Farris's strategy was twofold. First, he must silence the dead Jasper Francis. If the jurors were exposed to Francis's words from his last week on earth, and if they believed them, Charlie Blackburn was toast. They directly contradicted Blackburn's "farm sale" story, and Jap's voice, piteous from the grave, would weave a condemning web around Blackburn. A web of lies, deceit, and a compelling motivation for murder would speak insistently to the jurors. No, the dead Jasper Francis's every utterance in the days and hours before his death must be gagged. His lips must be sealed with arguments grounded in the legal principles of hearsay evidence. If Jap was to be heard, living beings would need to speak for him. The jury must not be allowed to consider such testimony. The motto must be: "Dead men shall tell no tales." If Judge Skinker let the hearsay testimony in, strenuous objections must be made, noted, and become part of a "bill of exceptions." Farris would then play his ace—an appeal to the Missouri Supreme Court. He had already been there once and he liked his chances.

"Reasonable doubt" is the underpinning of a murder defense. It takes only one stubborn skeptic to hang a jury. A few determined doubters might even sway the whole and pull off an acquittal. Blackburn's lawyers would throw in a dash of confusion, a sprinkle of alternative scenarios for poor Jasper's demise, a pinch of "blame the victim's family" innuendo, and most importantly, portray their client as an honest, reputable citizen. They would put Charlie on the stand and have him deny with steady hand and unblinking eye that he "had anything whatsoever" to do with Jasper Francis's death. Portray him as a sympathetic character, abused of his rights and put in fear of his life at the Stoutland inquest. Finish it all with some "make the welkin ring" oratory and there might be a clean shot at setting their client free. Nobody likes to send someone to the hangman. Most abhor the thought of incarcerating someone for life. The burden of proving Blackburn guilty beyond a reasonable doubt would fall on Sid Roach. All Frank Farris had to do was plant a doubtful seed and cultivate it.

In spite of the heat, the lawyers (except one) and the judge were dressed in dark vested suits, suspenders, and white shirts with high, starched, detachable collars. Roach's winged version added a note of distinction. Frank Farris had flung his flamboyant cattleman's pinched-crown Stetson hat on the post of the balustrade behind his chair. All were uncomfortable. All save one. Young Phil Donnelly, ready advocate for the defense, was nattily attired in a crisp two-piece, blue-striped, cotton seersucker suit; a button-down collared white shirt; and trousers held up with a belt. A striped tie and highly polished cap-toed shoes finished off the youthful look. Brooks Brothers would have been very proud. Fashion-conscious Don Vernon was envious but apprehensive for his opponent. Donnelly appeared cool—very cool. Too cool. The judge's eyes kept wandering to the young barrister, scanning him up and down. Skinker believed in equal misery for all in a second-floor courtroom with small windows, no ceiling fans, and without the hint of a breeze. The future Governor of Missouri would appear the next day in more conforming garb.

Charlie Blackburn had never looked better. Hair neatly trimmed and wearing a navy-blue broadcloth suit with a shirt and tie, Charlie could have passed for a church deacon ready to offer a prayer or pass the collection plate. Displaying no anxiety, he lounged confidently in his chair, leg hung over knee, coolly appraising the faces of the jurors. Chin resting on laced fingers, he struck a pose he would hold through much of the trial—that of a detached observer rather than a man on trial for his life.

The Supreme Court, in setting the terms of his bond, had been especially generous in placing no limitations on Charlie's travel. After his release, he had stayed a few weeks with his brother, Bob. Feeling out of place and weary of the family's daily routine, he had visited Minnie and Ray at nearby Lee's Summit. He then bought a ticket on the Atchison, Topeka, and Santa Fe for California. There, he had stayed a few weeks with Blackburn family friends who had migrated to the small town of Orange in the middle of the citrus country. The pristine Pacific air, brilliant sunshine, and a temporary job packing fruit had put color in Charlie's face. Gaining some weight, he appeared "fit as a fiddle."

The Blackburn family was well represented. Seated in the front row of the gallery were his aging parents, McGary "Mack" Blackburn and his wife, Araminta Annaronia (Hogue) Blackburn.[1] Charlie's mother was known variously as "Annie" or "Dolly" all of her life.[2] Both were dressed in their Sunday best. Dolly had on a long, dark-blue dress with a white lace collar on which she had pinned a little corsage of lilac blooms. Mothers never believe their sons capable of murder and Dolly Blackburn was no exception. She would go to her grave believing Charlie the innocent victim of a misplaced and vindictive prosecution by the Francis brothers. Charlie's sisters would agree.[3] Charlie's brothers, Bob and Lynn (at 17, the youngest), and Uncle Smith were on hand to lend moral support. Another brother, Gladys (nicknamed "Purg"), had stayed behind to mind the farm. Unmarried sisters Mattie, Della, and Imogene had also stayed home. Their mother had decreed a court trial "no fit place for nice young girls."

With both parents and a sister deceased, and his two brothers sequestered in the witness room, Jasper Francis's family went unrepresented in the courtroom. Friends and neighbors and a contingent of Odd Fellows Brothers were there to pick up the slack.

Glancing at his pocket watch, Judge Skinker gave the firm order, "Mr. Roach, you may proceed." And so the trial began.

"That man [pointing to Charlie Blackburn] brutally and without mercy took the life of Mr. Jasper J. Francis, one of the outstanding citizens of Stoutland, Missouri," opened Prosecutor Roach. He continued:

"Why did he do it? [pause—head shaking] *Plain and simple greed.* It's a story as old as time. Jasper Francis had things that Charlie Blackburn, sitting there [pointing], wanted. Mr. Francis had a farm, cattle, and money in the bank. That man [pointing] concocted a scheme to not just take Mr. Francis's property, every single dime of it, but his very life! In fact, his plan *relied* upon the death of Jasper Francis. He couldn't hope to pull it off with Mr. Francis alive. You go to prison for fraud and grand theft in this state if your victim is alive and around to complain about it. No, it was never a matter of *whether* Jasper Francis must die—but *when*. Gentlemen of the jury, when all the evidence is presented you will agree—without a reasonable doubt—that the man sitting there so relaxed and casual [scornful] is a cold-blooded killer and is guilty of murder in the first degree. As such, it will be your duty to punish him according to the laws of the great State of Missouri. Thank you very much."

Frank Farris was pulling no punches and in no mood, as at the preliminary hearing, to throw bouquets at the prosecution table:

"There is not one good piece of evidence that my client, Mr. Charles Blackburn, had anything *whatsoever* to do with the death of the unfortunate Mr. Francis. Throughout his life, Charles Blackburn has been a model citizen of this county. Witness after witness will attest to his sterling character. When you have seen the emptiness of the State's case, you will agree that this prosecution is not only misplaced but even vindictive. As you will learn, my client was selling his farm to Mr. Francis. Does selling your farm suggest murder is in a person's heart? *I hardly think so!* The prosecution would have you believe that just because you are in the process of selling your farm to a man, and the man turns up dead, you are the killer. What kind of logic is that? [looking at the jury, shrugging] It escapes me, too!

"The truth of the matter is that Charlie Blackburn had every reason to want Mr. Francis to live—so the farm transaction, satisfactory to both sides, could be completed. When all the evidence is presented, I believe that you will agree that proof of guilt, *beyond a reasonable doubt*, is *nowhere* to be found, and you will vote to acquit this good man and return him to his home, his loving wife, and young son. You may also suggest to those who have been so quick to bring this prosecution that they could be better employed seeking the *real* killer or killers of Mr. Francis instead of encircling and harassing this innocent man. Thank you for your kind attention."

The first witness was Simpson Francis. He repeated all the same testimony he had given at the preliminary hearing, including the substance of his conversations with Charlie Blackburn and Virgil Evans while his brother was missing. Francis swore that his brother's signatures on the checks and note purportedly made in partial payment for Blackburn's farm were forgeries. Over strenuous "conjecture" objections by the defense, Francis was allowed to state that his brother had never "even hinted" at buying the Blackburn farm and that he would have been "very surprised" if Jap would have entered into such an important transaction without telling him.

Roach gently led Simp Francis through the discovery of his brother's body and the grim task of identification. Simp hesitated for a moment, swallowing, and composing himself, as the enormity and finality of the scene was reprised in his memory. Roach wanted the jury to feel Simp Francis's pain. The "twelve good and lawful men" attentively leaned forward to hear every word. Finally, Simp added a new bit of testimony. He swore that while making inquiries in Stoutland about his missing brother, he had bumped into Minnie Blackburn on the street. When he asked her how long she had known Charlie intended to sell the family farm to his brother, Minnie had replied, "Oh Simp, Charlie never tells me what he's up to—my mind is just so frazzled—I reckon it's only been a day or two."[4]

Irwin "I.W." Mayfield, cross-examining for the defense, made much of the fact that Francis, with the advice of "lawyers that are now well-paid members of the prosecution," had first brought a lawsuit "attaching every single thing that my client owned."

Q: "Then, after Mr. Blackburn agreed to settle the matter of the farm sale in an amicable and friendly manner—it was only *then,* after my client had *voluntarily* given up any claims to your brother's assets, that you and your brother swore out a warrant for the arrest of Mr. Blackburn charging him with this crime—isn't that right, Mr. Francis?"

A: "Yes sir, that's right, we did not file the affidavit [murder charge] sooner because I wanted to get a settlement out of him and get back the note and the money he had received from my brother."[5]

"I.W." implied that this smacked of bad faith and cruel manipulation on the part of Francis and his lawyers. It was nothing more than adroit legal advice. Once Charlie Blackburn was charged with murder, any prospect of gaining his cooperation in returning Jap Francis's assets would have gone out the window. Nothing more readily propels a lawyer into a state of indignation than the demonstrated skills of another lawyer—especially one's brother.

Again trying to define his client as a victim, "I.W." continued:

Q: "At the time that you made a settlement with my client concerning the checks and note, did you make any statement whatsoever claiming that those documents were forgeries?"

A: "No sir, I did not."

Upon redirect, the "well-paid" Claude Mayfield took over for the prosecution. It was now brother on brother:

Q. "Mr. Francis, when did you first discover this note and these checks [holding them up] were forgeries?"

"I.W." leapt from the table, "Objection, Your Honor! That's a statement not proven in fact and not in evidence."

"Objection sustained—the jury will disregard the question."

Q: "When did you first tell they were forgeries?"

A: "I don't recall."

Q: "Do you know when you said they were forgeries? [a bit impatiently] Did you not take a position in the first place that they were forgeries?"

"Objection, Your Honor! Counsel is leading and being argumentative with his own witness."

"Objection overruled."

A: "Well, after I found there had been no papers made over [on the farm sale] and these checks were turned in after my brother was missing, then I took the position they were forgeries."[6]

Over the reach of 90 years, this little face-off between the Mayfield brothers is amusing and demonstrates how hard each side fought this contest.

Further questioning of Simp Francis broached the important question of admissibility of statements made by Charlie Blackburn at the inquest. Whether and when Charlie had been advised that he was a suspect in the murder of Jasper Francis quickly came to the fore. Aware that their client had appeared uncooperative, contriving, and contradictory, the defense could give no ground.

Roach:
Q: "Did you hear him [Blackburn] state, there at the inquest, that this $1,200 check [Blackburn's $1,200 check to Francis] was given for the cattle and also state that it was put up as a bonus on the land deal?"[7]

The entire defense team rose. "Objection Your Honor, may we approach the bench!" A lengthy argument ensued. Inexplicably, Frank Farris was then permitted to cross-examine Simp Francis with the original question yet unanswered. Farris asked a series of questions and got the replies he desired:

Q: "At that time [inquest], Mr. Blackburn had been suspicioned [sic] and was suspected by you and others with the killing of your brother; is that true, and he was summoned there as a witness?"

A: "Yes, sir."

Q: "And was sworn as a witness?"

A: "Yes, sir."

Q: "And as such, [the] witness was giving testimony?"

A: "Yes, sir."

Q: "Nobody, at the time he was sworn, informed him that he was suspected of the crime of killing your brother and of his rights in the matter?"

A: "Not that I know of."

Q: "He was not represented by counsel at that time?"

A: "No, sir."

Q: "And under those conditions he made statements you are about now to detail?"

A: "Yes, sir."

Farris: "Your Honor, we object!" [8]

Confusion reigned in the court with the prosecution, defense, and the judge questioning the witness simultaneously. Finally, a heated sidebar discussion was held. Stenographer Templeton, writing furiously, pleaded for everyone to slow down. The defense argued vehemently that Charlie's testimony at the inquest, prior to being advised that he was a suspect in the murder, should not be heard by the jury. Roach tried to clarify matters:

"I will state that Mr. Blackburn had been examined at some length before he was informed [that he was a suspect]. I did not inform him for the purpose of disqualifying him at all. I merely asked him the question if he was aware that he was suspected of the crime and that was done after some length of the examination had been conducted. Mr. Blackburn was examined as to any knowledge he might possess as to the cause of the death of J.J. Francis. There was no purpose on the part of counsel of informing him of his statutory right. There was some suspicion against Mr. Blackburn, but that was not of such a character that counsel was justified in notifying him he had a statutory right [to remain silent and engage counsel]; he was simply called as a witness from the community in which they both had lived."[9]

Judge Skinker stated, "I think it [the inquest transcript] clearly shows that the defendant was suspected of this crime at that time, and it seems to me that the indications are that he testified voluntarily. I think the rule as to matters of this kind deals largely upon whether or not the testimony given at the coroner's inquest was given voluntarily or not."[10]

Frank Farris replied heatedly, "Our idea is that there was nothing voluntary about it; that the man was summoned and sworn and required to testify!"[11]

Sid Roach replied with what seemed a common-sense argument:

"In conducting an inquest, it does not devolve upon the person conducting the inquest to inform the persons called that there might be some suspicion against them. Anybody might be *suspicioned* [sic] or any number of persons might be *suspicioned* [sic]. They might have knowledge that would be very beneficial. It is not the rule of law in this state that a person under suspicion of a crime cannot be called and examined at a coroner's inquest!"[12] [emphasis added]

Frank Farris continued to object to the impending testimony from Simp Francis. Judge Skinker overruled each objection. Simp was then allowed to answer the original question and affirmed that Charlie Blackburn had, indeed, first testified at the inquest that the $1,200 check from Blackburn to Francis was made in payment for the cattle and then later testified that it was given as a "bonus" on the land deal.[13] The conflicting statements were then confirmed in the transcript of the inquest proceedings and made a part of the trial record.

The discrepancy in Charlie Blackburn's inquest testimony could be deadly for his defense. Two different stories told at the same hearing suggested confusion inconsistent with an innocent man explaining a common business transaction. It reeked of deception and a guilty state of mind. It shook a damning finger at Charlie. A finger little moved by a third explanation that the check was given as a favor to temporarily cover up the sale of his farm to Francis. Over all objections, Judge Skinker had allowed the jury to consider this damning testimony.

By 12:30 P.M. of the trial's first day, Frank Farris was already worried. If the defense could not win exclusion of testimony forced from a suspect unapprised of his rights, how could it keep out hearsay testimony quoting the late Jasper Francis? In the back of Farris's mind, a Supreme Court appeal was looking more and more likely.

Chapter 39

At 2:00 P.M., Roach and Vernon resumed their methodical questioning of the State's witnesses. Having learned the "drill" during the inquest and preliminary hearing, they answered crisply and confidently.

Dave McClure and Clint Fulbright described the finding of the horse in the morning and discovery of Jasper Francis's dead body "just before noon," Monday, November 22. Doctors Pool and Carlton repeated the results of their examination and dissection of the body. In cross-examination, Pool opined that ". . . the gunshot wound would not have caused the crushing of the skull." The testimony defeated an attempt by the defense to shed doubt on one of the two murder charges, i.e., the one premised upon death by "crushing and fracturing the skull" with "some instrument or weapon . . . unknown."[1] Other than this clarification of the physicians' testimony, the defense attorneys sat quietly disinterested in the clinical details of the havoc wreaked on Francis's body. Why dwell upon it? Why help the state imprint the gory images in the jurors' minds?

Charlie Blackburn's attention wandered during much of the trial. Appearing bored, he often glanced to the ceiling or toward the open window while avoiding eye contact with the jury. The description of Jap Francis's remains was another matter. He sat upright and listened intently with his mouth pursed as if to whistle. Charlie was never a very good poker player.

W.W. Cox testified that he had discovered the blood pool "within three feet of the wagon track and on the same side of the road near where the Francis body was found" on Sunday, the 28th of November, nearly a week after recovery of the corpse.

An otherwise minor witness, Ben McShane, who had been among the searchers who arrived shortly after the body was discovered, was allowed by the judge to give controversial testimony.

Roach:
Q: "Mr. McShane, how many days did you assist with the search for Jasper Francis?"

A: "Well, I reckon it was three or four days?"

Q: "Were there any days in which Sheriff Hufft of Laclede County and Deputy Paxton of Camden County, sitting over there [pointing], had search parties out looking for Mr. Francis that you were not among them?

A: "No sir, not to my knowledge."

In a *Matlock* moment, Roach, pacing and rubbing his temple with his forefinger, quickly turned and asked:

Q: "Did you ever see Charlie Blackburn out there looking for Jasper Francis?"

A: "No."[2]

[interruption] "Objection, Your Honor—we object!"

Full of a large meal and having suffered through tedious medical testimony, Farris and the Mayfields had been caught napping. Young Phil Donnelly hadn't. Taking the initiative, he jumped to his feet. "Your Honor, this testimony is immaterial and incompetent and should not be allowed!" Glancing approvingly at his young sidekick, Farris demanded a sidebar with the judge out of hearing of the jury. Farris made a heated and seemingly persuasive argument:

"Whether he did or did not join in the hunt is completely immaterial. He may have been under the press of his own private affairs. In any case, no person, including our client, has any obligation to join in a search for anybody, under any circumstances. The defendant is not called upon to speak, nor does the law require him to act until a charge is made to him and against him. Mr. Roach is blatantly trying to prejudice the minds of the jurors!"[3]

Roach responded: "Your Honor, the actions, or inactions, of the accused during the search for Mr. Francis is very material. Mr. Blackburn testified at the inquest and at his preliminary hearing, and will presumably testify in this trial, that he was attending to the final details of selling his farm, at a very substantial price, to Mr. Francis when Mr. Francis went missing. Other than his immediate family, Mr. Blackburn should have had more interest in the whereabouts of Mr. Francis than anybody in the world! Why, Mr. Farris, in his opening statement, made that very point! Yet, Charlie Blackburn was completely indifferent to the search and took no action whatsoever to find the *one and only person* [emphasis added] who could readily consummate the alleged transaction. Actions speak louder than words and Charlie Blackburn's actions speak to a guilty state of mind."

"Your Honor," Farris answered, "the defense strongly disagrees and objects to this line of testimony. Why, if my client *had* [emphasis added] joined in the search, they [the prosecution lawyers] could just as easily be claiming it was a sham to throw off any suspicion of guilt or perhaps even a ploy to mislead the searchers in the wrong direction. Whether he did or did not join the search is absolutely immaterial and should not be considered by the jury!"[4]

"I think I'm going to allow it," Judge Skinker decided. "The witness, having participated actively in the search, seems competent, and the actions and words of Mr. Blackburn during the period of the search seem material and relevant for the case at bar.

"Objection overruled. Mr. McShane, you may answer the question."[5]

The witness then confirmed that he had never seen Blackburn assisting in the search, ". . . even when we searched right across his farm three or four times!"

Roach continued:
Q: "Did you see Mr. Blackburn upon any of these occasions?"

A: "Yes sir, he was picking and shucking corn with his hired hand, Skip Archer."

Q: "Did he ever approach and ask you what you were doing?"

A: "No sir, I couldn't tell that he ever even looked in our direction."

"That's all, Mr. McShane."

On cross-examination, Farris established that McShane was a close personal friend of Jasper Francis:

Q: "You'd like to see someone punished for this crime, wouldn't you, Mr. McShane?"

A: "I would, of course I would."

Farris then changed the subject:
Q: "Isn't it true that Mr. Francis, by habit, always carried money with him?"

A: "Yes, I reckon so—he usually did to my recollection."[6]

Q: "How much money?"

A: "Well, I don't rightly know—quite a bit."

With a "calls for speculation!" objection by the prosecution, Farris withdrew the question and dismissed the witness.

With the preliminaries out of the way, Roach called the first of five witnesses who could relate what Jasper Francis did and said on the day before he was killed (the "Informed Five"). Charles Winfrey, who attended the farm sale at Toronto with Francis, took the stand. A real donnybrook began. When Winfrey was asked to "detail your conversation with the deceased," the defense immediately objected on the grounds that the testimony would be hearsay. The jury was then excused (the first of several occasions) and Winfrey was permitted to relate his statement to the judge.[7] The jury was then recalled and Roach asked the same question again. Again, Frank Farris rose to object and loudly proclaimed a litany that would be repeated, over and over, during the remainder of the trial:

"Your Honor, the defense objects, for the reason that it [testimony] would be hearsay and not a part of the *res gestae* and not a dying declaration and not made or had in the presence of the defendant and would be incompetent and irrelevant for any purpose."[8]

The defense voiced the same objection so many times that the attorneys began taking turns leaping to their feet and shouting, "Objection, Your Honor!"

The strategy conserved energy and reduced titters in the audience prompted by the sight of four grown men, leaping as one, with pointed fingers extended heavenward. The jury was not amused. The interruptions were frustrating and annoying. As time went by, jurors glanced at each other and shook their heads impatiently. Clueless of what the phrase *res gestae* meant, they were put off by its constant repetition. Pronounced "race-guess-tie," the Latin phrase literally means "things done." In a court case, it refers to the "litigated event."[9] In this case, the physical murder of Jasper Francis.

Over the centuries, lawyers and doctors have padded their lexicon with Latin words and phrases uncommon to common folk. They facilitate clear and precise communications among those who understand the "code." It separates the learned from the unlearned. It cloaks such professionals with an air of awe and mystery. Use of these words proclaim: "I have the key to the code and I will use it on your behalf." For a fee. Repetitive use of the unexplained Latin phrase didn't help the defendant with this jury. Most had only attended a few years in a one-room public school—a long way from New England Latin schools. Planting and harvesting the crops gave time only for the learning of the three "R's."

As interrogation of the "Informed Five" continued, it became clear that Judge Skinker was going to overrule nearly all the defense's hearsay objections. In order to build a firm basis for appeal, it was incumbent upon the defense to object in each and every instance. Farris and company missed no such opportunities.

"Hearsay is often defined as an out-of-court statement offered to prove the truth of the matter being asserted."[10] The exclusion in court of most hearsay evidence has its roots in English common law and probably even ancient Roman law. The reasons are manifestly logical and aim toward fairness. "Hearsay is inadmissible, unless an exception applies, because the declarant is not subject to cross-examination about the statement, the declarant is not under oath, and the fact finder is not able to assess the demeanor of the declarant."[11]

The "declarant" in this case was the murdered Jasper Francis. Mr. Francis certainly could not be cross-examined nor put under oath. Lying six feet beneath newly turned soil, his demeanor could neither be assessed. If so, it's a safe bet it would have been adjudged rather somber.

Admission of hearsay statements made by Jasper Francis was crucial to the prosecutor's case. Defense counsel knew it and the judge knew it. In making the same objection, over and over, the defense stated the three common exceptions to the hearsay rule of evidence, asserting that none applied.

None of Francis's statements were "dying declarations." He was alive and well when he made them. If someone had found Francis wounded and dying and heard him say, "Charlie Blackburn did this to me!" the statement would likely have met the "dying declaration" test. Similarly, Francis had not made any "statements in the presence of the defendant" overheard and related by a third party. If he had, Blackburn would have the opportunity to explain or refute such hearsay. No one had heard an argument between Francis and Blackburn in which Francis said, "Charlie, I think you're trying to cheat me out of my cattle!" or "If you don't make that $1,200 check good, I'm going to garnishee everything you've got!" The defense's final assertion was that Francis's conversations with the "Informed Five" were not a part of the *res gestae*, i.e., the "thing done."

Duhaime's Law Dictionary defines the rule of *res gestae*:

"A peculiar rule, used mostly in criminal cases, which allows hearsay if the statement is made during the excitement of the litigated event. For example, the words 'stick 'em up!' during an armed robbery would be admissible in evidence under the *res gestae* rule. So too would spontaneous statements made by the defendant during or right after the crime."[12]

No one heard Jasper Francis, as he was being beaten, say, "Charlie, please don't kill me!" If a passerby on Rouse Hill had heard such a pitiful cry, the statement would assuredly have been a part of the *res gestae*. Sadly, any such pleas went unheard, except by the killer.

In arguing that the judge should be flexible in defining the *res gestae*, the prosecution came well prepared. It cited 11 state cases as precedents (including two Missouri cases), along with numerous legal reference books and dictionaries.[13] "In the very nature of things the *res gestae* must vary as the facts of each case vary," they argued.[14] Because of the materiality of the statements with respect to a motive for the crime, the interests of justice would be served by a broader definition. They also argued that:

"The subsidiary act [Francis's conversations with the "Informed Five"] need not transpire at the same instance with the main one [the actual murder], or always even on the same day; and, in reason, as well as in accordance with the current of the authorities, the time which divides the two is not the controlling consideration, though it may be taken into account. It is presumable that, distinctly and palpably, it *influenced* or was influenced by the main act, or proceeded from the same motive? If so, it is admissible, otherwise not."[15]

Finally, the State argued that, "Any evidence [even hearsay] that tends to show motive for killing the deceased is always relevant as rendering more probable the inference that he did kill him."[16]

The defense responded long and vehemently that the hearsay testimony should be excluded. Citing (but differently interpreting) many of the same cases, they reasoned that all the conversations were made ". . . prior to the night of November 9, or the morning of November 10, at which time the deceased is supposed to have met his death, and at places from one to five miles distant from the scene of the killing . . ." and, under the law, could not have been a part of the *res gestae*.[17]

Weighing the arguments, Judge Skinker was likely influenced by the consistent nature of Jasper Francis's words and uninterrupted and determined actions once he was informed by Virgil Evans that the cattle had been shipped. The juxtaposition of the hearsay conversations in time and place to the murder was probably deemed "close enough."

Sid Roach didn't hurt himself with his final statement arguing for inclusion:

"To hold the evidence of these witnesses inadmissible is to destroy one of the strongest links showing motive, intent, and matters of influence upon the main act. The lips of the dead are mute, but those things spoken, as here, when there is no incentive to manufacture evidence, echo back like the words of the Holy Writ: 'What hast thou done? The voice of thy brother's blood crieth unto me from the ground.'"[18]

Frank Farris only wished that he had summoned such biblical eloquence. Cain and Abel had come in very handy to the prosecution. Roach proved that lofty phrases and good oratory are not confined to those of the Democratic persuasion. In the interests of justice, Judge Skinker would prove very accommodating to the State. Those who spoke with Jap Francis on the day before he died would be heard. Jap Francis would be heard.

Throughout the afternoon of the trial's first day and the morning of the second, Sid Roach called the remainder of the "Informed Five" (except defense witness Virgil Evans), one by one, to the stand. They had spoken with Francis after he learned that he had likely been duped by Charlie Blackburn, after he discovered that Charlie had shipped his cattle without his knowledge, and after he realized he had nothing to show for his trade but a pair of useless mules and a bum $1,200 check. These were the people who could testify to Jap's state of mind and suspicion of Charlie Blackburn's intentions. To them, he had revealed his plan to investigate the whereabouts of the cattle returns by traveling to Stoutland early on the morning of November 10, the same morning that a lone gunshot had been heard on Rouse Hill. They would repeat his threat to take immediate legal action against Blackburn if the "returns had not come in."

The "Informed" would establish that Francis believed that Blackburn was selling his farm to Joe Givins and even helped Charlie fill out a check and a note for Givins's signatures. Jap was so convinced of the Givins story that he had counseled the People's Bank of Stoutland to require Charlie to repay his bank loan from the proceeds of the sale. "You boys be sure and get your money" were his last helpful words to a bank that would turn its greedy back upon him. Finally, the "Informed" would give lie to Charlie's claim to selling his farm to Jap. To the contrary, Jap had scoffed at Blackburn's expressed interest in buying the *Francis farm* when he couldn't scrape the money together to "pay for what he's got."[19] For the jury, it was compelling testimony. They listened carefully.

"Objection overruled" became Judge Skinker's mantra as Charles Winfrey, John Frey, Rube Winfrey, and Rolla Smith were questioned at length by the prosecution. During their interrogation, the defense team objected 21 times on the grounds of "hearsay." Judge Skinker sustained only three of their objections.[20] By noon of the second day, the prosecution had been successful in getting nearly all of these witnesses' testimony heard by the jury. It had been a good 24 hours for Sid Roach.

The mosaic was starting to reveal a portrait. Coming into focus was an ugly likeness of Charlie Blackburn.

Chapter 40

By two o'clock P.M. on Thursday, it was 90 degrees in Linn Creek[1] and at least that warm in the courtroom. An enterprising undertaker had brought over a box of "funeral fans" quickly snapped up by the spectators. This act of mercy undoubtedly worked against the good mortician's interests. Those sufferers who had not yet fled the courtroom expressed the universal opinion: "It's suh danged hot, I'm 'bout to die." The stiff cardboard images of Jesus rising into heaven, stapled to flat wooden handles and waved vigorously, brought some relief from what could only be described as hellfire. Judge Skinker had permitted a five-gallon crock of fresh water to be placed on a table in the back of the courtroom. Partaking of the precious liquid was limited to occasional breaks in the proceedings. As testimony droned on, the jurors licked their dry lips and glanced longingly rearward. In 1916, no one seemed to mind using a communal dipper made from a hollowed gourd.

Taking the stand as a State's witness, Rolla Smith provided the details of his meeting with Jap Francis, November 3, 1915, as well as his and Virgil Evans's conversations with Francis the evening that he was last seen. Most importantly, Rollie wavered in his earlier opinion that the signatures of Jasper Francis on the checks and note presented as Exhibits A, B, and C were authentic. Under close questioning, he admitted that he "wasn't positive." This gush of truthfulness likely numbered his days as the assistant cashier of the People's Bank of Stoutland.

Roach used numerous witnesses in seeking to prove that the signatures on the note and checks cashed by Charlie Blackburn the day after the murder were forgeries. Simp and Ben Francis swore they were. E.W. Cook, cashier of the Bank of Lebanon and J.M Vincent, a banker with 20 years experience, compared the questioned signatures with several authentic samples and opined that they were "inauthentic." On cross-examination, Vincent unhelpfully concluded that it was a "close proposition" and "If it is a forgery, it was a good one."[2] Finally, Roach put his "big city" expert witness on the stand. His name was Gus Mechin, a title investigator and partner of Mechin & Voyce, 812 Chestnut Street, St. Louis, Missouri.[3]

Mechin offered his credentials, including service as an expert witness in several other trials and hearings where signatures needed authentication. Without hesitation, he declared the signatures forgeries[4] likely traced from one or two authentic signatures. He further stated that the signature on the note, which had been overstamped "PAID" several times by the bank, was the poorest forgery. "The note was printed on very heavy paper, making it nearly impossible to trace through. All the signatures were probably made from the same refillable fountain pen, the same pen used to fill out other writing that is authentic." Like his velvet collared overcoat, Jap Francis's fountain pen was never found.

Frank Farris had his own cadre of handwriting experts at the ready. He scathingly attacked Mechin as nothing more than a witness for hire. Mechin admitted that he was being paid $50 per day, plus expenses,[5] including his railway ticket on the Missouri Pacific line all the way from St. Louis to Bagnell. In 1916, it was a princely sum, but Roach needed an urban professional whom he could portray as an ultimate authority in the matter. Besides, the State of Missouri was footing the bill.

Roach got his money's worth. At the behest of Mechin, the overstamped signature on the note had been photographed and an enlarged print produced that brought the signature out, making it easier to examine. The process likely employed a colored filter and was the only known use of modern forensics in the trial. Farris argued strenuously against use of the copy when "the original was in court and already in evidence."[6] He was overruled.

Edna Kissinger repeated her gunshot testimony. Edna also testified that Minnie Blackburn, in a candid moment at the inquest, had confessed she was "nervous and unstrung" and had been shocked by the boy delivering a telegram relative to shipment of Jasper Francis's cattle. Relishing her 15 minutes of fame, Edna was unshakable regarding the date, time, and direction of the gunshot that undoubtedly took Jap Francis's life. The blast had propelled her from obscurity into life's spotlight. Crestfallen at her brief questioning and dismissal, Edna addressed the judge: "Is that all you wanna know about?"

"Yes ma'am, you may step down."

Sid Roach was determined to shake any credibility that the jury might assign Miz Mary Craddock's sworn alibi for her son-in-law. In her deposition, she would claim he had been at the farm all night and was there for breakfast at around 5 A.M.—the very time of the murder. Claude and Ellen Castile's property adjoined that of Minnie's town home within easy "hollerin' distance." Repeating their preliminary-hearing testimony, they claimed to have seen Charlie Blackburn at Minnie's house early in the morning "about 6:00 A.M." the week of November 9. Ellen was positive the day was Wednesday, the 10th. Claude wasn't so sure, placing it "between Monday and Thursday." Claude said he spoke with Blackburn and "asked if he had stayed in town that night and he said no, he had come in that morning." Both of the Castiles said they had seen a black horse saddled and tied in the Blackburn yard.[7]

Placing Charlie "out and about" in Stoutland several miles from home and in the direction of the killing was deemed helpful by the prosecution. Although shaking Claude Castile's certainty of the date, the defense never produced an explanation of Charlie's presence in Stoutland, at that early hour, on any date that week. If he was there on the 10th, it was likely within an hour of the murder and his purpose was very murky. Could the "black" horse tied in the yard (in poor light conditions) have been Sam *before* he was taken and tied in the woods? Was Charlie there to change clothes, dump incriminating evidence, and deliver Jap Francis's fountain pen to someone with a steadier hand for the art of forgery?

Only a little more than 24 hours later, Charlie would present the note and checks for payment at the bank. If the documents were forged, who was the forger and when were they forged? Was it Charlie's work, tracing off authentic signatures pilfered from Jap Francis's leather valise? Apparently written with Jap's own pen, the forgeries were almost certainly completed after the killing with the instrument taken from the body. Examination of Charlie Blackburn's unsteady signature samples hardly gave evidence of a clever forger. Perhaps the more deft touch of a woman was required.

Minnie Blackburn traveled by horse to the farm the morning of the murder. Was this just a routine visit with her mother as she claimed? Or was she on a mission? Daylight would have been required to properly conceal the large bloodspot on the road. The risks to Charlie of being observed in Stoutland after beating and shooting a man to death just outside of town were huge. Yet, the risk of proceeding directly home and coming under the curious gaze of Skip Archer while seeking to dispose of bloody clothes and Jap Francis's missing possessions would become self-evident. Skip would never testify that he observed Charlie hiding or disposing of anything—just being gone all night and washing blood off his hands in the early morning. His forthcoming trial testimony would cast more suspicion upon Minnie Blackburn.

There *were* those persistent rumors down through the decades that Minnie was observed burning clothes in her backyard! Were they Charlie's bloody shirt and trousers? Maybe Jasper Francis's for-ever-missing overcoat? Today, where are the metal buttons of that overcoat? Where is the moldered leather of Jap's wallet and valise? And where is his treasured fountain pen? Could they be buried in Minnie's backyard in Stoutland?

By 4:00 in the afternoon, Judge Skinker adjourned the court due to "heat and discomfort" to be reconvened the next morning. Skinker was anxious to get the case to the jury before Sunday. It was a time when God-fearing folk still observed the Sabbath.

Admonishing both tables to proceed with "deliberate speed," Judge Skinker gaveled his court to order Friday morning at 8:00 A.M.

The aging Judge W.I. Wallace was called. Placing one foot tenuously upward and grasping the railing, he hoisted himself onto the platform. Appearing ill at ease, he carefully lowered his bulk into the witness chair and hunched forward resting his hands upon a gilt-headed walking stick. Speaking with a cultured eastern accent, he told Roach of his loan to the Blackburns secured by a second mortgage on both the farm and the town property. The original loan of $1,000 had grown to a balance due of $2,223.80, with $1,223.80 of interest in arrears. Although stating he had taken no direct legal action to recover the debt, Wallace admitted sending several "re-mindahs" threatening forcible eviction. He stated he was "verree pleesed" to be "paid in fool" by Blackburn during a personal visit to his home Wednesday, November 11.

Sid Roach graciously avoided asking Wallace what the interest rate was on a loan where the unpaid interest exceeded the principal outstanding. Under respectful cross-examination by Irwin Mayfield for the defense, Wallace stated that he had lent money to "Mr. and Mizzus Blackburn" before and had always been repaid. Furthermore, he would "prob-bub-lay" make additional loans to "Mr. Blackburn and his very chah-ming spouse—if they so desired."

The state called Joe Givins, who denied any intention or interest whatsoever in buying Charlie Blackburn's farm. Sid Roach then put on his star witness.

Skip Archer had gone from a nonwitness to a reluctant witness to a ready and willing witness. Skip repeated his preliminary-hearing testimony and made some new revelations. He swore that he knew that Charlie had been "gone all night" on the 9th and 10th because he heard Charlie depart the house about midnight without ever hearing him return. Charlie was not in the house when he arose. Preparing to feed the stock around 5:00 A.M., he had dressed and passed through Charlie's bedroom adjoining the kitchen. Skip had later breakfasted with Miz Craddock, and they both wondered where Charlie was. After doing some more chores, Skip had come to the house "just after sun-up" and observed Charlie "washin' blood off his hands" at the pump by the back porch. "Charlie say'ed he'd cut hisself on some barbed wahr[8] and he wrapped up his hand with a white cotton cloth." When asked if Charlie had saddled and ridden any of the two horses that morning, Skip said, "Nossir, I fed the hosses and all the stock a'fore brake-fuss—besides, when I hooked 'em to the wagon to haul corn that mornin', I'd a-noticed if they'd a-just been rode."

Whatever Charlie Blackburn did on the morning of the murder, he had set out from home on foot and returned on foot.

Roach continued:

Q: "Now then, Mr. Archer, on the morning that you saw Mr. Blackburn washing blood off his hands did his wife, Miz Minnie Blackburn, come to the farm?"

A: "Yay-ess, she shore did."

Q: "And about what time was that?"

A: "I'd reckon it wuz about nine o'clock in the mornin'."

Q: "When she got there, what did Miz Blackburn do?"

A: "Way-ell, 'stead of goin' into the house the way she would reg'lar do, she follered Charlie around t'other side of the barn, along with the hoss, and they talked quite a little spell around thar.[9] It was kind-a like they wuzn't a-wantin' me to hear what they wuz a-sayin'."

Defense: "Objection! Your Honor, this line of questioning is immaterial and irrelevant! It calls for speculation on the part of the witness."

Judge: (after side arguments) "The jurors are instructed to disregard the witness's last sentence. Mr. Templeton, will you please read it back? Otherwise, the defense objection is overruled."

Under cross-examination, Farris got Archer to admit that farming was "kind of a dangerous business" and that "cutting your finger or your hand isn't that unusual." Skip also admitted that it might have been possible for Charlie to have returned to his bed after Skip dozed off:

"Yes or no, Mr. Archer?"

"Way-ell, mebbe so, but . . ."

[interruption] "Yes or no, Mr. Archer?"

"Way-ell—I reckon."

Farris then tread in dangerous territory when he asked: "Mr. Archer, you are aware that Miz Mary Craddock, living in the same house, has previously testified and will testify at this trial that Mr. Blackburn never left the house and was there all night and was present at breakfast with both you and Mr. Blackburn?"

Archer's reply was a blockbuster: "Yay-ess, I know, but Miz Mary don't hear too good and b'sides, that thar old Craddock house is all made out a' cee-ment 'cludin' the inside walls.[10] Why, from her room thar on the front a' the house—I don't reckon she could hear a soli-tar-ee thang!" Miz Mary's alibi for Charlie had suddenly gone on a diet.

Upon redirect, Roach asked Skip: "Mr. Archer, did you testify truthfully before this jury when you said it was your honest belief that Mr. Blackburn was gone from his house all night of November 9, 1915, and the early morning of November 10, 1915?"

"Yay-ess, I shorely did, I always got up a'fore Charlie to feed the stock and he warn't in his bed and I didn't see him no whar on the place."

The dollar-a-day hired hand, Harrison F. "Skip" Archer, had testified to the best of his ability. He had placed his employer away from home the early morning of the killing, had observed him washing blood off his hands and dressing a wound only a couple of hours later, and he had noticed the accused and his wife acting in a suspicious manner the same morning. Skip had done the right thing. His ma and pa would have been "right proud" of him.

Sid Roach was on a roll and he had one last witness. Wes Scrivner, the most well-informed man in Stoutland, took the stand. Unworried about his appearance, Wes was attired in mattress ticking striped bib overalls, a blue work shirt, and scuffed brogans. After a few establishing questions, Roach got down to business:

Q: "Mr. Scrivner, did you have occasion to speak with the defendant, Mr. Blackburn, a little before noon, Thursday, November 11, of last year?"

A: "Yes, I did. I was a-settin' up at the depot and Charlie Blackburn come in to buy hisself a ticket."

Q: "On that occasion, did Mr. Blackburn tell you he was in the process of selling his farm to Jasper Francis?"

A: "That's right, he asked me if I had seen Jap. He said they wuz supposed to take the train to Leb'non to draw up the papers."

Q: "That's fine, Mr. Scrivner. Now then, did you also have a conversation with Mr. Blackburn one week later—let me see here [looking at papers]—on Wednesday, November 17?"

A: "Yessir, I did. I seen him on the sidewalk right in front a' Calkin's store."

Q: "At the time that you saw Mr. Blackburn, were you aware that Mr. Jasper Francis was missing?"

A: "Yes sir, I wuz."

Q: "At that time, when you spoke with Mr. Blackburn, did you ask him whether there was a written contract for him to sell his farm to Mr. Francis, and if so, what was his reply?"

A: "Mr. Roach, I asked him that very question and he said, 'Yes, we have a contract and that contract is wrote out on two sheets of paper and is folded together, and it is put down in that little red book that Jap always carried in his pocket.' He said, 'Whenever they find Jap, they'll find that little book with that contract in it.'"[11]

Q: "Mr. Scrivner, Mr. Simp Francis, brother of the late Jasper Francis, has testified in this courtroom that Mr. Blackburn told him on November 16 that a contract had been written in a 'little red book' in the form of a memorandum. He also testified that Mr. Blackburn said nothing about any other written contract. Are you absolutely certain that Mr. Blackburn spoke of the existence of a separate two-paged document?"

A: "Mr. Roach, I'm just as sure of that as the sun'll come up tomorrow."

Q: "Mr. Scrivner, did it seem odd to you that Mr. Blackburn spoke of Mr. Francis in the *past tense*, when he said that Mr. Francis always 'carried' a little red book?

Defense: "Objection, Your Honor! Immaterial and calls for speculation on the part of the witness."

Judge: "Sustained."

Q: "Mr. Scrivner, did it seem odd to you that Mr. Blackburn presumed that Mr. Francis would be searched when he was found? If the man was found alive, why would they be searching him?"

Defense: "Objection! Your Honor, this whole line of questioning calls for speculation, is improper, and is designed to unfairly bias the minds of the jury!"

Judge: "Sustained! The jurors will disregard the last question. Mr. Roach, please confine your questions to matters actually seen or heard by Mr. Scrivner."

Roach: "No further questions, Your Honor."

Roach then quickly recalled Dr. C.E. Carlton to the stand and determined that Carlton, along with H.W. Singleton, was appointed by Coroner J.L. Jackson to search the body of Jasper Francis when it was found November 22, 1915, atop Rouse Hill.

Q: "Dr. Carlton, did you or Mr. Singleton find on Mr. Francis's person a small red notebook or ledger book?"

A: "No, we did not."

Q: "When you and Mr. Singleton searched the body of the late Mr. Francis, did you find on his person or anywhere nearby where they might have fallen, sheets of paper on which was written a contract for the purchase of the defendant, Charles Blackburn's farm?"

A: "No, we found nothing of the kind."

Roach: "Your Honor, I have no more questions for this witness. [Loudly] *Your Honor, on behalf of the State of Missouri, the People rests its case, while retaining the right to call witnesses in rebuttal!*"

Frank Farris was immediately on his feet, pleading with the judge to direct a verdict of "not guilty . . . based upon the law and the evidence."[12] The motion was denied.

[gavel] Judge Skinker: "The State having rested its case, we will break early for our midday meal and reconvene promptly at 1:00 P.M." [gavel]

It was a strong finish by Sid Roach. The overheated jury was already peeved about suffering through dozens of objections, sidebar arguments, and banishment to the airless jury room. Missouri's State Flower, the Hawthorne, has lovely blossoms that grow on a gnarly and spiny bush. Missourians proudly display the equally prickly "Show Me" motto on their license plates. The defense of Charlie Blackburn had been left to trod a thorny, uphill path.

Chapter 41

Charlie Blackburn's defense team abided by the well-known lawyer's maxim: "When the law is against you, argue the facts. When the facts are against you, argue the law." With the facts pointing resolutely at their client as the killer of Jasper Francis, their mission had been to keep those facts from the jury through tedious application of the law. Charlie was "suspected but not advised of his rights" at the inquest, testimony of the "Informed Five" must be excluded because it was "hearsay," and Blackburn's unconcern with the search for Jasper Francis was "irrelevant and without significance." Having failed in their efforts to keep such adverse testimony from the jury, Farris, the Mayfields, and Phil M. Donnelly squared their legal shoulders, took a deep breath, and put on the best case they could muster. Given what they had, it was a yeoman's effort.

When Judge Skinker's gavel hit the block at 1:05 P.M., the outside temperature was 91 degrees and headed for a high of 97.[1] Augmented by body heat and the searing sun on the building's roof, a thermometer in the courtroom would likely have read 100+ degrees. Row upon row of spectators rhythmically waved their soul-saving "funeral fans." Like drones cooling an overheated queen bee, they produced a steady whir.

When Clarence Darrow and William Jennings Bryan tangled in the "Scopes Monkey Trial" in July of 1925, H.L. Mencken wrote that Dayton, Tennessee, had the "atmosphere of a blast furnace."[2] One wonders what the "Sage of Baltimore" might have said about Linn Creek? (Incredibly, Warsaw, a town only 37 miles distant, holds the Missouri records for *both* high and low temperatures: 118 degrees, July 14, 1954, and -40 degrees, February 13, 1905.)[3] Frank Farris and Sid Roach took no backseats to their famous peers in enduring summer's misery. Believers, atheists, and agnostics alike dared not presume to "Inherit the Wind." Just a small whiff of fresh air would have been appreciated.

The defense's first witness was Virgil Evans. Protecting the interests of the People's Bank, he confidently testified that the signatures on the checks and note were the authentic signatures of Jasper Francis. Otherwise, Virgil wasn't especially helpful to Charlie Blackburn's cause. A reading of the record reveals Evans to be a reluctant witness. The two highest officers of the People's Bank of Stoutland, Virgil Evans and Marvin Calkin, seemed little interested in finding justice for their former director whose account they had so coveted. In the business world, it seems there are many acquaintances but few friends.

Grudgingly extracted under cross from the prosecution, Virgil Evans's testimony was punctuated with the usual barrage of hearsay objections from the defense. Nevertheless, Evans corroborated almost all the sworn statements of the rest of the "Informed Five." With one exception. To a man, they had sworn that Francis said he had spoken with Charlie Blackburn early in the morning before leaving for Peters' sale. Jap was indignant that Charlie had not told him that he had shipped the cattle and had expressed skepticism about the claimed farm sale to Joe Givins. Evans denied that Francis had told him anything of the sort but instead had said, "I seen him pass there [Jap's house] about sun-up this morning, *but I did not have a conversation with him. He rode by and waved his hand and spoke to me.*"[4] [emphasis added] The contradiction was striking and simply made no sense. Virgil may have wished to assist the defense by casting doubt upon Sid Roach's dark theory that Blackburn had intended to kill Francis that same morning, dissuaded only by the sudden appearance of Simp Francis. Later, Charlie would himself contradict Evans by testifying that he had, indeed, spoken at some length with Francis that morning.

Roach saved the best for last. Evans confirmed that at the time of the murder, Blackburn was deeply into debt at the bank and delinquent in his interest payments. Virgil was forced to admit his concern that Blackburn might resort to desperate measures.

Roach:
Q: "Mr. Evans, on the evening that Jasper Francis was last seen, did you advise that man not to go by Charlie Blackburn's house and confront him about the cattle returns?"

A: "Yes, I guess I did."

Q: "Did you or did you not advise Mr. Francis to not go by there for fear that if Blackburn was planning on leaving, he might get away?"

A: "Yes, that's right."[5]

"Your Honor, I have no further questions."

Happy to escape the spotlight, Virgil Evans stepped down.

Frank Farris then called Harry Taylor who had spoken to Jasper Francis the evening he was last seen. Harry had motored past Jap astride Sam and apparently headed for home. Taylor said that he saw a man "that he did not know" riding on horseback behind Francis.[6] Desperate for a reasonable doubt, the defense team had found a suspicious stranger "riding a few steps behind" Francis on Rouse Hill where his decomposed remains were found.[7] Unfortunately, this serendipitous killer had deficiencies. Riding in the same car with Taylor, Jim Marshall said he had no recollection of seeing the man. Only a short distance away, Marshall got out of the car and walked home. He heard "no discharge of firearms nor any outcry, nothing to attract attention."[8]

A succession of witnesses, including Marvin Calkin, L.D. Franklin, and Fred Huff, passed the Blackburn farm on the morning of November 10 after about 7:15 A.M. None saw nor heard anything unusual, just Charlie Blackburn and Skip Archer hauling and unloading corn. Calkin added that he was present when the financial settlement was made at the bank in Stoutland and that neither of the Francis brothers had claimed the signatures affixed to the $3,000 note, $1,500 check and $1,200 check (Exhibits A, B, and C) to be forgeries. Predictably, Calkin's opinion was that the signatures were "that of the deceased."[9]

Joe Piercy, who lived near the Castile and the Blackburn residences in Stoutland said he passed by and talked with Claude Castile the morning of the November 10 "about six o'clock" but saw nothing of Charlie Blackburn and saw no "stock in his yard."[10]

This was the exact time that Mrs. Castile recalled seeing Blackburn at Minnie's house and overheard her husband's conversation with him. She had recalled a "black horse" tied in the yard. Oh, the pesky memories of eyewitnesses! Nevertheless, score one for the defense.

Hardware salesman Fred Jacobs provided the defense's only hint that Jap Francis shared a stealthy secret with Charlie Blackburn to conceal his plan to buy Blackburn's farm. Jacobs recalled being at the Blackburn farm Saturday, November 6, when Jap had stopped by looking for Charlie. When departing, Jap had said to Skip Archer, "Tell Charlie that everything is alright and that he [Charlie] would know what he [Jap] meant."[11] This statement was dramatized by the defense as meaning "I'm making progress on selling my farm and I'll soon be ready to finish the papers to buy your farm." Under cross-examination, Jacobs admitted that Francis might possibly have said, "Tell Charlie I want to know if everything is alright—he'll know what I mean." This statement could easily have meant something very different, i.e., "I'm wondering if you have the money from Joe Givins. I haven't tipped off Skip Archer that your farm is sold." It didn't matter. The impact of Jacobs's testimony was that of a gnat's wings in a hurricane.

Then came Guy Stanton. Anxious to place the late Jasper Francis and his horse anywhere but on Rouse Hill at 5 A.M. Wednesday morning, November 10, 1915, the defense ginned up this amiable con man posing as a real-estate agent. Born in Michigan in 1868, Stanton and his wife, Mildred, had appeared in Lebanon before 1910.[12] By 1912, industrialists were proposing a 130-foot-high hydroelectric dam on the Niangua a few miles above the stream's confluence with the Osage River.[13] Rumors and speculation were rife in Lebanon about money to be made in real-estate syndicates buying and holding land near the proposed dam. Representing both buyers and sellers, Guy Stanton was making money hand over fist—at least, that's what Guy said.

Stanton claimed to have met with Simp Francis in Lebanon Friday evening, November 19, and told him that he had seen a horse and rider matching the description of Jap Francis and Sam as they passed through Lebanon on Wednesday, November 17. He observed them leaving town, heading south toward Hartville. The rider was wearing a "white Stetson hat, had a mustache and was riding a sorrel horse with white legs and white face."[14] Stanton also reported that he had "seen the same horse about two miles from Conway" a few days later.[15]

Stanton's testimony suggested that Jap and Sam were still cruising the town of Lebanon a full week after the prosecution's claimed November 10 date of the murder. If Jasper Francis was alive on the 17th, he was well able to dispute any fraudulent checks and notes turned into the bank by Blackburn on Thursday, the 11th. It cut deeply into the prosecution's thesis that Blackburn knew with morbid certainty that Francis would not be returning. Placing Francis's death at another time, or perhaps even another place (with his body and horse brought to Rouse Hill), might shake the State's case. They need not have worried.

Simp Francis was recalled to the stand and gave his version of Stanton's story after which the flamboyant Guy Stanton, in black Stetson hat, silver-buckled belt, and fancy hand-tooled western boots, meekly fell apart in cross-examination (paraphrased):

Well, yes, maybe it was Tuesday the 16th rather than Friday the 19th that he had talked with Simp Francis in Lebanon. Yes, it was true that although he was acquainted with Simp and Ben Francis, he did not know Jap Francis well enough to recognize him on sight. Yes, the second horse and rider that he saw near Conway was really "a different outfit" from the first but that "one or the other" of the horses and riders could have been the missing duo. Actually, the man he had seen riding the second horse had been later identified as Dewey Conray. Yes, after Sam was found, Simp Francis had brought the horse to Lebanon and he had been unable to pick him out of several horses until he was backed out of the stall and separated from the others. And finally, yes, when he was subpoenaed for the first scheduled trial at the February circuit-court term, he had told Sheriff Hufft: "From what I learned, it was not the horse; the horse I saw was just a good butt of a pony."[16]

Sam, at more than 16-hands tall was considerably more than "a good butt of a pony."

Miserable from the heat, the jurors must have wondered why they had to suffer through all of Guy Stanton's blatherings and flimflam. For Mr. Stanton, the time was well spent—he took the measure of some of the best lawyers in Laclede County. By August of 1921, he would need a good attorney or two. Stanton had been charged in adjoining Webster County with "obtaining money by false pretenses." Guy Stanton hired Phil M. Donnelly and Don O. Vernon to defend him. They not only defended him, but personally signed his $2,000 recognizance bond to keep him out of jail and guarantee his court appearance.[17] By 1930, Stanton was plying his real-estate trade in distant Kansas City.[18] Caveat emptor.

Having exhausted their "arm's length" witnesses, the defense began calling Charlie Blackburn's family to the stand. In succession, Ray Blackburn, Minnie Blackburn, and Miz Mary Jane Craddock (by deposition) testified.

When pale, moon-faced Ray Blackburn was called, he promptly slid forward in the witness chair and assumed a crossed-arm, defiant slouch. If Minnie had been there, a "Sit up straight!" remonstrance would surely have been heard. Ray's appearance portrayed Charlie Blackburn as a family man, perhaps plucking the heartstrings of a juror or two. Ray denied seeing his father at the Stoutland home on either Tuesday evening or Wednesday morning the week of the murder. He stated he "put a man's saddle on his sorrel pony Wednesday morning before he went to school." He had tied the animal to a peach tree for his mother to ride to the farm later that morning. Before answering each question, Ray glanced nervously toward his stone-faced father. He said he had heard his father tell his mother he was "taking them (the cattle) in on the trade in selling the place and was giving $44 a head for them." Ray claimed he had heard the conversation "two or three weeks" before Francis was missing.[19]

Under cross, Ray said that he was at school when he first heard that J.J. Francis had been found. When he returned home, he found his father, mother, grandmother, and Uncle James Craddock there together. Shortly afterwards, Skip Archer came into the room. He stated that his father and grandmother moved back into town the day the body was found. He admitted that he had never heard his father say he was "at home" (at the farm) Tuesday night, November 9th.[20]

For a 13-year-old, Ray Blackburn was composed and told a story that jibed with that of the rest of the family. He wasn't asked if he had ever overheard his father speak with Jasper Francis about the sale of the farm. There had been ample opportunities before and after the Sunday cattle drive from the Francis to the Blackburn farms. But then, Ray had vamoosed back to Stoutland as soon as he was paid. Charlie Blackburn did not flip a silver dollar to his son as he left the witness stand, but he deserved it.

When Minnie Blackburn marched up the courtroom's center aisle, the audience turned and gawked as if awaiting a blushing bride. Minnie did not disappoint. She was dressed in a long, white, silk dress, draped in yards of lace and embellished with seed pearls. Her white patent-leather, high-buttoned shoes glistened. With her long dark hair braided and pinned primly under a matching white feathered hat, Minnie swished confidently to the stand. Her posture as erect as a finishing-school ingénue, she sat and took the oath. But that wasn't the best part. Her imported lavender cologne, diffused by the fanning crowd, quickly permeated every nook and cranny of the courtroom. The atmosphere was significantly improved. The French really do know a thing or two about dealing with perspiration and unbathed bodies.

Judge Skinker was so moved by the appearance and essence of Miz Minnie Blackburn that he shocked the entire decorum of his court by generously stating to the attorneys and officers assembled: "Gentlemen, in recognition of the extraordinary heat and resulting discomfort, please feel free to remove your jackets if you so desire." Carpe diem. The sheriffs and deputies breathed a sigh of relief and, grasping their reprieve from Hades, removed their suit coats and flung them on the backs of their chairs. Mr. Donnelly stood to follow suit but noticed that no other lawyer had moved. He quickly reseated himself and watched the judge intently. Skinker, with a faint, even devilish smile, glanced at both tables and left his jacket on. Not to be adjudged more comfortable than the judge, the lawyers remained jacketed.

Minnie Blackburn provided no alibi for her husband but claimed that he had told her of the farm sale to J.J. Francis "about two months" before going to Lebanon to start the legal paperwork. She denied that Charlie had been at her house early on the morning of the 10th. Under cross-examination, Minnie slid sweetly into deeper denial. She had never said to Edna Kissinger, "I thought

I would fall dead," when a lad showed up on her porch with a telegram about the cattle. She had certainly never said, "I didn't know what in the name of God they [Clay & Robinson] wanted to send us a telegram for." She denied that she had told Simp Francis that she had known of the farm sale for only "a day or two" when the two met on the street Tuesday, November 16. She indignantly denied going "around the barn, away from Skip Archer" to talk to her husband on the morning of the 10th. "He went with me to the barn to put the pony away and we spoke only a few minutes."[21]

Finally, Minnie Blackburn swore that she had bandaged "a sore" on Charlie's hand the same afternoon he had come to Stoutland to read the telegram from Clay & Robinson.[22] If true, this precluded Charlie from receiving the injury during the commission of the crime. No powder burn from a gun held close to a man's neck, no kick by Sam's iron-shod hooves, just a barbed-wire nick received *before* the murder.

Full of chivalry, Frank Farris, in his most genteel tones, thanked Minnie Blackburn for her testimony. He held her soft, white-gloved hand as she stepped from the platform and apologized for the "Ozarkian summer heat" that had made her trial experience so "disagreeable." Like the freakish blossoming of a lily in a patch of nettles, Minnie had briefly appeared and then, as if uprooted by a cool zephyr, disappeared to adorn a distant and shady dell. For those mortals consigned to the courtroom's fetid swelter, she would be missed—and envied.

Too aged and ill to attend court, Miz Mary Craddock's written deposition was read to the jury and entered into the record. Having inoculated the jury with Skip Archer's testimony, the prosecution seemed little concerned with her claim that Charlie had been in the house during the night and morning of the murder. Read without emphasis or emotion by the circuit clerk, Miz Mary's testimony fizzled. She too, claimed to have known of the farm sale for "quite a while, a month or six weeks" before the murder. But under cross-examination, she stated that prior to moving to Stoutland the day Francis's body was found, Charlie "had said nothing to her about moving to town."[23] Unasked was the question, "Ms. Craddock, if you knew that the farm was being sold, why hadn't you inquired, and why hadn't anyone told you, when and where you were going to move?"

Roach had one last, very relevant question, the answer which he had re-read to the jury:

Q: "Miz Craddock, during the month of November of last year [1915] did your son-in-law, Mr. Charlie Blackburn, keep a breech-loading shotgun at the farm where you and he lived?"

A: "Well yes, he did have such a gun."[24]

Without objection, Miz Craddock's statement was entered into the record.

Farris: "Your Honor, the defense calls Mr. Charles Blackburn."

The weary jury turned, as one, and looked squarely at Judge Skinker. Tired and dehydrated, their message was clear.

"Mr. Farris, in consideration of the lateness of the hour, I believe it advisable to adjourn this court until tomorrow morning."

"Your Honor, the defense has no objection."

It was nearly 6:00 P.M. of a long and grueling day. Charlie would have a few more hours to rehearse a one-act play requiring his best performance. He would open as a Saturday matinee before twelve discerning critics.

Chapter 42

Saturday, July 1, 1916
Approximately 11:00 A.M.

"Mr. Charles Blackburn, did you directly or indirectly have anything to do with the death of Mr. J. J. Francis?"

"No sir, no sir, I did not. I did not!"

"Do you know anything about how J.J. Francis came to his death?"

"I do not; no sir!"[1]

"The State's witness, Your Honor."

It had taken Charlie Blackburn almost two hours, under the gentle, almost paternal guidance of Frank Farris, to reprise, with additional details, his testimony at the preliminary hearing. In a rambling monologue, he portrayed himself as just a common farmer, unlearned in the world of real estate. He had been caught up in Jasper Francis's scheme to conceal for a time the fairly agreed upon purchase of Blackburn's farm for $11,500. The reason? "He told me the talk was around that he [Francis] had bought my farm; he says, 'If some parties gets hold of that, it will knock me out of the sale of my farm.'"[2]

The devious plan to conceal the farm sale? After receiving the $3,000 note and $1,500 check from Francis as partial payment for the farm, Charlie had agreed to write Francis a $1,200 check to be deposited at the bank. So that "if anyone come in there and said anything to Virgil [Evans] about Jap buying my farm . . . Virgil could show them this check which would show that he had *sold* the cattle to me."[3] Only as a belated move to protect himself from a "live" $1,200 check, sitting ready to hit his nearly empty personal account, did neophyte Charlie meekly ask for a counterpart $1,200 check to hold for his own protection. In the mind of Charlie Blackburn, the mystery of those darned double-crossing checks had been solved.

The magical mystery tour continued. Then came a contradiction of both Virgil Evans's and Charles Winfrey's versions of Jap

Francis's meeting (or nonmeeting) with Blackburn the morning before he was murdered. Charlie freely admitted going to the Francis farm and talking with Jap before he departed for the Peters sale. Charlie was trying to speed the farm sale along. "I wanted to go to Stoutland and wanted him to go with me [so] that we could take the papers [checks and note] to the bank and turn them through the bank that day."[4] Charlie claimed to have told Francis that he had already gone to the bank promising to come in and pay off his debts. He was just trying to do the honorable thing:

"I told Virgil Evans a few days ago—I forget now the day I told him—a few days ago or last week sometime, that I would come in and settle up with him. I had told him, 'I will bring you in some papers and settle up with you.' So I told Francis that I had told Virgil Evans that. I had made the promise to Virgil that I would do that. He said, 'If that is all, don't let it bother you 'bout that.' He says, 'You wait a few days; I am a little bit interested in the bank myself.' He said, 'You wait a few days, if that is what is pushing you up.' He says, 'I will probably go with you in a day or two."[5]

Charlie's assertion that he had met with Virgil Evans and promised that he would soon be paying off his debt to the bank may have surprised both sets of attorneys. Charlie had never before claimed it and Virgil Evans had never mentioned it. A pious "promise" to pressure Francis to consummate the farm sale was a new twist. Both sides had ample opportunity to recall Evans to the stand. He was right there in the witness room. Cannily, Blackburn had not claimed to have told Evans where the money was coming from for such a "settling up." The opportunity to expose a blatant lie before the jury must have been tempting, but the prosecution didn't bite. *"Never ask a question to which you don't know the answer."* They let it pass. Putting a reluctant and adversarial Virgil Evans back on the stand was too risky. Besides, Blackburn's tale was so improbable, why further confuse the jury?

The defense strategy was to just let Charlie keep on talking about his alleged farm sale. Maybe if the jury heard it long enough, they might believe it. He went on and on about Jap's failure to appear at Stoutland, his failure to appear at Lebanon, and his failure to appear at Linn Creek. That darned Jasper Francis just wouldn't keep his appointments! Finally, under pressure to repay his creditors, Charlie cashed the check and note, swapped the $1,200 checks, paid his debts to the bank and W.I. Wallace, and went on about his business. He made no inquiries about the whereabouts of Jasper Francis. He was amazingly unconcerned about when he might expect the $5,800 balance due from the buyer of his farm.

Charlie finished his testimony by looking in the direction of the jury box and adamantly denying involvement in the death of Jasper Francis.

It was Sid Roach's turn. With the temperature rising (it would be another scorcher at 98 degrees[6]), he was anxious to get started. He had familiar ground to plow with the jury and a blockbuster to spring upon the defense. He started with a bit of theatre. Notes in hand, he strode directly and confidently toward Blackburn, stopping abruptly within inches. Pausing, he pointed an accusing finger at Charlie and then withdrew it slowly to his mouth, as if considering which lie he wished to address first. Shaking his head in sadness and frustration, he turned his back and strode away. With every eye fixed upon him, he did a slow pirouette in front of the defense table and waving his papers in the air, opened his mouth as if to speak. Again, nothing came out. The falsehoods were too large, the crime so unspeakable, the guilt so apparent. The gestation of this pregnant pause seemed almost elephantine. *Where to start? Where to start?* But then, someone must do this distasteful job. Taking a deep breath and exhaling slowly, Sid Roach began.

Roach's 90-minute grilling of Charlie Blackburn began with how Charlie's unpracticed testimony before the coroner's court, only one day after the body was found, differed with what he had just told the jury. When recollection of the most important financial transaction of his life should have been fresh in his memory, he had been contradictory and evasive.

The inconsistencies were legion. In November, Charlie had said the note and all the checks were written the same day. Today, they were written on different days. In November, his $1,200 check to Francis had been "to pay for the cattle," or, take your pick, a "bonus" written back to Francis to correct a misunderstanding or a contrivance to help hide the sale of his farm to Francis. At the inquest, the checks had come out of Charlie's checkbook. Today, they had come out of Francis's book. At the inquest, Charlie had been hesitant and unsure of his testimony, often remaining silent for several minutes before answering questions. Some he had not answered at all. Today, he had delivered his story without hesitation. Roach homed in on this point, but Charlie fought back:

Q: "How much of the time that day did you sit and refuse to answer the questions; how much of the four hours that you put in on the witness stand?"

A: "I don't really know. I did not answer every time. You know you were sittin' right there and the jury and you winked and grinned and tried to run something over me."

Q: "You took plenty of time?"

A: "I had to. . . . That was the way I had to do."

Q: "You would sit for some minutes sometimes and would not answer a question at all . . ."[7]

Farris: "Objection, Your Honor!"

Judge Skinker: "I don't think this is proper for the jury to hear. Sustained!"[8]

Just as they had objected to Jasper Francis's words (as repeated by unimpugned witnesses) being heard by the jury, the defense was determined to keep Blackburn's inquest testimony out of the record. Judge Skinker let almost all of it in. Farris, with the confident insistence of young Donnelly, believed that if an appeal was necessary, it would all be thrown out.

Time after time, the objection, "He was summoned as a witness and testified under duress of oath after he was suspected of the crime of killing of J.J. Francis, without counsel and without notice of his rights,"[9] rang out in the courtroom. Their man had been wronged before the law by "these very people [Farris pointing], representing the State, charged with upholding the law."

Roach then homed in on the fact that Blackburn had received, used, and treated as his own, "Five thousand seven hundred dollars of Jasper Francis's money and property and he had nothing from you to show for it—nothing in the form of a signed contract." No corroborating witnesses to the farm sale (except immediate family). No contract in his possession. No nothing.

Roach then took Charlie back to Jim Sullivan's pool hall in Lebanon the day after the murder. Charlie denied sounding every bit like a farmer planning the spring planting:

Q: "When Jim Sullivan, as he has previously testified to this jury, asked you, 'Did you sow any wheat this year?' didn't you reply, 'No, I am going to corn, grass, and pasture my land; I think there is more money in it'?"

A: "No sir, I never had such a talk with Jim Sullivan."[10]

Q: "When you got back from Lebanon, after using Jasper Francis's money, note, and his cattle to pay off your debts, did you make any inquiries about Mr. Francis? Did you try to call him or his brother up?"

A: "I don't remember—I reckon not—but Simp Francis called me."

Q: "Did you go out to his house?"

A: "No."

Q: "So you did nothing until his worried brother called you three days after Jasper Francis failed to meet you in Lebanon?"

A: "No, I figger'd he'd turn up."

Sensing the weariness of the jury and confident that the State's case would hold, Roach finished with incendiary leading questions that he knew would be disallowed. They would be part of his summation as well, but Roach firmly believed in the rule: "Tell 'em, tell 'em again, and then tell 'em what you told 'em."

Q: [incredulous] "Mr. Blackburn, do you really expect this jury to believe a cockeyed story that Mr. Francis agreed to buy your farm?"

"Objection!"

"Sustained."

Q: "Mr. Blackburn, isn't it true that Mr. Francis sold his cattle to you and trusted you to pay for them and you sold them and took the money and paid off your debts?"

A: "No, that's not the way of it."

Q: "Mr. Blackburn, isn't it true that you lied to Mr. Francis?

"Objection!"

"You defrauded Mr. Francis! And when he found out about it, *as you knew he eventually would*, you took his life!"

"Objection, Your Honor, he's browbeating the witness!"

"Brutally and without mercy!"

"Your Honor! Objection!"

"Sustained—Mr. Roach, I won't tolerate further questioning along these lines. If you keep it up, I will hold you in contempt!"

[sarcasm] "Your Honor, I have no further questions for this man."

Frank Farris knew that his case was weak. There was simply nothing to corroborate Charlie Blackburn's version of events. It was Charlie and Minnie and Ray and Miz Craddock, all interested witnesses, against a wealth of unimpeached testimony pointing to only one man—his client. He had one bullet left in the chamber—Charlie's reputation as a law-abiding citizen.

Farris marched eight character witnesses onto the stand: Marvin Calkin, Dr. C.E. Carlton, Frank Schlicht, Hensley Palmer, J.C. Reynolds, John Esther, Ousley Claiborne, and John Williams. All attested to Charlie Blackburn's good reputation. A couple hedged with, "I've never heard anything to the contrary," but it was a credible close.[11]

"Your Honor, the defense rests."

The jury breathed a sigh of relief, shifted in their seats, and turned to the judge. But Sid Roach had brought a little surprise to the party.

Confident that the jury would appreciate a different interrogator at this late date in the proceedings, Roach entrusted his *fait accompli* to an experienced veteran, Claude Mayfield. Roach fully understood the value of "primacy and recency" long before the concept had been articulated by psychologists. When listening to a lengthy presentation, people tend to best remember those portions at the beginning and the end. The middle is a wasteland. By holding it until the end, Sid Roach wanted to headline and underscore one of the prosecution's most important arguments. To add to the affect, it would be presented in a different voice.

"Your Honor, the state wishes to call a few rebuttal witnesses," announced Mayfield.

"Very well, Mr. Mayfield."[12]

"I call Dave McClure."

The defense lawyers looked warily at each other. McClure had previously testified about the finding of the body. What possible additional insight might he add?

After establishing that McClure was familiar with the people and land values in the neighborhood of the crime, Mayfield posed one of the most important questions of the trial:

"What was the value of that [Blackburn] farm, we will say, from the tenth to the thirtieth day of October—last October?"[13]

As one, the defense lawyers rose to object. They argued that McClure's testimony was not a matter of rebuttal and such testimony would be "immaterial and incompetent."[14] Judge Skinker took charge:

Q: (to Farris) "Has not Mr. Blackburn testified of an agreed sale price of $11,500?"

A: "Yes, Your Honor."

Q: (to McClure) "Are you a farmer?"

A: "Yes, sir."

Q: "Do you live in that part of the country?"

A: "I was born and raised in that locality."

Q: "Are you familiar with land values in that neighborhood?"

A: "Yes, sir."

"Objection overruled! You may answer Mr. Mayfield's question."[15]

"I think about $6,000."[16]

The jury had become bored with much of the long and tedious testimony. But disputes about the price of things can always perk a man up. The twelve men in the jury box had to be cautioned to stop whispering among themselves about this startling new testimony. Evidence that the Blackburn farm was worth only about one-half the sale price claimed by Charlie had come as a bolt from the blue.

The defense's "perfect storm" wasn't over. Two more local farmers, Ben McShane and Leroy Fulbright, were similarly questioned. Over strenuous objections, they valued the Blackburn farm at "somewhere about $5,000" and "I would say between $6,000 and $7,000."[17]

It was preposterous that Jasper Francis, an astute businessman and director of the bank, would agree to pay $11,500 for a farm worth no more than $7,000. Significantly, the defense never offered any witnesses to support an $11,500 value.

The prosecution had hit a home run. They had driven it farther than Rogers Hornsby, a rookie in 1915, would ever slug a baseball in St. Louis's old Robison Field.

"Your Honor, the State has no more witnesses."

It was nearly 5:00 in the afternoon. In July, Missouri days are long. With four hours of daylight remaining and hoping not to infringe upon the Sabbath, Judge Skinker recessed his court for 30 minutes and then called for closing arguments. "Counselors, in the interest of time, I would urge that you be brief and to the point. Mr. Roach, you may begin."

Outside, it was a cloudless day. The torrid sun had driven the thermometer to 98 degrees[18] and all humanity off the streets of Linn Creek. Word had circulated that the much-anticipated face-off of Farris and Roach was about to begin, and the courtroom quickly filled beyond capacity. The funeral fans paused—the moment had arrived.

Chapter 43

Sid Roach obeyed Judge Skinker's appeal for brevity. He positioned himself directly in front of the jury box, closer to individual jurors than at any time in the trial. They were the only audience that mattered. He wanted eye contact and their undivided attention, and he got it. He paced back and forth relentlessly, never turning his back upon them. He reminded the jurors that each and every one of them had agreed, during *voir dire*, that they could convict on circumstantial evidence alone. It was a subdued, personal conversation. Roach posed the questions and Roach provided the answers:

"Nobody saw Charlie Blackburn take Jasper Francis's life in the early morning darkness on Rouse Hill just outside Stoutland, Missouri. If they had, they might have stopped it. That good man might be alive today. There was only one eyewitness, J.J. Francis's saddlehorse named Sam. I'm told he is a fine animal. After the murder, he was led away in the dark to a distant ravine by a man who lived nearby. Someone who knew every ridge, valley, tree, and brush pile along the way. There, he was tied securely and left to starve. [sadly] If Sam could speak—if only Sam could speak—our task would be very easy, wouldn't it?

"No, nobody saw it—and, of course, Charlie Blackburn denies it—he always will. [shrug] I would too. Nobody heard Charlie Blackburn, in a fit of anger, threaten to kill Mr. Francis. No, this was a calculated and cold-blooded act, committed without warning. Did officers of the law find Mr. Francis's wallet or his valise with cancelled checks in the possession of the defendant? No, there was ample time, almost two weeks, in which to dispose—we know not where—of those items stripped from Mr. Francis's lifeless body.

"So, gentlemen of the jury, what do we have? How do we find justice for Jasper Jacob Francis? From his cold grave, there by the Liberty Church house, he cries out for it. That's my job. And gentlemen, that is your job. You and I have a sacred trust—we are Jasper Francis's only hope. What you have heard from sworn witnesses in this trial and what I am about to repeat, are circumstances that can lead to only one conclusion. Taken alone, these circumstances might be explained by coincidence. But taken together, one after the other, they are threads tightly woven into the whole cloth of *murder*. As pieces placed together in a picture puzzle, these circumstances form the image, *to the exclusion of all others*, of only one man—the defendant, sitting there [pointing], before you and this court."

Those threads inextricably woven around Charlie Blackburn, those puzzle pieces revealing his likeness, summed to a tidy baker's dozen. Roach reviewed them for the jury:

- He was hopelessly in debt with no prospects for repayment.
- He fraudulently obtained Francis's cattle with a bad check and sold them without his permission.
- He used the cattle returns to pay W.I. Wallace instead of Francis.
- He created a clever and convincing forgery by tricking Francis into putting his own hand to a note and check that he presented for payment at the bank the day after the murder. He had at least two opportunities to obtain samples of Francis's signature, and several expert witnesses had declared the signatures on the checks and note to be forgeries.
- He was present in Stoutland late in the afternoon the day before the murder. He could have easily overheard or been told by a number of people that Jasper Francis would be returning to Stoutland early the next morning.
- He possessed a single barreled, breech-loading shotgun capable of inflicting the ghastly wound found on Jasper Francis's head and creating the gunshot heard by Edna Kissinger at 5:00 A.M.
- He was "gone all night" before the killing and was seen by Skip Archer "about sun-up." This was 1 hour and 40 minutes after the gunshot.[1] Charlie

Blackburn had ample time to hide the body, be seen in Stoutland before sun-up, and dispose of Sam. He then walked a little more than a mile to his own back door, where he was observed by Skip Archer washing his bloody hands.

- Living near the crime scene, he possessed intimate knowledge of the roads and terrain. Positioning himself near the intersection of the Linn Creek and Fulbright Roads, he could listen for and intercept Francis, regardless of which route he took to Stoutland. In near darkness, the killer easily found a remote hiding place in which to tie Sam. A place where he expected the horse would never be found alive.
- While relaxing in a Lebanon saloon and pool hall he had vowed come springtime, to plant corn, sew grass, and pasture his farm. The same farm he now claimed to have sold to Jasper Francis.
- Against all reason, he took no part in the search for Jasper Francis.
- He had told a witness that he had a contract with Jasper Francis to sell Francis his farm. He said it was written on two pieces of paper and placed in Jap's "little red book." No such contract was found on the body. On the witness stand, Charlie admitted that he had never entered into a written contract with Francis.
- At the coroner's court, he had told wildly inconsistent stories of the alleged sale of his farm to Jasper Francis and the reasons for Francis's $1,200 check dated the same day as his own $1,200 check to Francis.
- His claimed $11,500 sale price for his farm was ridiculous. Jasper Francis would never have agreed to pay that much. Not one person, other than members of Charlie's immediate family, had come forth

> to corroborate a single detail of the alleged farm sale.

The evidence of guilt was so bounteous that Roach saw no reason to bring up Minnie Blackburn's admission to Simp Francis, well after the killing, that she had known of the farm sale only "a day or two."

In closing, Roach repeated his impassioned condemnation of Charlie Blackburn as a man who had killed for money: "The Bible calls it filthy lucre." With cool premeditation he had lied to Jasper Francis, he had stolen from Jasper Francis, and when Jasper Francis "found out about it and determined to do something about it," he waited for him on Rouse Hill and "while that good man undoubtedly pleaded for his life, bludgeoned him senseless." And then, fearful "that the victim of his deadly attentions might be found alive," he placed "a large gauge shotgun to the back of his head and pulled the trigger." Roach wished it could be otherwise. His close was measured, collegial, and intense:

"I truly wish that I didn't have to be here today, and I know each and every one of you [jurors] feels the same way. But circumstances—that word again—created by that man [pointing to Blackburn] bring us here, under the law, obligated to carry out the law. The facts are clear. They prove beyond any reasonable doubt that the man sitting before you, Charles Blackburn, is guilty, as charged, of the murder of Jasper Jacob Francis. It is your duty, and yes, *your solemn obligation*, to return a verdict of guilty of murder in the first degree." Thank you for your attention and thank you for your service."

Roach had taken all of 20 minutes. He never raised his voice. Frank Farris would take almost an hour.

Recognized as the best orator and "running debater" in the Missouri Legislature, Frank Farris did not disappoint. He loosened his western-style bow tie and began. At 5'8" and a skinny 130 pounds, Farris was a small man, even by 1916 standards.[2] But his presence was so commanding and his words so riveting that observers swore he possessed great stature. Without notes, he paced constantly, stopping briefly to punctuate his important points.

Occasionally he would pause, at some length, head bowed as if to plumb the depths of some bottomless reservoir of wisdom and intellect. The floor was his, and the entire courtroom, his audience. His resonant, bass voice reverberated off the walls, through the open rear doors and down the twin stairwells to the crowd amassed below. Sometimes as gentle as a Chinook wind, blowing warmly off the Rockies, signaling the coming of spring. At other times, a subwoofer, vibrating the building's load-bearing timbers, then drifting away as a disquieting rumble, signaling the crash of a tsunami on some distant shore. Silver mane flowing, his hands gesturing grandly, he might have been Wellington orchestrating the destruction of Napoleon's Imperial Guard at Waterloo. This was Frank Farris. It was the greatest thespian performance ever staged in Camden County and the ticket was free for those few—those lucky few.

Just two weeks earlier, Farris had helped lead a Missouri delegation that, amid wild cheers at St. Louis's Coliseum, had nominated President Woodrow Wilson for a second term. In a few short years Farris would campaign ardently and eloquently in support of Wilson's League of Nations.[3] Frank Farris was a man who could move people. He was a man of influence. A man who wielded extraordinary power. But today, before this jury of twelve, he wished only to be "one of them." A common citizen of an uncommon state, living in an idyllic, almost utopian, world.

Frank Farris wrote and published whole speeches extolling the natural beauty and the perfectly healthful living conditions of the Ozarks. Every drop of water was a "crystal fountain" or a "babbling brook." There was no breeze that was not a "balmy zephyr of spring." There was no crop that could not thrive, no mineral that could not be mined, and alas, no industry that could not profit in his beloved Ozarks. And if a human was hungry, the fertile Ozark soil would satisfy "with its juicy grapes, its rainbow-tinted peaches, and deep red apples, tender as tempting and delicious fruits, as were ever kissed by the sunset of the Pacific slope, or moistened by the tears of the warm Gulf Stream."[4]

Mark Twain might have suggested he was "laying it on a little thick" or even guilty of an outright "stretch," but Frank Farris was a true believer in the land that he represented and ruled. Unabashedly summing it all up, he declared, "Nothing too good can be said of the Ozarks and the Ozark Mountaineer."[5]

Confident that a passel of fox and coon hunters sat before him in the jury box, he squeezed in a choice phrase from one of his speeches as a metaphor for the search for truth:

"Like, I suspect, some of you . . . with baying hounds I have chased the coon and fox across these streams and over these mountains, and as I sat upon some craggy peak . . . under the mellow radiance of a southern moon, while listening to the music of the hounds . . . I have wondered from whence they came and whither they goeth . . ."[6]

It was poetry—sheer poetry.

Enough of fine elocution; today it served Farris's purpose to dwell upon the inherent skepticism, common sense, and fairness of those inhabitants of God's "Other Eden," the Ozarks. Properly directed and applied in the jury room, these attributes might acquit his client:

"While serving this proud state in the United States Congress, my friend Willard Vandiver, a plain spoken man from Boone County, once said, 'I come from a state that raises corn and cotton and cocklebürs and frothy eloquence neither convinces nor satisfies me. I am from Missouri! You have got to *show me*!'[7]

Not wishing to offend Republicans on the jury, Farris cannily left "and Democrats" from Vandiver's proud list of Missouri's products.

"Gentlemen of the jury, when you really think about it, just what has Mr. Roach and his assistants, *shown you*, for sure? Things that are for certain, things that you can see, things that you can *get your hands around* [clasping hands], something that makes *sense*—good Ozark common sense [finger pointed to temple]? I submit, very little—almost nothing.

"My client, a good man, never in trouble with the law before in his life, made only one mistake! His mistake was agreeing to sell his farm to Jasper Francis during a time in which *some* person or persons unknown took that man's life. That *coincidence*, over which he had absolutely no control and no forewarning, has taken him from his family and the normal pursuits of providing a livelihood. That *unhappy, tragic coincidence* has put him in jeopardy of prison and even his very life![8] [long pause]

"*Coincidences* happen—they happen all the time. Things are not always as they might appear. Very *reasonable* explanations often account for events that might, at first consideration, seem suspicious. But life teaches us not to condemn too quickly. And the law requires you, as jurors serving your community, with little pay and in this heat, at some considerable inconvenience, to do only one thing. *Be reasonable*. As men whose mothers and fathers and grandmothers and grandfathers settled and civilized, for the betterment of all humanity, these beautiful, rugged Ozarks, neighborliness and fairness and honesty is a part of your *char-ac-ter*. Reason and common sense is your *leg-a-cy* from those good people who have gone before us. [pause]

"The law does not require a man charged with a crime to prove that he is innocent. If it did, we would not have this grand democracy, the envy of the world. We would not enjoy those rights so eloquently enumerated within this nation's founding documents. No, we would have a tyranny! All of us would live, every hour of every day of our lives, in fear of a hateful, spiteful, or greedy false accuser. No, *human reason* is what the law demands. The law requires that you, the jury, presume my client, Mr. Charles Blackburn, innocent until proven guilty! In order to convict, each and every one of you, sitting before me here today, must conclude, after careful and thoughtful deliberations, that you have not one single *reasonable doubt* of the State's case! Not one! [pause]

"I submit that there are a *mul-ti-tude* of such doubts. I submit that the foundation of the State's case rests on the shifting sands of hearsay and twisted logic that doesn't make any sense, *common sense*. It is burdened with *supposes*, riddled with *maybes*, and frought with *doubts*, and yes, *reasonable* doubts!"

Having nailed down the high threshold over which the jury must step to convict, Farris proceeded, with all his intellect and persuasion, to stub the jurors' collective toes. Most of his arguments are quoted or paraphrased below:[9]

- He admitted that Jasper Francis was "foully dealt with" and the crime was committed at or near where the body was found. He also admitted that it occurred sometime between sundown of November 9th and Wednesday, the 10th, 1915.

- "Who killed him and why? No one knows. Could it have been the defendant? It is possible, but criminal prosecutions do not rest on possibilities."
- There was no proof that Jasper Francis ever reached home on the evening of November 9, 1915. Close by to where his body was later found, a witness saw Mr. Francis being followed by a stranger that he did not know.
- There was no proof that the defendant was at the time and place of the homicide and had the opportunity to commit the crime, "except farfetched presumptions and unfounded suspicion arising from the business transactions between defendant and the deceased."
- The state had failed to establish a motive or a reason why the defendant would seek the life of the deceased. "In fact, the record, taken as a whole, shows a hundred reasons, if the witnesses tell the truth, why the defendant would want the deceased to live."
- "There is but one feature in this case that tends, in any way, to give a motive for defendant to take the life of the deceased and that is the claim that the instruments of writing that passed from the deceased to the defendant were forgeries . . . when it is apparent to judge, lawyers, and laymen that it is a question of serious doubt; and the forgeries claimed of such skillful character that it would have been impossible for the defendant to have committed."
- The claim of forgery was "greatly augmented by the opinion of an expert witness, anxious for a per diem of $50 and expenses, and who in most cases are ready to shape their testimony to suit the largest compensation."

- Then it started to get nasty. Blame was cast upon Simp and Ben Francis, alleged to be most concerned about claiming their brother's substantial estate and then, and only then, punishing someone—anyone.

The brothers' lawyers also took some abuse.

- The charge of murder against the defendant had been "an afterthought, hatched in the minds of deceased's brothers, who were overzealous in a desire to punish somebody for the killing of their kin, and a wish to succeed to his estate free of charges and liens, which was aided and encouraged by keen-sighted and aggressive counsel."
- The defendant had delivered two mules to the deceased who had them for more than a week. In turn, the defendant had received 32 head of cattle of which he had possession for more than a week and had "*openly* driven the cattle to market under claim of ownership and title two days before the killing."
- The defendant had taken the note and checks, deemed by the State to be forgeries, and passed them "*openly and publicly*" in the normal course of business and the cashier, assistant cashier, and president of the bank, where the deceased had an account, and three others ". . . who could be and were familiar with the writing of the deceased, stated at all times that the alleged forged instruments were the genuine writing of the deceased."
- The claim of forgery was never made "until after brothers of the deceased, slyly and cunningly . . . treated them as genuine," until a rescission of the agreement was obtained. And then, "After tying his hand and foot, and removing from him, as they thought, every instrument of defense, they pro-

claimed to the world the forgery of the documents and made the charge of murder" against the defendant.

Farris wasn't finished throwing brickbats:

- "The disappearance of the deceased did not even excite his brother for five days, and not until Sunday following Tuesday, November 9th, did he announce that his brother was gone." He then "called up the defendant—why, no one knows—and defendant *openly* and *freely* told him of their business transactions."

The sheer brazenness with which Charlie Blackburn had gone about his business was a pillar of the defense's case. Would a man trying to defraud and then kill another man do so much of it out in the open? And in the normal course of business? The obvious rejoinder was, if he were to be successful, how could he do otherwise? Especially if he knew that no complaints would ever issue from the mouth of his victim.

Farris continued:

- The state was permitted, over objection, to make a part of the record the defendant's testimony at a hastily convened inquest where the defendant was sworn under oath and questioned and abused while surrounded by a hostile mob of Stoutland residents.
- "Under such threatening circumstances, you or I might have been equally unwilling to speak. You or I might have had trouble recalling the exact details and order of events of a complex business arrangement. An arrangement agreed to over some passage of time and involving the trading of livestock and real estate. All amid the professed desire of the deceased to keep it quiet for a while."

- "Although suspected of the crime at the inquest, the defendant was not properly advised of his right to engage counsel and to decline to testify. The same people who failed in their application of the law at that inquest are now here prosecuting my client!"

This brought forth a rare, but permitted, interruption and objection from Roach in the middle of Farris's closing argument: "Your Honor, the defense can't be permitted to stand there and make such a statement, impugning the integrity of State's counsel, when the court itself has held that the defendant's statements, as related by witnesses and uncontested by the defendant, were admissible."

Judge Skinker agreed and cautioned Farris that it was "inappropriate" and the wrong venue to argue matters previously settled by the court. The statement was stricken. Farris paid little attention and continued:

- Neighbors of the deceased were permitted to give their opinions as to the value of defendant's farm, making for the purpose of this prosecution, such opinions the opinion of the deceased and "creating the idea that the defendant, by his trade, was cheating the deceased, and because he was cheating him, he thought it necessary to kill him."

Same objection and rejoinder by Roach. Same caution by Skinker. Statement stricken.

- Contrary to all rules of hearsay evidence, numerous witnesses had been permitted to relate statements alleged to have been made by the deceased "at times and places far away from the time and place of the killing." By this means, the deceased had been made a "living testifying witness."

Same objection and rejoinder. Same caution. Statement stricken.

Farris finished with an impassioned return to his central argument that his client had every reason to see Jasper Francis alive, not dead. The only record of contract "according to his [Blackburn's] statement," between Francis and Blackburn was written into the little red book which the deceased carried on his person. "If defendant killed him, he evidently took this book and destroyed it, thereby removing the only evidence which made the contract enforceable. Why should he do so?"[10]

Likewise, "The defendant knew that his trade was not completed; that no deed had passed by him to the farm; and that all consideration therefore had not been paid by the deceased; he knew that the death of the deceased would interfere with, if it did not wholly destroy the sale and make impossible its conclusion. Why should he remove and destroy the little red book?"[11]

Frank Farris must have realized how transparently specious such arguments were. They only made sense if the jury believed that Charlie Blackburn was telling the truth. If they believed Jasper Francis's words, as told by numerous witnesses, Blackburn had compelling reasons to see Francis dead.

Farris's close was essentially that "stuff happens" in life that can never be fully explained, and the jury should let his client go home. He took a stab at alternative explanations for Francis's demise. Fascinatingly, he never brought up a simple highway robbery gone bad, committed by a felon who happened to know the countryside. Mercifully, he didn't attempt to revive Guy Stanton's fleeting and faulty sightings of Jap and Sam.

Frank Farris continued:

"Many human lives have been lost and the cause, the manner and the means by which it happened shrouded in the deepest mystery, which years have never explained. Accidents have happened in ways and manners which the human mind could not understand, and for which no reasonable human theory could be advanced. But mystery and inexplicable circumstances are not sufficient bases to warrant the taking of a man's life and liberty.[12]

"When last seen, deceased was riding leisurely on the highway; he could have tied his own horse in the woods near the road and gone back, if needs be, to his trysting place, to meet companions of his own choosing; it is as possible for hundreds to have killed deceased as the defendant; within a hundred yards of where his body was found some person not known to Harry Taylor was seen riding a few steps behind the deceased; he, whoever he was, was near the deceased, and in much better position to have killed him than was the defendant.[13]

"In conclusion, I submit that the State has failed, and failed miserably, to show sufficient circumstances to rebut the presumption of innocence of this good man, unjustly accused and brought by the full force of the State before you. It is manifestly clear that the circumstances of this case are every bit as consistent with Charles Blackburn's innocence as his guilt.[14]

"Yours is an awesome responsibility. [walking behind Charlie and placing both hand on his shoulders] If any or all of you [the jury] have a reasonable doubt about the guilt of this good and honest man, you are obliged under the law to acquit. I plead of you! I beg of you! *For God's sake*, return him now to his home and family! The stakes are too high, the consequences too grave, to make a mistake. [long pause] Mr. Donnelly, Messrs. Mayfield, and I admire your patience and trust your good judgment. [nodding] We thank you."

The State always gets the last word. Sid Roach kept it short:

"The soul of the dead Jasper Francis cries out for justice. He knows that Charlie Blackburn lied to him, just as he has lied to this court. Jasper Francis was a good neighbor, a trusted friend and generous benefactor of many. That man [pointing to Blackburn] took everything that Mr. Francis had in this world. [choking with emotion] He stole his money. He stole his cattle. And then, as he knew from the beginning he would, he coldly and without mercy took the only thing that honorable and trusting man had left. He took his life. [voice rising] Jasper Jacob Francis and the people of the State of Missouri are relying upon you to bring justice for this terrible crime. I know that you can be trusted to do your duty! Your Honor, I have nothing else."

And it was over.

Chapter 44

"Mr. Foreman, has the jury reached a verdict?"

"Yes, Your Honor, we have—we shore have."

"Will the defendant, Charles Blackburn, please rise and face the jury."

It was 5:00 in the afternoon, Sunday, July 2, 1916. Predictably, in Linn Creek the weather was unbearably hot. Relief provided by a brief morning shower had proved short-lived. Heated by the sun, the refreshing drops had traitorously converted the town into a steamy cauldron. The drama played out at the courthouse for the last six days had reached an edgy, short-of-breath, catch-in-the-throat conclusion.

At 4:30, a bell, pulled by a cord through a small wall port, rang several times, signifying the jury had reached a verdict. Judge Skinker, dozing in his chambers, immediately ordered court deputies to summon the defendant and lawyers for both sides. Families of both the victim and the accused filed silently in, filling the front rows. As word spread that the jury had come in, a horde of dismissed witnesses, newspapermen, determinedly vengeful residents of Stoutland, and general curiosity-seekers scurried toward the courthouse. No one spoke aloud—only nervous whispers were heard.

Sequestered in the jury room, down a short hall and across from the Judge's Chamber, the jurors waited expectantly for the Judge's call. Skinker was in no hurry. He peered several times into the courtroom and, much like a minister delaying opening prayers for late arrivals, lingered for a while. The citizenry had patiently, even heroically, observed court decorum under difficult circumstances. They deserved to tell their grandchildren they were present when the famous Blackburn murder trial verdict was read.

Nearly 24 hours earlier, following closing arguments, Judge Skinker had turned and read detailed instructions to the jury. Nine in number, they seemed to cover the subject. Among other things, they carefully defined "willfully," "deliberately," "premeditatedly," and that evil phrase, "malice aforethought." All were necessary to convict for murder in the first degree. Circumstantial evidence was defined as "proof of certain facts and circumstances from which the jury may infer other connected facts which usually and reasonably follow, according to the common experience of mankind."[1]

Judge Skinker had carefully crafted his charge to the jury to include instructions that had passed muster with Missouri's Supreme Court. They covered "reasonable doubt," "weight of character witness testimony" and "jurors as the sole judge of the credibility of the witnesses, including his or her interest, if any, in the result of the trial." With the latter, Charlie Blackburn's alibi and corroboration of a farm sale to Jasper Francis took a judicial hit.

Finally, Skinker repeated the two counts of the information charging Blackburn with first-degree murder, i.e., murder resulting from the use of a "gun loaded with gunpowder and leaden balls" and the other, murder resulting from the striking of the victim's head with "some instrument or weapon."A finding of Charlie Blackburn's guilt to either count would require the jury to "assess his punishment at death, or at imprisonment in the penitentiary for the term of his natural life."[2]

Skinker then permitted the jurors to have supper and return for deliberations at 7:00 P.M. With a caution not to discuss the trial with anyone, including themselves, he placed them in the accompaniment of deputies and gaveled the trial into a temporary recess.

Skinker held a glimmer of hope that a quick verdict would permit sentencing, if necessary, yet that evening. A devout Presbyterian, he earnestly desired to leave the Lord's Day inviolate. It didn't happen. An inquiry was made at 10:00 P.M. The jury's elected foreman, a 50-year-old farmer by the name of Grant Eldred, stated a lack of a consensus and a need to continue. It had been a fatiguing day, long and eventful. The jury would have to sleep on it. Skinker dismissed them until 2:00 P.M. Sunday, when their work would resume. He urged them to attend a "church of their choice" in Linn Creek.

Judge Skinker could have put off deliberations until Monday morning, but he abhorred long interruptions. Momentum toward a verdict might be lost. Jurors would have too much opportunity to harden stated positions. And for some wavering souls, too much time to think, rethink and "over think" the case. The 6-day trial had generated 52,000 words of testimony and a bill to the State for court fees totaling $1,455.55. A frugal and tidy man, Skinker did not want a hung jury.

The good judge also happened to know that the steamboat *Homer C. Wright*, operating out of Tuscumbia, Missouri, would be making its regular Monday morning docking at Linn Creek. Passage on the *Homer C.* could convey a prisoner and his guards quickly and cheaply the 70 miles downriver to Osage City and then by prison car or Missouri Pacific train to the Missouri State Penitentiary at Jefferson City.

Once reconvened on Sunday, the jury took another two and a half hours to arrive at a verdict, suggesting serious disagreement. Now they were ready to speak as one.

The women in Charlie Blackburn's life were dressed in black. Forty-one-year-old Minnie was in black satin, corseted, trussed, and cinched to accentuate her buxom, yet wasp-waisted figure. Sixty-one-year-old Dolly Blackburn wore a plain linen frock, accented only with a white tatted collar. Both sat grim-faced and silent, Minnie with her arm pressed tightly around Ray. McGary "Mack" Blackburn, 65, sat stoically, leg crossed over knee. Mack was only 11 when his father had been killed in the Civil War. He knew a lot about bad news and was prepared for the worst.

Sid Roach leaned forward, elbow on table, thumb supporting chin; his three co-counsel sat upright, hands clasped in laps.

Sheriff Salsman, Chief Deputy Paxton, and another deputy moved into positions within an arm's length of the defendant.

With cupped hand, Frank Farris whispered a final word of encouragement into Charlie Blackburn's ear as the defense lawyers rose with their client. Charlie's California tan seemed considerably paled. He crossed his arms defiantly across his chest and assumed his odd pursed-lip mannerism, half-whistle and half-grimace.

Foreman Eldred stood and read from a handwritten paper. He intoned:

> "We, the jury, find the defendant, Charles Blackburn, *guilty as charged* in the second count of the information, of murder in the first degree, and assess his punishment

[pausing, as if losing his place] at imprisonment in the penitentiary for the term of his natural life."[3]

Minnie gasped as if to faint. Ray looked questioningly to his mother. With trembling voice, Dolly uttered a tragic, "Oh, no!" Mack stared at the floor, shaking his head in denial. At least Charlie would not be hung, but the news was bad, very bad. How would they tell the children at home—back on the farm at Decaturville? The object of their affection stood mute and expressionless, pale blue eyes imprinting the jurors' faces in his long memory.

Speechless, Ben and Simp Francis turned and embraced for a moment, clapping each other's backs, a rare show of emotion for men of hardy West Virginia stock. Their resolute belief in the guilt of Charlie Blackburn had been confirmed by a jury of "twelve honest men." They took no pleasure in it. Their brother Jap was gone.

Friends of J.J. Francis made exclamations of "Yessir!" "Yeah!" and "They gotter right!" One bold fellow opined, rather too loudly, "They should a' hung the S.O.B." Overall, reaction in the courtroom was muted. Missouri's July heat and humidity had wrung the emotions out of most observers. Content that justice had been done, they just wanted to go home.

Salsman and Paxton immediately handcuffed a compliant Charlie Blackburn. They need not have bothered. He had high hopes that he and his distinguished lead attorney would eventually prevail. Those efforts began immediately. Before sentencing by Judge Skinker, Frank Farris and young Phil Donnelly, the novice lawyer Farris had taken a liking to, had motions to make.

Motion for granting of a new trial for all the reasons that they had objected and excepted to during the trial, and in addition, the Judge's alleged errors in instructing the jury; because the verdict was against the weight of the evidence; because the jury verdict was the result of prejudice, passion, and a misconception of the law and the evidence; and the verdict of the jury is not supported by any substantial evidence.[4]

"Motion denied!"

For similar reasons, "Motion for arrest of judgment."[5]

"Motion denied!"

Asked if he had anything to say, Charlie replied, "No, sir. No, I don't."

With his soft Virginia drawl, Judge Skinker repeated the jury's verdict, formally sentencing Charlie: "To be confined in the Penitentiary of the State of Missouri, for the period of your natural life from the first day of July, A.D. 1916. . . ."[6]

As Charlie was led away, he was allowed a brief encounter with his family. As Mack, Smith, Bob, and Lynn Blackburn looked on, Minnie briefly took Charlie's hand but never embraced him. Sobbing openly, Dolly Blackburn hugged him and cried, "Son, I know you didn't do it!"

"Ma, we'll fight this to the Supreme Court—it ain't near over yet."

Then came a final goodbye to his little ring of family supporters. Never an affectionate man, Charlie hugged his son Ray and told him, "You keep goin' to school now and look after your ma—I'll be back before long."

Charlie could not have known that the next time he would see Minnie Blackburn, she would no longer be his wife.

Charlie was then returned to familiar surroundings—his cell in the bleak Camden County jail. The Blackburns had been away from their livelihoods too long. Food and lodging expenses were mounting. They left immediately, not staying overnight to see Charlie off on the *Homer C. Wright* in the morning.

In chambers, defense lawyers had another request. They presented an affidavit requesting an appeal directly to the Missouri Supreme Court. An accommodative man, Judge Skinker granted it.[7] Frank Farris saw no reason to test the waters with a lower court. He would immediately make his case within the imposing supreme-court building in Jefferson City. The red brick structure with a Corinthian-columned entrance faced the nearly finished new Missouri State Capitol building. Well known to the court's seven justices and three commissioners, Farris's pleas would be well considered there.

Interestingly, the jury had found Charlie Blackburn guilty only on the second count of first-degree murder, committed with some "instrument or weapon" and not the first count of death by "gun, gunpowder, and leaden ball." They apparently had given weight to

Doctor Carlton's opinion that although injuries from both would have been fatal, the crushing of the skull was "sure to have caused death in a very short time." The decision contravened the prosecution's theory that the gunshot had likely been administered as a *coup de grace*.

Later, it was learned that the jury agreed upon Charlie Blackburn's guilt almost from the outset. Whether Charlie should die for his deed or spend a lifetime in prison was a different story. Evenly divided, the matter was discussed hotly and at length. One side demanded an "eye for an eye." The others could not bring themselves to impose death with circumstantial evidence only. As the second afternoon waned on, those seeking a more merciful and less "final" sentence held firm and persuaded their hot-blooded brethren to go along. It was, after all, the blessed Sabbath.

Chapter 45

The 110-foot-long, triple-decked *Homer C. Wright* was right on schedule, whistling its arrival at Linn Creek before 10:00 A.M. Veteran pilot Clarence "C.B." Wright was in the wheelhouse with chief engineer Charlie Jenkins tending the steam engine.[1] A fireman and a couple of burly deckhands completed the crew. Braking for landing, the giant stern wheel was reversed, creating a fine-misted rainbow in the morning sun. With the ship's bell clanging relentlessly, the shallow draft boat nudged securely upon the mud-flat landing. The sturdy craft was then tied off to a couple of trees and its loading ramp lowered. This would be the last visit of the *Homer C.* to Linn Creek until fall rains would bring a rise on the Osage. The danger of grounding the craft on a shoal or sandbar had become intolerable.

As freight was unloaded, Charlie Blackburn was hustled the two blocks downhill from the jail to the landing. Dressed in stripes and bound with ankle irons and handcuffs, he was "prepped" and ready for his journey to the penitentiary. A contingent of county officials, law-enforcement officers, merchants, and farmers were there to see him off. Their numbers were swelled by the usual lounging yokels, children, and numerous dogs aroused by the excitement of "steamboat a-comin'!"

Like the Blackburns, Simp and Ben Francis had gone home. Just as they had stopped a Stoutland crowd intent on lynching Charlie, they entrusted the last rites of justice to the Law. Neither Sheriff Salsman nor Chief Deputy Paxton would be accompanying Charlie on his one-way trip downstream to Jefferson City. That task had been delegated to two deputies, armed with sidearms and double-barreled shotguns. A man would have to be a fool to attempt escape while shackled in irons on a boat in the middle of a river.

Some 30 minutes later, the ramp was hoisted and the *Homer C.* prepared for departure. Standing safely on the bank, Sam Paxton had one last jab to land on his favorite prisoner. In an era when a life sentence meant "life," it was worthy of the whiney sadist "Captain" in *Cool Hand Luke*. With hands cupped to mouth, he shouted, "Charlie, next time yore in the neighborhood, come by and see us!"

Shuffling up the steps to his appointed place on the second deck, Charlie's anger was riled. He turned and shouted, "I wouldn't get too damned comfortable if I was you, Sam Paxton; I just might do that!" With this disquieting threat, Charlie Blackburn left Camden County.

Its 16-foot paddle wheel spinning, the big steamboat backed into the main channel. Drifting briefly, it righted itself and gaining headway, disappeared around the grand bend of the Osage. Two peremptory whistles announced Charlie Blackburn's departure. Most, including Sam Paxton, felt that it would be for good.

Records on file with the Missouri Department of Corrections show that "Chas. Blackburn" was received at the penitentiary in Jefferson City, Tuesday, July 4, 1916, and assigned prisoner number 18591. Undoubtedly, the *Homer C. Wright* had "laid up" for the night because of darkness and difficulty of low water navigation. Ironically, its bound human cargo had been delivered to prison on Independence Day. Charlie was the only prisoner logged in at the "pen" that day. He was described as 5'9" tall with an 11" foot; medium-brown hair, bald on top; eyes blue and complexion fair. Charlie professed to be a "Baptist," with "temperate" habits of life, and having an education (literate). The Prison had not yet begun taking mug shots of incoming prisoners. Hence, the world is deprived of a photographic likeness of the man.[2]

Charlie Blackburn's experiences in the Missouri State Penitentiary are unchronicled. His "rap" of first-degree murder may have stayed the hand of gangs and predators who seek to impose their will on new inmates—or maybe not. Undoubtedly, it was a very unpleasant experience. In any case, Charlie didn't hang around long. Sam Paxton's mocking farewell had been premature.

February 16, 1918, one year, 7 months, and 12 days after arriving at prison, the Missouri Supreme Court "reversed and remanded" Charles Blackburn's life sentence.[3] Charlie was returned to the Camden County jail for a new trial scheduled for August. He was then released under the conditions of his original bail. He apparently took up residence in a rooming house in Lebanon and began working off some of his legal bills. Although Charlie would never serve another day in prison, his troubles were far from over. Sidney Crain Roach would see to that.

Minnie Blackburn didn't wait around for the results of Charlie's appeal before filing for a divorce. She started proceedings against Charlie almost immediately after his murder conviction. Jackson County court records show the divorce was granted April 19, 1917, ten months before Charlie was released from prison. There would be no welcoming arms on the home front. The case file was either destroyed or misplaced by local officials. It might have made interesting reading.

Charlie's Supreme-Court appeal had included all the "duly excepted" trial testimony, as well as Judge Skinker's alleged errors. A "bill of exceptions" was extracted by the defense from a verbatim trial transcript drafted by stenographer Templeton. Both sides then prepared a detailed "Statement, Abstract of the Record, Brief and Argument" for the benefit of the court. Prosecutors Roach and Mayfield were aided by Missouri Attorney General Frank W. McCallister and his assistant, Henry B. Hunt.

There were no oral arguments in the case entitled: *Supreme Court of Missouri; October Term, 1917; State of Missouri, Respondent v. Charles Blackburn, Appellant, No. 20,332*. Written briefs and arguments were deemed sufficient, and an opinion was prepared by Commissioner Reuben F. Roy. Roy's work was reviewed by Commissioner John Turner White, who agreed. Like all functionaries, Missouri Supreme Court justices employed three full-time "commissioners" to do the tedious work for them. The seven justices, sitting *en banc*, liked what they saw. Roy's opinion was adopted as the decision of the court. "All the Judges" concurred.[4]

Predictably, the Supreme Court divided the baby:[5]

- "Admission of evidence as to alleged statements made by defendant at the coroner's inquest was clearly an error. . . . The constitutional protection of the defendant against compulsory self-incrimination was thereby denied." Sid Roach would never again be allowed to show that Blackburn had told wildly conflicting stories at a time when the details of a business arrangement he had with Francis should have been fresh in his mind.

- Much of the alleged "hearsay" evidence from the "Informed Five" was permitted to stand, but some of it wasn't. With legal nuances and hairsplitting so fine some attorneys still remain flummoxed, portions of John Frey's and Charles Winfrey's testimonies relating their conversations with Jap Francis were disallowed. Only Francis's direct statements bearing on the reason for the $1,200 cattle check [since Blackburn provided an entirely different reason] would be permitted as "competent" evidence in any future trial.
- The opinions of local farmers as to the value of Blackburn's farm were permitted to stand. Since the existence of a contract between Blackburn and Francis was contested by the State, "such evidence is competent for the purpose of showing that no such contract was ever made, on theory that a good businessman would not probably contract to pay $11,500 for a farm not worth over $7,500."
- Testimony that Charlie Blackburn showed no interest in the search for Jasper Francis was permitted to stand: "We hold that the failure of the defendant in this case to join in the search for the deceased was a competent circumstance to be shown in evidence. Its weight was for the jury [to decide]."

And finally, a stinging rebuff to the defense for arguing that Judge Skinker erred in failing to direct a "not guilty" verdict for lack of evidence:

"Defendant contends that there is no sufficient evidence to support a conviction. We are sorry to say we are of a contrary opinion. The judgment is reversed, and the cause is remanded for a new trial."[6]

As a side note, the Supreme Court forever cast suspicion on the People's Bank of Stoutland. Having examined the alleged forged checks and note, along with "about fourteen genuine checks of Francis . . . we venture no opinion [about authenticity]." However, the court continued:

"The 'paid' stamp of the bank is placed twice over the signature to the note, very much obscuring it. The cashier of the bank testified that it was the custom to thus stamp paid notes. In this case the note is also stamped by the bank 'paid' on the back. The genuine checks before us are only stamped on the back."[7]

A not-so-subtle hint to Camden County that it might wish to pursue an obstruction-of-justice charge by an officer(s) of the bank? It never happened. Sid Roach and Ivon Lodge would be much too busy trying to put Charlie Blackburn back in prison.

The Supreme Court had spoken. With a well-reasoned opinion, it had accomplished two salutary results. It had given the powerful Chairman of the House Judiciary Committee what he wanted, a new trial for his client. A sort of "Go away, Frank Farris—be happy" decision. At the same time, it did not appear the court had grievously wounded the State's case against Blackburn. But such was not to be.

Judge Skinker granted Charlie a change of venue to Marshfield, the county seat of Webster County. Marshfield is 42 miles southwest of Stoutland on the Frisco Line and some 90 miles overland from Linn Creek. Sid Roach would be a long way from home and his well-deserved reputation with the Camden County jury pool.

Between his discharge from prison and November 8, 1921, more than 5 years after his original conviction, Charlie Blackburn would be tried 3 times before Webster County juries for First-Degree Murder. These years would be dotted with disputes, continuances, and delays. The circuit court files for the period are littered with stillborn trial dates. Sid Roach demanded them, Judge Skinker ordered them, and Frank Farris and company maneuvered out of them.

Even the great influenza pandemic of 1918 got into the act. At the height of the contagion, Attorneys Donnelly and Farris would seek continuance of a trial set for November 21 of that year because Charlie, "living at his home in Lebanon, Missouri, has been suffering for three weeks from the Influenza." An affidavit from Dr. J.L. Benage noted that the poor man "is still in a very weak and highly nervous condition with digestive organs deranged and other complications."[8] Continuance granted. It would not be the only medical reprieve.

While living with his youngest brother, Lynn Blackburn, in Escondido, California, Charlie eschewed attendance at a trial scheduled for May 10, 1920. Dr. A.L. Gregory provided an affidavit swearing that he was acquainted with Charlie, had treated him for several months, and that "Charles Blackburn is suffering from inflammatory articular and muscular rheumatism and that in addition to this his heart is affected." Helpfully, Gregory opined that it would be "dangerous" to his health to travel from "here [Escondido] to Missouri and . . . he would not be able to travel any distance for over 6 months."[9] Continuance granted.

Other delays were caused by Frank Farris's duties as a Representative in the Missouri General Assembly and his appointment by the Governor in 1918 to a commission to revise Missouri's criminal and civil codes. Farris was an important man whose services were needed in Jefferson City for the greater good. First-degree murder trials must stand in line.

Webster County Circuit Court dockets note at least seven trial dates set for which the cause was continued, sometimes after witnesses were subpoenaed, and in at least two cases after jurors had been summoned. Against all odds, three trials were actually held with a full compliment of witnesses and jurors. The first, a 4-day affair in June of 1919, resulted in a hung jury and a mistrial. A poll of the jurors found "seven for acquittal and five for conviction."[10] It was not a good omen for Sid Roach and the State.

The case had taken on a new persona, helpful for the defense. First, the prosecution was no longer seeking the death penalty. Only the life-imprisonment option was presented by Judge Skinker to the jury. The "Informed Five" were now limited by the Supreme Court in repeating only those utterances of Jasper Francis respecting the purpose of the $1,200 check from Blackburn to Francis. Most importantly, any mention of Charlie's confused and contradictory testimony at the inquest was denied the prosecution. Even the stalwart Judge Skinker, weary of his rulings being reversed by the Supreme Court, did a little editing of his jury instructions. A line-by-line comparison of instructions for the Linn Creek jury and the Webster County juries is revealing:[11]

- The jury was allowed to make its own comparison of the alleged forged signatures of Jasper Francis against signatures "admitted to be true signatures of J.J. Francis." The signatures, disputed by squads of experts on both sides, had been requested and looked at, without opinion, by the Supreme Court. They were now in the hands of the only people who really mattered—the jury. Judge Skinker told them to "use your own judgment."
- Skinker removed all references to character witness testimony. In the original instructions, he had said, "If you are satisfied of the defendant's guilt then his good character cannot justify, excuse, or mitigate the offense." Since Charlie Blackburn's lack of a criminal record and the calling of numerous character witnesses was a bulwark of the defense, this deletion may have helped the defense.
- Regarding the credibility of witnesses, Skinker had originally said, "You will take into consideration . . . his or her interest, if any, in the result of the trial." Not so subtly, this had put the spotlight on Charlie Blackburn's only alibi and corroborating witnesses, i.e., his immediate family. For inexplicable reasons, the Judge decided to delete this seemingly reasonable instruction. This could only help the defense.
- He took the "recommendation" of the Supreme Court and instructed jurors that "The alleged declarations of J.J Francis as to the $1,200 check given him by the defendant, Blackburn, were admitted to show for what purpose said Francis held such check, and should be considered by the jury for no other purpose whatsoever."

It would be 15 months until the next trial, begun September 24, 1920. It took only three days to achieve the same result. A hung jury and a mistrial. The headcount would be different. This time, those voting for acquittal had increased from seven to nine with only three jurors willing to put Charlie Blackburn back in the penitentiary.[12] With a well-tainted Webster County jury pool, the prosecution's prospects had gone from mediocre to downright dismal. But Sid Roach was not a man to flinch when confronted with adversity. The case had become his magnificent obsession. A dogged determination in the face of reality. Roach seemed prepared to prosecute Charlie Blackburn until death took one or the other. He may have had other reasons.

Sid Roach had taken time out from a successful run for Congress to prosecute Charlie Blackburn at his third trial in September of 1920. He had sought no delays or continuances. He took on a murder trial only six weeks before the election. Talk about multitasking? Roach was elected to represent Missouri's Eighth District, which included 8 counties and 138,807 people, defeating his Democratic opponent by 4,200 votes.[13] He had parlayed his experience in the legislature and reputation as a tough law-and-order prosecutor into a congressional seat. It hadn't hurt that newspaper coverage of the notorious Blackburn trials had kept his name in the papers for four years. Republican pols and voters alike knew who Sid Roach was. Temporarily, Roach had won the political battle with Frank Farris. A sitting congressman trumps a state senator.

The trying of Charlie Blackburn had become a cottage industry with deputies of several counties, in and out of Missouri, dispatched thither and yon, rounding up increasingly weary and reluctant witnesses for trials that might or might not happen. The Blackburn trials were a plague upon Stoutland society. Mark Twain supposedly said: "Everybody talks about the weather but nobody does anything about it." To be sure, deputies delivering subpoenas were as common as the sun coming up and the wind blowing. Nobody knew how to stop them—they just kept coming. Witnesses got up in the morning and couldn't remember whether to go to work or go testify. Testifying had become as natural as grumping at the spouse and swatting the kids. The case had taken on an eternal "Groundhog Day" life of its own, repeated without end. Justice had become a public nuisance and was gaining a downright bad reputation.

The tide of public opinion had begun to turn in Charlie Blackburn's favor. "Mebbe they oughta jest quit houndin' thuh man, seein' as how two differ'nt juries cain't decide nuth'in no-how," was drawled more than once on the streets of Stoutland and Lebanon.

One witness had become reluctant and surly. When served for the umpteenth time at her residence in Lee's Summit, Missouri, Minnie Blackburn was succinct. She told County Marshall H.C. Staffman, "I've been sick. I don't have the money to make the trip. I'm not coming."[14] By August 23, 1919, Minnie had married a man by the name of Lankford. She just wanted to be done with Charlie and move on with her life. But those infernal deputies, dispatched like clockwork at the request of Sid Roach, kept knocking upon her door, month after month, year after year. "My God, will it never end?"

After the second mistrial, the defense pounced.

In January of 1921, Farris, Mayfield, and Donnelly filed a motion with Judge Skinker asking him to dismiss the charges against their client. They pointed out that a majority of the jurors in both retrials had voted to acquit. They noted the "cost and expense" of bringing "a great many" witnesses from different counties and "some of them live in other states." They then sprung their hole card. They reminded the good Judge that he had made an entry on the docket after the most recent mistrial that the case was to be "continued generally." They continued:

"It is the practice and custom in this state where a criminal case has been continued generally after two or more mistrials of the same, to dismiss the same and not require the defendant to defend the same any longer."[15]

The prosecution seemed baffled. They had misunderstood the consequences of agreeing that the case be "continued generally" without the setting of a new trial date. The defense argued that this was tantamount to a dismissal of charges. In May of 1921, with Congressman Sid Roach ensconced in Washington D.C., the new Camden County Prosecutor, Charles Calkin, along with trusty Claude Mayfield, showed up in Judge Skinker's court. In a hand-scrawled motion, they asked Judge Skinker to set aside his order "continuing the case generally." Their reason? The order had been made by mistake. It was pretty lame, but Skinker bought it. "The motion to dismiss is overruled."[16] He then set a new trial date for September.

Charlie Blackburn had been feeling a whole lot better about things. Led by his attorneys to believe that his troubles were over, he had left Missouri, taking up residence in California. He should have known better. When his presence was "undetermined on inquiry," Skinker issued an *alias capias* warrant for his arrest. The long arm of the law found him not in California but in Kansas City, Missouri, where he may have been visiting his 17-year-old son Ray, still living with his mother. Charlie was arrested and transported to the Webster County jail to await a fourth trial, now set for the third Monday in September.[17] Reliably, his Uncle Smith and brother Bob posted the $10,000 bond to get him released.

In September, with jurors summoned and witnesses subpoenaed, the case was continued until the first Monday in November. Congressman Roach was not present, but the fight over "general continuance" raged on. Another motion for dismissal was submitted by the defense repeating their earlier contentions and arguing with some indignation that:

". . . this cause was by agreement made with the Prosecuting Attorney of Camden County, Missouri, and the defendant's attorneys, continued generally, and was so entered upon its docket, *with the understanding that the case should never be retried, and should be dismissed* [emphasis added] and that the defendant, acting upon said agreement left the State of Missouri, and in good faith was living in the State of California, when attorneys for the State, without notice to this defendant or his counsel appeared in this court, and made application to it to have said cause reinstated and redocketed, which the court did. . . ."[18]

Congressman Roach fired back with a sworn affidavit, filed with Judge Skinker, stating that:

". . . during the period of time which the above cause has been pending in this court up to June 1, 1921, that affiant was Prosecuting Attorney for Camden County, Missouri and that as such officer *he never at any time made any agreement that said cause was not to be again tried or was to be dismissed, and never authorized any such agreement to be made by any of the Counsel associated with him in the case* [emphasis added]. Affiant states that he and Hon. Frank H. Farris had some talk as to the disposition that might be made of the case in event of mistrial, but that *no agreement was made or even sought to be made that same was to be dismissed*[19] [emphasis added].

Country comedian Jerry Clower once told a wonderful joke about himself and his buddy Marcel. They were out coon hunting one night and treed a big coon. Marcel climbs up the tree to shake the coon out, but when he gets up there, he finds out it is a lynx, not a coon, and it gets after Marcel and is about to tear him up. Marcel hollers down at Jerry, "Shoot, shoot, this thang is killin me!"

Jerry hollers back, "I'm afraid to shoot, I might hit you."

Marcel hollers back down, "Shoot up here amongst us; one of us has got to have some relief."[20]

Relief—that's what everybody needed. The judge, jurors, and legions of tormented witnesses needed it. Sweet relief. The gritty, cinder-strewn town of Stoutland needed it. Even Simp and Ben Francis needed it. Minnie Blackburn was surely having fainting conniption fits and needed it badly. The soothing balm of blessed relief. Charlie Blackburn, teetering at the precipice of death or life imprisonment for nearly six years, could certainly use some relief. Sid Roach and Frank Farris, each as tough as the other was stout, needed a closing bell. Like arm-weary pugilists in the fifteenth round, unable to raise their gloves, they glared at each other and needed it badly. Yes, sweet relief.

And yes, there was one more trial. Saturday, November 12, 1921, six years and two days after the killing of Jasper Francis, a third Webster County jury reported itself "unable to reach a verdict." For the third time, Judge Skinker declared a mistrial and again ordered the case "continued generally."[21] This time all the parties understood what that meant. Although the case was not formally dismissed, Charlie Blackburn would never again be tried unless new evidence was found. For 81 years, no one went looking for any. Never found "not guilty," the sword of Damocles would hang over Charlie for the rest of his life.

Epilogue

Charlie Blackburn died October 22, 1964, at the age of 91 years, 8 months, and 4 days. He had outlived Jasper Jacob "Jap" Francis by almost 49 years. His grave in Fairhaven Memorial Park, Santa Ana, California, is marked with a surface monument deemed "basic" by the caretakers of those lush and impeccably manicured 70 acres. A promotional brochure boasts of "1,000 trees originating from around the world" and membership in the "coveted" American Association of Botanical Gardens and Arboreta. Fairhaven guides point with pride to the mausoleum, replete with marble, gilt, and Tiffany stained-glass windows. Yes, Charlie lies with the "old money" of Orange County. The pioneers, the builders, the captains of industry. His unpolished 12" x 24" stone is predictably black and appears to be some sort of basalt. The etched name and dates are as blurred as Charlie's enigmatic past. It is a monument to a man whose name and deeds are all but forgotten.

Charlie died at the Golden Age Convalescent Hospital in Pomona of "medulary failure, sepsis, and lobar pneumonia" with contributing factors "age, inanition, and debilitation."[1] It was the picture of a comatose patient, slowly suffocating from pneumonic-fluid buildup in the lungs. Finally, starved for oxygen, the "old brain" malfunctions and dies. Without its autonomic signals to the lungs to breath and the heart to beat, a deep sleep slides into death. An old man with a worn-out body had died. There was no deathbed confession. The panting and wheezing just stopped.

The Blackburn Family Speaks

Soft-spoken Robert "Bob" Blackburn of Citrus Heights California, near Sacramento, remembers "Uncle Charlie" very well. Bob, an 80-plus-year-old navy veteran of WWII, was extraordinarily gracious and helpful in tracing Charlie Blackburn's life after his last murder trial in Missouri. Bob is the son of Charlie Blackburn's youngest brother, Lynn, 26 years Charlie's junior. Bob's account follows:[2]

Bob was a teenager when first acquainted with Charlie. Sometime before his third trial in September of 1920, Charlie came to live with Bob's newly wedded parents, Lynn and Edith Blackburn in Escondido. Bob recalls that his dad mentioned accompanying Charlie back to Missouri for at least one of his trials. While awaiting the trial date, both Lynn and Charlie worked on a Missouri farm that may have belonged to one of Charlie's lawyers.

Bob Blackburn recalls his father saying Mack and Dolly Blackburn "mortgaged the farm, sold off the stock and spent every dollar they had trying to get Charlie exonerated" from the Missouri murder charge. Nearly bankrupt, Mack and Dolly uprooted the family and moved to Ada, Oklahoma, "where they didn't do too well." Pulling up stakes again, they "landed in Escondido, California," where they stayed. California was not kind to Mack Blackburn. The old man was hit and killed by a car "driven by a kid" in downtown Orange in 1939.

While living with Lynn and Edith Blackburn, Charlie had a "run-in" with his brother Gladys, variously known as "Purg," "Guy," and "Jack." Like Johnny Cash's "Boy Named Sue," a boy named "Gladys" learned to use his fists early in life. Remembered as a volatile and unpleasant man, Purg took offense at Charlie giving the bassinet holding Purg and his wife's newborn child a kick. Setting on the floor, Charlie deemed it to be "in the way." According to Bob, his Blackburn uncles had short tempers and tended to "personalize" arguments. The "run-in" resulted in Charlie having Purg arrested and jailed for a period of time. Being on the dispensing end of an arrest warrant must have been an odd sensation for Charlie. Shortly thereafter, without fanfare or farewell, Charlie Blackburn disappeared for 15 or 20 years. No one knew where he was or whether he was alive or dead. As a boy, Bob remembers his father sadly wondering aloud, "I wonder where Charlie is?"

In the mid 1930s, during Charlie's long disappearance, his son, Ray Blackburn, surfaced in California. The 1930 census shows 27-year-old Robert R. Blackburn living in a lodging house in Kansas City, Missouri, "unemployed" and doing "odd jobs." The Depression was on and things were tough, but it seems Ray Blackburn was well on his way to becoming a con man and a drunk. Ray Blackburn tracked down his California relatives and, claiming to be destitute and sick with tuberculosis, begged for the money to transport himself and his wife to California. His uncles, aunts, and cousins dug deeply and even "sold some jewelry" to rescue the poor fellow and bring him to a better climate in California. He arrived in about 1935, accompanied by "an Indian woman" who quickly disappeared. Ray seemed in excellent health with no symptoms of tuberculosis. He was just the "spoiled rotten" child of Charlie and Minnie that everyone remembered.

Ray lived and mooched off his Uncle Lynn and Aunt Edith for some time. Eventually, Lynn bought Ray a car, thinking it would improve his employment prospects. Ray set off with the car, claiming he was going "junking" for scrap metals to sell. He promptly got drunk and wrecked the car in San Diego. When the authorities called Lynn to see if he wished to bail Ray out of jail, Lynn thought for a moment and then quietly told them to "leave him there." Robert Ray Blackburn was never heard from again.

In 1939 or 1940, Charlie Blackburn reappeared. Like the "prodigal son," he was joyfully welcomed by the family back into the fold. He related a few "interesting" stories from his long sojourn. A taciturn man by nature, most of his missing years went unreported. The family presumed that he had worked as an itinerant "hand" on ranches and citrus farms up and down the valleys and coastal plains of California. But he apparently told his nephew, Bob Bloomer, son of his sister, Maude "Maudie" (Blackburn) Bloomer, a little more. Actually, a lot more.

In a videotape provided the author by Donna (Bloomer) Crim, great-niece of Charlie Blackburn, "Uncle Bob" Bloomer (now deceased), for the benefit of family assembled, once sketched the history of the Blackburn family. Some of it is demonstrably incorrect or embellished, but none seems entirely hatched from imagination. Bloomer said that after being let go by Missouri authorities, "Uncle Charlie" had gone into the sheep business with a partner near Fruita, Colorado. Fruita is in ruggedly wild country on the border of Colorado and Utah. One day, returning from town, Charlie and his sidekick found four cowboys with rifles in the process of shooting their sheep. Charlie then "shot two of them" (the cowboys).

Afraid they had "started a big fuss," Charlie immediately "left on foot so he could not be tracked," finding his way through wild country to Salt Lake and eventually back to California.

A fanciful story told to entertain the kids? Maybe. But Fruita and environs has a long history of violence over the grazing rights of cattlemen and sheep herders. Historians say that most such violence had abated in the area by the 1920s and 1930s. A thorough search of local newspapers and other records disclosed no mention of the incident.[3] Some speculate that the shooting could have happened at a remote location, possibly over the state line in Utah. Maybe the cowboys were itinerants, never reported missing by those who sent them on such an illegal mission. Were their bones left to bleach in the sun of that desolate country? If this story is believed, Charlie and his partner likely ran from the wrath of cattle ranchers seeking retribution. This tale was Charlie's version. There may have been another story—a very different one.

In 2003, the author met with the lovely and gracious Donna (Bloomer) Crim and her husband, Jim, on their ranch in the foothills of the Sierra Nevadas east of Sacramento. Donna Crim owned two things that were priceless for the production of this book and only she possessed them. Donna distinctly remembered what Charlie Blackburn looked like *and* she is an accomplished portrait artist. With no extant photos of Charlie, the author was overjoyed to learn that Donna could produce his image. Her detailed recollection was:

"He had the milky white skin [of the Blackburns] but the sun played spots and ruddiness on his complexion . . . unlike his brother Purg, Charlie had blue eyes and they were very blue. His hair was white when I knew him, and I didn't know that he had sandy colored hair. He looked quite a bit like Uncle Purg, but his face was not quite as long, and he did not have the puppy-dog eyes that Purg had. Their mouths were almost identical. *They had pursed lips, always slightly openmouthed* [emphasis added], and Charlie had a parrot nose. And yes, there was a fairly deep cleft in his chin. Purg had a very weak chin, and though Charlie did not have a nice, strong jaw line when he was an old man, it was stronger than Purg's."[4]

Confirmed by Bob Blackburn, Donna's creation, in the form of a color portrait, appears on the cover of this book. Thank you,

Donna! Donna also cooks great Mexican food and can bake a mean lemon meringue pie.

As a slender, doe-eyed teenager, Donna Bloomer lived for some years with her widowed Grandma "Maudie" Bloomer. During those years, in the late '50s and early '60s, Charlie Blackburn made his home there as well. As an artist, Donna's keen powers of observation give unique insights into the aged Charlie Blackburn and maybe the younger man as well. In her own words:

"The preliminary sketch of Uncle Charlie just seemed to flow from the end of my pencil. I sat down with paper and pencil and said, 'Come on, Charlie; help me out.' I think it is very close.

"He [Charlie] received a small pension, probably social security, and he gave my grandma $100 a month for his care. His care was very intense, and sometimes around the clock. When he was ill, he would stay in bed for days, without a bite of food or a drink of water. I didn't know how he could possibly live, and then suddenly he was back!

"This was Charlie's routine and it did not vary unless he was abed. Around 6 A.M., he would shuffle down the hall and go straight to the head of the table. He was always fully dressed in button-down front shirt, brown slacks with suspenders to hold them in place, and his leather slippers. Everything was catered around his place. The table was always set with the 'Franciscan Desert Rose' china, and coffee was served in a china cup in a saucer. The clatter of china would begin, as his hands shook violently. Breakfast was always very hearty with bacon, oats, eggs, and toast or biscuits. He went straight from his place at the table to his chair for the day. Other than visiting the bathroom once or twice a day, he never moved. He never went outside. His radio would get tuned to the horse races and he would get his wad of tobacco going. . . .

"*Then at some point in the day his battle would start. He would start out mumbling to himself, then it would get louder and he would occasionally shout out. He fought out loud and flung his fists and he cursed—it was apparent that he was in one heck of a fight. 'It was a cattle deal gone wrong,' Grandma would say. I learned to tune him out, as we all in the family tuned him out, and just left him in his own world*[5] [emphasis added].

What horror was it that Charlie Blackburn relived over and over in his daytime nightmares? Was it just the mad ravings of an old demented man? Donna Crim doesn't think so.

"Strange, but I never thought of Charlie as being demented, he seemed quite in tune to everything that was going on in our house . . . until he went to his chair and slipped into that 'other world.'[6]

Repressed memories of the murder? If he committed the violence on Jasper Francis, it hadn't been much of a struggle, and it certainly was not a fistfight. "Surrounded by a mob" in Stoutland? Maybe. A man condemned to battle each day of his life against taunting bullies who had come for him. Come to force that rough hemp rope over his head and draw it tightly under his chin. Or maybe it was prison assaults. Offenses in which he was overpowered and rendered helpless by men who violated his manliness. Men for whom he harbored a seething hatred, without limit and undiminished by time.

"My grandmother nurtured and fussed over him as if he was the most important person in the world, but he lived out the years that I knew him as a tortured soul and never at peace!

"Grandma maintained that Charlie's life was ruined over a crime that he did not commit. That he lost everything, including his family, and also their parents spent every penny they had defending him. I never questioned his innocence, as Grandma's word was all I needed."[7]

Charlie Blackburn may or may not have been a man killer but he was a human being—not without pity or generosity. Donna Crim continues:

"One morning after the sprinklers had run on the lawn, I found a raw baby bird glistening with water and lying in the grass. . . . I found a shallow box, made a nice soft nest and planned my strategy on how I was going to keep it alive. I decided to use raw hamburger soaked in warm water and I would use tweezers to mimic mama bird's beak. The little bird flourished!

"Charlie observed everything I did for the bird. When the bird feathered out, I moved it to a wire cage on a stand and sat it close to Charlie. That sort of made him the guardian of the bird.It was a tiny little sparrow. I would take the bird out for flying lessons and

Charlie and Grandma observed all of this from the front windows. . . . Soon the bird was flying but I couldn't get away from 'Chirpie.' She would fly around over the yard and right back to my shoulder.

"Summer ended and I returned to my school schedule. Grandma had all her instructions of what to feed Chirpie but the bird went into a slump—it would not eat or drink while I was gone. The first thing that Charlie would do when I came home is point to Chirpie with a real look of concern. . . . When I would open the cage door, the bird would show signs of life once again and Chirpie would eat and drink.

"My days grew very long as I took a job after school and I did not get home until quite late. Charlie continued to show great concern for the bird . . . not talking, just pointing. *Then I bounced into the house one day after work and Charlie [acted] as if he had lost the only friend he ever had. Chirpie was lying dead in the bottom of the cage. I feel that his huge concern was over how it would affect me . . .* [8] [emphasis added]."

Imprisoned in his own "Alcatraz" of tortured memories and physical debilitation from advanced Parkinson's disease, Charlie Blackburn could show concern for a tiny bird and the girl who loved it. Old age and impending death may also have loosed a streak of generosity that his nephew, Bob, still finds hard to imagine. Donna Crim adds:

"I had just graduated from high school and [had] taken a job in Covina, California, a few miles away. I had bought my first car with money that I had earned working after school. My car quit, just as I was depending upon it for my job. I sat at the table with Grandma, just stewing and worrying about what I was going to do. There was a 52 Mercury for sale across the street. They wanted $200 for it. Grandma nor I had any way of getting that much money. . . . *I just about fainted when Charlie reached for his back pocket, pulled out his wallet, and he took two $100 bills out and handed them to me* [emphasis added]. Never in my life, to that point, had anyone but my grandma been that generous. I shall never forget that act of kindness. I made sure that I paid back every penny . . . but he had no way of knowing the money would come back. He gave [it] freely."[9]

Donna recalls an even earlier time in her life:

"As a very young girl, I can remember when Charlie would come to Grandma's house and stay a few days or weeks. His routine was about the same as when he came to stay permanently. . . . My sister Dianne and I spent a lot of time with Grandma Maude, and when Charlie was there, she warned that we were not allowed to go near his chair. I was fascinated with the scene that he created and when Grandma wasn't looking, I always danced around as close to him as I could get. He would hold his finger out for me to take his hand. . . . I would do just that. He never did anything inappropriate. He seemed to thoroughly enjoy my company."[10]

Donna Crim's late-life version of Charlie Blackburn is that of an elderly man, coherent and aware, but severely debilitated and mainly uncommunicative. Aside from his "other world" angry fits and his sister's royal treatment (perhaps still catering to his lifelong vanity and feelings of self-importance), we have few clues of what thoughts mulled in Charlie's aged head. It can be said that with Parkinson's shuffling and shaking him toward a certain death, the small but touching acts of kindness described by Donna are remarkable and somehow pityingly redeeming.

"Personally, I didn't care much for him," was Bob Blackburn's teenaged view of "Uncle Charlie" some 20 years earlier. "Although she was nice to him, my mother never liked having Charlie around. She hated the fact that Charlie was always negative—always a pessimist. When my cousin and I went into the service, Mother expressed the optimistic view that we would both come back alive. Charlie offered, 'They'll never make it back!'"[11]

According to Bob Blackburn, his Uncle Charlie never remarried nor expressed any interest in women. He was never again known to be in trouble with the law and had no drinking or gambling habits. For years, he lived in a little trailer parked on Lynn Blackburn's property. He always wore khaki work pants, suspenders, and matching shirt. He smoked a pipe, chewed tobacco, and when not listening to horse races on the radio, "just sat and stared into space." Since Charlie was a horseman and enjoyed the races, Lynn would occasionally take Charlie to the new racetrack at Riverside. They would also make an annual trek to Santa Anita. Charlie never bet on the horses, just watched. He once took a job at a nearby horse-breeding farm.[12]

"Charlie was thrifty, you couldn't pry a dollar out of him," was Bob Blackburn's recollection. Once, when Bob was 17- or 18-years-old, he drove Charlie "up to Whittier, California, where his sister met him there. He didn't offer to pay for the gas."[13]

Bob's most vivid memory of Charlie was supplied by his father, Lynn Blackburn. When Bob was about 16, he got into a disagreement with his Uncle "Purg" (It seems that Purg and disagreements went hand in hand.) When he told his dad about it, Lynn said, *"Oh, I wouldn't worry too much about what Purg says, but don't cross Charlie. . . . He'll kill you!"*[14] [emphasis added].

Lynn Blackburn's earnest advice to his young son speaks volumes. His chilling words still echo persuasively over a chasm of time. Lynn accompanied his brother to Missouri for one of his murder trials and helped "work off" his legal bills. Lynn believed Charlie to be a dangerous man—one not to be fooled with. No man would idly utter such words about a brother if he didn't believe them. *"Don't cross Charlie. . . . He'll kill you!"*

Bob Blackburn and Donna Crim agree on one thing. Neither believes that the Charlie they knew had the capacity to plan and execute a complicated fraud and murder scheme. Speaking of Sam, Jasper Francis's horse, Donna said:

"I am an animal lover too, but it is what happened to Jasper that really broke my heart. Such a cold and calculated crime was committed. It brings tears to my eyes, as it seems that Uncle Charlie committed this crime. . . . It certainly explains the extreme torment that he was in. . . . I think that perhaps the Francis murder occurred as a snowball effect. I believe it was impulsive. If Charlie had any great intellect, he would have lived his life differently."[15]

The Handwriting Expert

"I didn't like Charlie Blackburn at all—he has a vanity that won't quit and doesn't care what other people think. He is full of deceit and is weak in the morals and ethics area. He is impulsive and prone to erratic behavior. He has a belief that he can do no wrong."[16]

It seemed the perfect psychological profile of a killer. The above quoted comments are those of Betty Ann Butts, a certified graphoanalyist and member of the International Graphoanalysis

Society. Betty was commissioned by the author to do blind analyses of the signatures of four men associated with the Blackburn trials: Charlie Blackburn, Sam Paxton, John Fudge, and R.A. Corbett. She was provided two signature samples for each and the approximate dates of those signatures. Nothing else. During Charlie Blackburn's trials for murder, Sam Paxton was the Chief Deputy Sheriff of Camden County. John Fudge and R.A. Corbett were the respective Circuit Clerks of Camden and Webster Counties. Betty qualified her analyses by asserting:

> Graphoanalysis is a trademarked process of stroke identification to determine character and personality of an individual. Thus I can only evaluate the strokes presented. A signature is limited to what is evident.[17]

Predictably, Betty Butts's analysis of Fudge's and Corbett's signatures revealed traits that one might expect among elected public officials, all certified bureaucrats:

> Fudge—Friendly and emotionally responsive . . . good self-esteem . . . proud of his accomplishments and desires more responsibility. He will study the facts long enough to find what he needs to know, but he has limited imagination. . . . To preserve his ego, he may rationalize and make excuses to himself for any limitations he may have. He is honest with others. He is sociable and sincere.
>
> Corbett—Emotionally responsive to others . . . He is direct and honest in his approach to others. . . . He may at times be domineering with his wit and sarcasm. He also can be critical and may become irritable with others. He takes pride in his accomplishments. He is proud, dignified, and knowledgeable.[18]

These are fellows with whom you could trust your money and your daughters. Maybe even your life. As bosses, they might be a bit of a "pain," and to protect their jobs they would practice CYA in the best military tradition. But these two barely move the meter when it comes to homicidal tendencies.

What about brash, mustachioed, pistol-toting, spur-jangling, Slim-Pickens-talking Deputy Sam Paxton?

> Paxton—Emotionally responsive and very impulsive. At times his behavior is unpredictable. However, his emotions are somewhat controlled by his self-esteem and dignity. He is capable of investigating and analyzing factual information to arrive at his conclusions. He has high goals and ambitions, and he takes pride in reaching his goals. He has a strong, deep-seated emotional resentment from some past imposition or infraction, and he is not likely to forget it. . . . He is a private and hardworking man with a grudge.[19]

Well, it seems that Sam Paxton just might shoot somebody. He had. All in the line of duty of course. But what about: "dignity . . . self-esteem . . . investigating . . . analyzing factual information" and "high goals and ambitions?" For a law-enforcement officer these seem very laudable attributes. His capacity for violence seemed to push the danger dial but necessarily so. As for a grudge? Sam Paxton probably just hated crooks and killers.

And what of Charlie Blackburn? In addition to the traits of vanity, deceit, weak ethics, and morals, Betty Butts said:

> Blackburn—A slight tremor in Mr. Blackburn's handwriting would suggest some medical problem [excused twice from trials for medical reasons]. At this time, his energy level is low [jailed or on bond while charged with murder]. He is emotionally expressive and perhaps somewhat impulsive. He does not take time to research details or ask questions. At times, his behavior may appear erratic to others. He is restricted in philosophical imagination and may twist ideas to fit his own beliefs. He may feel culturally above others. He is opinionated

> and strongly communicates these opinions. When he makes up his mind on anything, he will stubbornly defend his position. He can be argumentative and defiant. One might call him cantankerous.[20]

It is an opinion offered without a single positive observation. Could such a person have twisted and distorted ethical boundaries enough to convince themselves they were "entitled" to Jasper Francis's money? A kind of *noblesse proprietaire droit*? It describes a man who needn't frame the whole plan before acting. Worry about the end game later.

A comment by Donna Crim is instructive: "The entire Blackburn family was very 'haughty.' I was always made to think that I was better than anyone else. . . . I knew better and I knew that it went way back to the Blackburn family. My Grandma Maude had been sent to a fine finishing school. She dressed for the day like the President was coming. . . ."[21]

Graphology has never been validated with an empirical scientific approach. At best, it is an art—not a science. But when a practitioner like Betty Butts can, without one self-doubt, select a likely "bad guy" out of a lineup of known "good guys," one must take note.

A Medical Examiner Weighs In

An expert with a startling theory about the murder must be heard. The author submitted all relevant newspaper articles, as well as the trial testimony by examining physicians Carlton and Pool, to Dr. Michael Graham, M.D., Chief Medical Examiner for the City of St. Louis. Dr. Graham is a Professor at St. Louis University School of Medicine and Co-Director, Division of Forensic and Environmental Pathology. In a report dated April 10, 2007, he states:

> Although assessment of the injuries is hindered by the lack of a verifiable, detailed, and comprehensive description of the wounds or photographs of the trauma, reasonable inferences can be made on the basis of the available information.

Given that the injuries, consisting of multiple skull fractures, were considered the result of a beating with a blunt object, Dr. Graham was surprised and puzzled by the examining physicians' inability to find any external abrasions or lacerations of Jasper Francis's skull. The skin was reportedly not broken except where the bullet entered and exited. Dr. Graham's theory is that the large caliber projectile, fired from a pistol, rifle or shotgun, with the muzzle held at or on the body surface (the hair was described as singed and the skin hardened at the entry point) may very well have "created cranial pressures and energy sufficient to have caused the numerous skull fractures." In other words, the observed fractures were the result of the skull breaking from within rather than external blows from without. Graham continues:

> The broken neck (if, in fact, it was truly broken and not simply lax as a result of decomposition) and nose (if any damage unrelated to gunshot-related facial bone fractures) could be explained by an uncontrolled fall of the body or the indelicate handling of the partially decomposed corpse when removed.

Graham suggests the following possible murder scenario:

> Both men were standing, facing each other. In near darkness, the killer produced a gun and pointed it at the victim. In an act of avoidance, the victim turned approximately a quarter-turn to his left, exposing the right side of his neck. The killer placed the gun muzzle on or near the mastoid bone, 1½ inches below the right ear, and pulled the trigger. The bullet took a leftward and possibly slightly upward path through the neck, inflicting major trauma to bone and soft tissue, likely perforating one or more of the pharynx, larynx, glottis, or epiglottis, and possibly disrupting major blood vessels such as the carotid arteries and jugular veins and possibly nicking the vertebral column. Perforation of the mastoid bone (and possibly other parts of the skull base)

> and the propulsion of muzzle discharge gasses into the wound could have resulted in extensive damage to the skull and facial bones, along with secondary damage to the brain.
>
> The bullet exited just behind the angle of the left jaw, creating a large exit wound. The victim likely immediately fell to the ground, and without moving from that spot, rapidly died. Death likely involved some combination of extensive bleeding, blockage of the airway by blood and damage to the brain associated with the fracturing of the skull. *The victim could have conceivably articulated sounds until rendered unconscious and, after becoming unconscious, made gurgling sounds from aspiration of blood or the accumulation of fluid (edema) in the lungs while dying (the so called "death rattle")* [emphasis added].

If Dr. Graham's theory is correct, Jasper Francis's death resulted only from the gunshot wound and not a beating with a club or other object. The Linn Creek jury that convicted Charlie Blackburn found him guilty only on the count premised upon death resulting from a "heavy instrument or weapon," not the gunshot. If he died only from the gunshot, one could argue that no jury ever truly found Charlie guilty of the murder of Jasper Francis. Some 91 years after the killing, it is a distinction without a difference.

A Search for New Evidence

If one draws a straight line on a map from the place where Sam was tied in a ravine east of the Linn Creek Road and follows it to the back door of Charlie Blackburn's farmhouse, the line passes directly by the old water well dug by Dick Craddock in the 1860s. The well has not been used for human consumption for a very long time. The well opening is sealed with a rough aggregate concrete retainer with a circular opening at the top. The thought occurred to the author's mother that if Charlie Blackburn did the deed, he may have used the well to quickly dispose of items taken from Jasper Francis's body. His wallet, his valise with the little red ledger-book inside, his velvet collared overcoat, and possibly the murder weapon itself; all weighted and sent to the bottom.

The prospects of recovering anything submerged in water for so long seemed remote. But the author could not resist the adventure of rolling the dice on a one-in-a-thousand chance. Maybe the crime could be solved once and for all. What might be found? An old gun barrel of the proper caliber? Matching buttons of a Chesterfield coat of the era? Or best of all, a soggy lump buried in the muck—a waterlogged leather wallet. Dreams of using space-age "freeze dry" technology to restore it and extracting papers with Jasper Francis's name on it were tempting.

Charlie Blackburn's well is on a portion of the Blackburn farm owned by county road maintainer Ricky Rogers. Only a couple years earlier, Ricky had found a solid gold Waltham pocket watch stuck in the dirt along the same line on the map. The watch's serial number disclosed it had been made in 1888, well before the murder. Although Jasper Francis's watch was found on his body, could Charlie Blackburn, in haste to return home after the killing, have dropped his own watch? Lebanon jeweler Blake Norman examined the lovely timepiece but could find no clues to its owner.

A financial payment and a liability release permitted a full-fledged "archeological dig" expedition to be organized. Large screening trays capable of processing tons of mud were custom-built from lumber and hardware cloth. Generators sufficient to power a small city were rented, along with numerous large and small pumps. Hand tools of every description, shoring lumber, power weed whacker to clear the high weeds, ropes, block and tackle, large trash cans to store wash water, and rescue ladders were all required. A 500-pound capacity, metal tripod derrick was assembled over the well. Large and small hoses were strewn everywhere. A 150-mph leaf blower to ventilate the well was tested. Hand disinfectant, bug spray, and sealable plastic tubs filled with distilled water in which to place our ancient waterlogged finds were laid out. And all of this hauled to the site by a 20-foot diesel-powered truck. We were ready—really ready.

Oh, yes, genuine Amighetti Italian sandwiches, chips, cookies, fruit, and pop headlined our planned high-calorie lunch. Oceans of iced bottled water stood ready to stave off dehydration in the expected 90-plus degree July heat. A festive, bright blue tent was erected to shield the workers from the broiling sun.

And what of the thick-bodied, cottonmouthed snakes reported by the Rogers to frequent the vicinity? When the great safari pulled in and set up for the night, they high-tailed it down the nearby stream. Our heavy vehicles, throbbing motors and thousands of human footfalls must have been as terrifying as the great New Madrid earthquakes of 1811 and 1812, those "tremblors" that sent the great Mississippi's waters roaring backward toward their origins in the lakes of Minnesota. Ask any Missourian, they all tell the same story with a straight face.

And the crew? What an intrepid bunch! James Wright, whose Eagle Scout knots may have been a life saver (literally). Ted Hamilton stood ready with his metal detector. Joe Rogers, son Ricky, and grandson 10-year-old Joseph, were willing hands. Baptist Minister Dan Sample, who moonlights as a Stoutland High School teacher, had enlisted the help of two lovely scholars, Amanda Hill and Kaylah Domer. Curious observers included Jasper Francis, great-nephew of the murdered man of the same name and local historian Bob Barr, a specialist in Stoutland murders. The wives of Joe and Ricky Rogers and hay bailer Bill Peterson stopped by. Two pet dogs, ever alert, stood guard over the proceedings.

At 10:00 A.M. it was showtime. Unwilling to permit anyone else to descend into the well, the author stepped forward. Too late to back out now. Someone had to disappear into the dark cavity, shovel the muck in buckets and send it up by hook and rope. With block and tackle, the crew lowered the author though the narrow opening into a deeply mudded, foul-aired place. It would need to be ventilated every quarter-hour. Rubber boots and a plastic disc used by children for sleigh riding were indispensable. The disc distributed body weight around, preventing the ankles from being sucked beyond retrieval into the mud.

The well was constructed very differently than had been imagined. Not a cylinder at all, its diameter increased with depth, forming a subsurface bell shape. Stacked, unmortared rocks formed the walls, tapering up to the 19-inch opening 10 feet above eye level. Would removal of tons of water and muck weaken the walls? The potential for collapse seemed very real. Only a narrow beam of sunlight from above supplemented a miner's lamp mounted upon a hard hat. Seeping water had to regularly be pumped out. More than once, the thought occurred that Charlie Blackburn's spirit might end this prying into his business with tons of crashing rock and earth. This risky venture would not be repeated!

It seems that vicious thunderstorms descend upon outsiders who come to Stoutland inquiring about the killing of Jasper Francis. This day was no different. A bluish-green squall line moved down from the north at about 2:30 P.M. and all operations ceased. After a one-hour delay, filled with nearby lightning strikes and heavy rain, the crew began anew. Excavating down to a solid rock shelf at the very bottom, the last bucket of mud was sent to the top. The well was "slick as a whistle."

During seven hours of hard labor, 1,000 gallons of water were pumped out of the well. Some 100 cubic feet of extremely fine loam and clay muck were hoisted out in 5-gallon buckets and water washed through 3/8-inch screens. The net find was underwhelming:

- A few tiny animal bones
- A couple of small wooden blocks
- A rusty remnant of a metal food can
- Shard of an old Mason glass jar
- 2 smoothly rounded creek stones likely tossed in by a child
- At the very bottom, a very old waterlogged 14-inch-wide circle-sawn board.

Consoling ourselves, we argued that something had indeed been accomplished. A nagging question had been answered. We now knew that nothing of interest resided in Charlie Blackburn's well. Wearily, we washed ourselves in the nearby stream, reloaded the truck, and began the long trek back to St. Louis. The old Craddock place gives up its secrets grudgingly.

Minnie (Craddock) Blackburn Lankford

Minnie Blackburn's life was shattered by what happened on Rouse Hill. By 1930, she was a single woman, either widowed or divorced. It's safe to say her days of big hats and satin dresses were over. As they say in Stoutland, she had "come down a notch or two." She was laboring as a cook in an Independence, Missouri, café. A census entry classified her as a "lodger" in the rented home of 19-year-old newlyweds William and Margaret Davis. Her connection to the Davises is unknown—perhaps just a cohabitation of convenience during hard times.[22] The woman that the Blackburn family considered "very haughty," "fancy," "high-toned,"[23] and "the most particular person he had ever known"[24] died June 24, 1953, at the age of 72 years and 2 days. She is buried in the Hillhouse Cemetery near Stoutland alongside her infant sons, Clyde and Floyd Blackburn. The babies' stones are identically inscribed:

"Sleep on dear child and take thy rest. In Jesus's arms forever blest."

Sidney Crain Roach

Sid Roach's stint in the U.S. Congress would be brief. He served only two terms, 1921–1925. He was defeated by Democrat William Lester Nelson from Boone County, the incumbent whom he had defeated in 1920. Roach would never hold public office again. After the 1924 election, Roach moved to St. Louis and resumed the practice of law. He died June 29, 1934, in Kansas City, Missouri, while on his way to St. Mary's Hospital to receive treatment for heart disease.[25] He was 58 years old. Wherever Charlie Blackburn was in 1934, his step must have suddenly gotten a little lighter. Maybe he even smiled. His murder case, "continued generally" in Webster County, Missouri, was forgotten. Sid Roach would not be coming for him again.

Sidney Crain Roach's remains lie in the Roach Cemetery, south of Camdenton, Missouri. His impressive monument reads:

AN ABLE LAWYER, STATESMAN AND TRUE AMERICAN HONEST, INDUSTRIOUS AND LOYAL TO HIS FRIENDS

—Erected by his friends

Austin Ivon Lodge

By 1920, the young Camden County Prosecuting Attorney was living in the City of St. Louis practicing law. By 1930, he and his wife Martha had moved to nearby University City.[26]

Frank Hiram Farris

Frank Farris would continue to be a political kingmaker and powerbroker for the rest of his life. But when the last jury of the last Blackburn trial declared itself "unable to reach a verdict," the man had less than five years to live.

Ever ambitious, Farris wanted to be Governor of Missouri. Alternatively, he sought appointment to the Missouri Supreme Court. He would get neither. Maneuvering for both these positions overlapped with his lawyerly duties in the interminable Blackburn case. Farris became more and more reliant upon the young Phil Donnelly to file the motions for continuance, prepare affidavits, and argue motions for dismissal. When an opening appeared in 1919, Governor Gardner would likely have granted Farris's fond wish to be a Supreme Court justice. But there was a problem. The Missouri Constitution prohibited sitting legislators from serving on the court during the period for which they had been elected.[27] The opportunity for political back-scratching on a grand scale had been wisely foreclosed.

Farris then entered the 1920 gubernatorial campaign, but a bitter, running battle with powerful U.S. Senator James Reed hurt his chances. In the Democratic primary election, Farris placed a distant second in a three-man race.[28] Reed actively opposed him, as did Tom Pendergast, political boss of Kansas City. Belatedly, Farris returned to Rolla and a last-minute effort to hold his seat in the Missouri Legislature. This, too, failed.[29]

Frank Farris would not be out of the public eye for long. Like the phoenix rising, the indomitable politician from Rolla would run and win a 1922 campaign for the state senate. Frank Farris was back in business. His Democratic contemporaries recognized a man with potential when they saw one and immediately elected him majority floor leader.[30]

As chairman of the Missouri State Democratic Committee, Senator Farris led his fellow delegates to the Democratic National Convention in New York City in 1924. As the "Boy Orator of the Ozarks," and a supporter of William G. McAdoo, he would give one of three keynote speeches to the throngs assembled in Madison Square Garden.[31] Farris would greet for the last time William Jennings Bryan, the man with whom his oratorical skills were often compared. His party's standard bearer in three failed presidential campaigns, Bryan would also address the convention. His performance was panned because: "Bryan was used to wandering around the stage. He wouldn't stay inside the railings by the microphone and lost his radio audience for most of his speech."[32] Bryan undoubtedly heard Farris's speech, but history records no professional critique. It was the longest convention in U.S. history (lasting 17 days and 103 roll-call votes.) Frank Farris shared the national stage with a paralytic Franklin D. Roosevelt. In placing New York Governor Alfred Smith's name into nomination, Roosevelt dubbed Smith "the happy warrior." The name stuck for the remainder of Smith's career.[33]

The 1924 Democratic convention may have marked the zenith of Senator Frank Hiram Farris's political power. It was a personal *tour de force*. He carried out an especially satisfying act of revenge by leading out-state Democrats in blocking the nomination of a fellow Missourian, Senator James Reed.[34] Reed's presidential ambitions were dashed by a realpolitik cudgel wielded by an embittered Farris.

Frank Farris's personal life was as flamboyant as his political career. He was married three times. His first wife, Anna May (Miller) Farris died of pneumonia in 1906 after bearing the couple's three children, Bessie, Josephine, and Anna May. Farris married St.

Louis divorcée Cora Shanks in the same year, but they divorced in 1922, childless. During the marriage, Farris adopted Shanks's daughter who became Charlotte Shanks Farris.[35] In 1922, he married 25-year-old Bertha Dent, secretary and stenographer in his Rolla law office.[36] The bridegroom was 55. The lovely Miss Dent was the daughter of Rolla storekeepers John and Mary Dent. The Dent family was from Virginia and pioneered a portion of Crawford County that later was named Dent County.[37] In December of 1924, Mary Susan Farris was born to Frank and Bertha Farris. Susan's proud papa "never tired of telling his political and personal friends about the cunning tricks of this baby."[38] Generation-skipping Mary Susan (Farris) Goodwin-Tubbesing is a retired attorney residing in Ballwin, Missouri.

Sadly, little "Sue" Farris and her famous sire were acquainted for less than two years. Frank Hiram Farris died of a "stomach ailment" September 1, 1926. He was 59-years-old. After part of his stomach was removed at the Mayo Clinic in 1925, he recovered enough to resume his law practice. Sadly, the malady returned, claiming his life at his home in Rolla.[39] Extensive articles recapping his career appeared in every major newspaper in the state and on the front page of the *New York Times*. A few were slavishly praiseful, while others were respectful and forgiving of his early career foibles. Many were downright maudlin. None were partisan and mean. Even the Republican-leaning *St. Louis Globe-Democrat* called him:

> A leader willing to make the effort and sacrifices essential to leadership and the Ozarks' ideal of a man of the people. . . . In his consistency to a certain rugged type of Missourian . . . surely there was much to admire. Undoubtedly much said about him was calumny . . . no charge against him was ever established and he played the game out to the end.[40]

"A man of the people." Frank Farris would have loved it. He desired no other epitaph.

The press fingered the likely culprit in Frank Farris's untimely death. The *West Plains Missouri Journal* noted that "Farris was known as a hail fellow and his fondness for the 'cup that cheers and sometimes inebriates' narrowed his usefulness and may have shortened his life."[41] The *St. Louis Post-Dispatch* elaborated: "At one time . . . he determined to 'cut out' alcohol and took a course of treatment in the St. Louis branch of the Keeley Institute. . . . The 'cure' was not permanent."[42]

Frank Farris's funeral was conducted in Parker Hall at the Rolla School of Mines, Sunday, September 5, 1926. Newspaper accounts describe an extravaganza never equaled in Phelps County history:

For three hours, hundreds of mourners filed past the bier. "The funeral was the largest ever held in this section of Missouri." Prominent men from all over the state were present. The St. Louis Police Department sent a ranking four-man contingent. Doctor R. Calvin Dobson of St. Louis, assisted by another minister, conducted a Presbyterian service. A male quartet sang Farris's favorite hymns. The Masons, including Rolla Commandery No. 59, Knights Templar, held their rites at the grave site in the Rolla Cemetery. State Senator Phil M. Donnelly, whom Frank Farris had mentored for 11 years, was an honorary pallbearer. He was accompanied by a large Senatorial committee appointed by the Lieutenant Governor. The Frisco Railroad, for whom Frank Farris was a District Counsel, sent their top executives. Enough flowers to fill four trucks were transported to the cemetery and placed upon the grave. Even in death, Frank Farris was bigger than life.

Phil M. Donnelly

The fresh-faced young attorney, who helped successfully defend Charlie Blackburn, would become Missouri's Governor, elected not just once, but twice. Senator Frank Farris's fondest dream became Donnelly's reality. Farris was surely a valuable friend and advisor of young Donnelly during his early years in the Missouri Legislature. Their mutual respect and friendship were ended only by Farris's death in 1926. Donnelly delivered a stirring eulogy of his friend on the floor of the Missouri Senate.[43] Although admiring and learning from Farris's vast knowledge of Missouri politics, Phil Donnelly was his own man. Sitting at the "foot of the master" requires critical thinking and the making of choices. "Straight-arrow" Donnelly chose wisely.

First elected governor in 1944, Donnelly guided Missouri through a difficult post-WWII transition. Having Harry Truman, the "Man from Missouri," in the White House probably helped a bit. Prohibited by the state's constitution from succeeding himself, Phil Donnelly went back to his Lebanon law practice in 1949. Persuaded to run again in 1952, he won nomination in spite of strong opposition from labor elements in the party, including the St. Louis "Callanan-Shenker machine."[44] Larry Callanan headed the hoodlum-infested steamfitter's union, and attorney Morris Shenker was reputed to be the St. Louis Mob's chief legal shill. In his first administration, Donnelly had taken decisive actions to prevent unionization of the St. Louis Police Department. He had also demanded that federal wage scales for state employees be returned to state control after WWII.[45] Angering organized labor and state employees, the underpinnings of the state Democratic party, was hardly the politic thing to do. But it was the right thing to do.

Republican Dwight D. Eisenhower trounced Democrat Adlai Stevenson in the presidential election of 1952, narrowly carrying Democratic-leaning Missouri by 30,000 votes. In spite of a huge turnout for Eisenhower, Phil Donnelly beat Republican gubernatorial candidate Howard Elliott by 97,000 votes. He bettered the Democratic national ticket by 53,000 votes and even polled ahead of Eisenhower by 24,000 votes.[46] Donnelly had swum against the tide of an unpopular Truman administration, an unpopular Korean War, and Eisenhower, a hugely popular national hero. He had left everyone in his wake. Donnelly proved that a man of character, determined to do the right thing, can still win the hearts and minds of voters. It was a magnificent political victory—perhaps the greatest in Missouri history.

According to his son, Phillip David "Dave" Donnelly, his father believed the "Governor should be the Governor." That he was. In his second term, murder and mayhem prevailed at the state reformatory for juveniles at Boonville. Donnelly fired the reformatory's board of directors (whom he had appointed) and the entire administrative staff. He then put the place in the firm hand of the Missouri State Highway Patrol, led by legendary Colonel Hugh Waggoner. Waggoner reported that the "inmates had taken over the institution." Three months later, things had been tidied up. A new administration and a building program soon brought the facility a high national ranking.[47]

In 1953, Governor Donnelly appointed a young African-American assistant prosecutor to a circuit judgeship in the City of St. Louis. His name was Theodore McMillian. Donnelly's appointment shattered the city judiciary's color barrier. McMillian didn't let Donnelly down. His distinguished legal career was capped with a nomination by President Carter to the Eighth U.S. Circuit Court of Appeals in 1978. Congressional approval took all of twenty minutes. The renowned and revered Judge McMillian would serve there until his death in 2006 at the age of 86.[48]

The most serious challenge faced by Donnelly was a disastrous riot and fire at the state penitentiary at Jefferson City in 1954. It began Saturday evening, September 22 at 6:00 P.M. when 80 hard-core prisoners broke out of a maximum-security cell block and began releasing other inmates, smashing windows in the dining hall and setting fires throughout the prison.[49] By seven o'clock, concerned that the rioters might breech the walls, Donnelly ordered all of Missouri's state highway patrolmen to Jefferson City as soon as possible. The radio call went out and by 11:30 P.M., some 265 troopers had arrived at the scene.[50] With sirens wailing and red lights flashing, they descended upon Jefferson City from every corner of the state at speeds exceeding 100 miles per hour. Patrol veterans state that more than one engine in newly delivered 1954 Ford police interceptor cars were burned up in the urgent dash to the State capitol.[51]

Governor Donnelly, along with Department of Corrections Chief Whitecotton, Prison Warden Eidson, and Highway Patrol Superintendent Waggoner took charge. Amusingly, photographs at the scene show an unarmed Donnelly, dressed in business suit and homburg hat, calmly conferring with officials. Lieutenant Governor James T. Blair came prepared for a shootout. A colonel in WWII, he had pulled on a Sam Browne belt and sported a holstered .45 caliber army-issue pistol.[52]

At 7 A.M. the next morning, Governor Donnelly ordered the highway patrol into the prison yard to put down the riot and arrest the ringleaders. By this time, a battalion of national guardsmen, a contingent of 60 St. Louis police officers and a hodgepodge of local police were on the scene, but Donnelly charged his own state police force with this dangerous assignment.[53] Not thought to have firearms, the inmates certainly possessed knives, clubs, and readily thrown projectiles.

Contemporary news photos show the troopers standing tall in cripsly pressed uniforms. Broad, straight-brimmed "Smokey Bear" hats, gray long-sleeved shirts with knotted necktie tucked away between shirt buttons, navy trousers with electric-blue leg stripes, and mirror-polished, strap-buckled shoes comprised the snappy getup. A black Sam Browne belt, supporting a Smith & Wesson .38 service revolver mounted on a .44 caliber frame, created a professional and intimidating appearance—as intended.

With riot shotguns carried at port arms, the state troopers marched four abreast, fingers on triggers, into the prison yard.[54] It was their finest hour. Long before SWAT teams, they advanced sans helmet or flack jackets. Before departing, they had received clear and concise orders. Superintendent Waggoner is reputed to have barked, "If you meet any resistance, kill 'em all."[55]

"We mean business," the troopers shouted to 400 convicts running loose in B and C halls. One inmate made the mistake of cursing and throwing a heavy object, probably a typewriter, down from a catwalk. He was immediately fired upon and went down with a head wound. The remainder of inmates rushed to their cells and stayed. The officers then moved along to E hall, where the riot's ringleaders had been holed up since 1:00 A.M. "Get back in your cells or you're not going to be able to," was the order. Upon entry, not a man was out of his cell.[56] The riot was over.

The riot's causes still remain murky but the results were not. Two inmates were murdered by other inmates and two killed by law-enforcement officers. Thirty-one inmates and several guards were injured. Six buildings burned,[57] incurring $20 million of damage.[58]

An investigation was launched and instigators were punished. A strong governor had carried out his first responsibility—public protection. With Donnelly's leadership, a $75 million bond issue was passed to improve several state facilities, including the ancient prison that once held Charlie Blackburn.[59]

September 12, 1961, after a series of strokes that left him aware but unable to speak, Phil M. Donnelly died at his home in Lebanon, Missouri. He was 70 years old. Marsh Clark, political editor of the *St. Louis Globe Democrat* had this to say:

"He looked like a governor and, when he was governor, he acted like one. He was tough and serious and feared and respected and, most agree, he was one of the best governors Missouri has ever had."[60]

Phil Donnelly's grave in the family plot in Lebanon's city cemetery is marked only with a small footstone. It reads:

Phil M. Donnelly
Mar. 6, 1891—Sept. 12, 1961
Governor of Missouri
1945/1949   1953/1957

That's all. At first, it seems too little to sum up the man's lifetime of public service and achievement. Upon reflection, simplicity and humility imbue those few words with a certain majesty. Sometimes, less is truly more. "The state wanted to erect a monument for my father at the cemetery, but my mother would not hear of it," wrote Dave Donnelly to the author. Juanita (McFadden) Donnelly got it just right.

The Mayfields and Don Vernon

Donald O. Vernon would continue to reside in Lebanon, Missouri, and practice law. L.C. "Claude" Mayfield and his brother, I.W. "Irwin" Mayfield, would do likewise, although never practicing together. In 1919, Claude Mayfield's son, W.C. "Waldo," moved up the Frisco Line to Maplewood, a suburb of St. Louis. There he practiced law until 1944 when he became a circuit judge. Waldo and Nellie Mayfield's son, Eugene "Gene" Mayfield, would continue the long line of Mayfield lawyers, retiring in 1980 as general counsel of the Pet Milk Company. He now resides on Hilton Head Island, South Carolina. Gene's first cousin, Edgar Mayfield, another grandson of I.W. "Irwin" Mayfield, would become general counsel for Southwestern Bell Telephone Company.[61]

Sam, aka "Sam Hill"

And what of Sam, Jap Francis's fine Missouri Fox-trotter? The only living creature who knew for certain who killed his master died in the late 1930s at the age of about 27 or 28. In human years, he was an "old man," about 81.[62] As he aged, Sam's sorrel coat became sprinkled with gray and he was often mistaken for a roan.[63] After the murder, Sam was adopted by Jap's brother Ben Francis. Ben then passed the horse down to his son Silas. Sam lived out his days as a Francis family pet, roaming the familiar fields where he had arrived as a 2-year-old in about 1912.

As a boy, Silas Francis's son, Jasper Francis (the murdered man's great-nephew and namesake) used to ride the elderly horse several miles to Stoutland to buy a few groceries or to have him shod at Ben Manes's blacksmith shop. By then, Sam was getting pretty stiff, and Silas cautioned his son, "Now you take care of Sam—and don't you dare run him!" Even after 20 years, when Sam approached the scene of the murder on Rouse Hill, he would become nervous, cross to the right side of the road and look to his left. On the return trip, he would repeat the same cautious routine, only in reverse.[64] Sam was determined to never let his rider suffer the same fate as his beloved owner, the long-dead Jasper Francis.

Famous racehorses like Man O'War, Citation, and Secretariat are buried like people in a fancy box on hallowed ground. A stone or maybe even a statute is erected to memorialize their greatness. "Regular" horses on "regular" farms in the 1930s were taken to a distant location and left to Mother Nature. Earth to earth, dust to dust. One winter evening, Sam did not appear at the barn to be fed. A light snow had fallen during the day and it had gotten much colder. A search found Sam lying dead in the snow at a remote corner of a distant field.[65] He had saved his human friends a lot of work. Sam was a mighty good horse.

Postlude

Sometime in the spring of 2000, Ruby (Allee) Wright called her son Alan, who lives in St. Louis. In a burst of excitement uncommon in a lady of fourscore and four years, she said, "I just had to call you; I've finally thought of something that I want to write a book about!"

Alan was not surprised—his mother had already authored two volumes, both written after her 75th year. Curiosity piqued by her enthusiasm and air of expectancy, Alan went for the bait and asked with feigned wonderment, "Gosh, Mom, what's it going to be about?"

Ruby exuded, "It'll be about an old murder that took place over by Stoutland, close to where we lived when I was a kid. Mildred [Ruby's older sister] and I talked about it the last time I saw her before she died."

"Who was murdered and what all happened?" Alan asked.

Ruby then sketched the story.

"A man by the name of Jasper Francis was waylaid and murdered on his way to Stoutland real early one morning. A fellow by the name of Blackburn was arrested and tried for the crime, but he finally got off."

"Mom, that sounds like a pretty run-of-the-mill murder to me; what is it that's got you so excited?"

"I'll tell you what—it was a terribly brutal murder, and it involved forgery and some of the most important people in the community. I remember quite a few of them. Why, one of the lawyers later became the Governor of Missouri, and not only that, Mr. Francis's fine saddlehorse, named Sam, was led down in the woods by the killer and tied to a tree. That horse survived almost two weeks out there with no food nor water and then lived another 20 years. Why, I've seen pictures of kids riding that horse when he must have been 25-years-old."

"Mom, that's going to take an awful lot of work to research and write a book like that—when did this take place?"

"It happened way back in 1915, but I remember my mom and dad talking about it a lot when we lived there," replied Ruby. "The next time you come out, I want you to take me over to Tunney's [Ruby's youngest brother, Gene Tunney Allee]. He knows the murdered man's great-nephew, and maybe we can go by and see him. Besides that, Tunney knows where the killing took place—he can take us right to it."

"You know I'll be happy to go with you, but I'm still surprised that you want to get started on something like this after all these years," surmised Alan.

Impatiently, Ruby replied, "Well, I need to get off of this long-distance line, but there is just one last thing." With her voice lowered in a manner that long experience signaled to Alan that a bombshell was about to land, she spoke slowly and meaningfully, "When I was twelve years old, Mildred and I heard Jasper Francis groaning and trying to call for help!"

"Mom, by 1928, Jasper Francis would have been dead for 13 years!" Alan exclaimed.

"Son, I know, and that's the real reason this book has to be written!" Click.

July 2, 2000

Alan helped his mother into the car at her lovely old sandstone home, "Melody Lane," near Tuscumbia, Missouri. Armed with Uncle Tunney's directions about how best to get to Stoutland and points along the way, Alan nudged his sedan onto State Highway 17, turned left onto Route C and headed south. It was a cloudless morning with the car radio promising highs in the 90s and isolated afternoon thunderstorms.

The first stop would be the Old Liberty Cemetery, some 7 miles from Stoutland. Jasper Jacob Francis is buried there.

"Tunney told me where it is and I want to see his marker—I think I'll be able to sense what kind of person he was."

"No problem," responded Alan. Anxious to please, he wondered just how much insight could be gained by viewing a block of stone. "On the other hand," he said to himself, "Mom has an uncanny ability to predict events—bordering on the psychic. Maybe things are revealed to her that remain hidden from workaday folks like me."

A half-hour and a couple of miscues later, the cemetery was found lying uphill just off a gravel farm road. Dried grass lightly covered the ground from a recent mowing in preparation for "Decoration Day." Still, it had the feel of a place rarely visited. The hum of insects and the distant sound of a farm tractor were the only sounds disturbing the souls sleeping there. Braving the heat and a 100-yard walk over rough terrain, Ruby was determined to stand near Jasper Francis's resting place and touch his tombstone. She confided that she received a sense of inspiration but felt the presence of a great sadness and a certain naïve innocence. Alan snapped Ruby's photo with her hand extended to the lovely pink and gray striated marble. Returning to the welcome cool of the car's air-conditioning, they continued on their way.

Arriving earlier than expected in Stoutland and not wanting to "run in" on Uncle Tunney and his wife during dinner ("lunch" for city folk), Alan parked the car at a small grocery on Main Street. In a dubious state of repair, the building appeared to have had numerous uses in its long life. The premises first appeared deserted, but a woman soon materialized from a back room and cheerfully offered, "Can I help yuh, mister?"

Alan ordered lunch meat and cheese hand-sliced from large rolls pulled from a refrigerated case. A weary motor reluctantly kicked on to replenish the chilled air. Bread, cookies, bananas, and pop rounded out this fulfilling lunch. Engaging the woman in conversation, Alan was met with a barrage of complaints about the heat, humidity, the oddities of folks living in small towns, and numerous other annoyances and perceived slights. While sacking up the items and making change, the lady never missed a beat in her well-practiced commentary. Alan grinned and accommodated by interjecting, "Isn't that the God's truth?" at each pause. Backing out the door and bumping his elbow on the faded "7UP, the Uncola" sign, he was bemused and a little disappointed that the woman had expressed such little interest in a stranger or his business.

Mother and son then drove to the Stoutland Cemetery on the southern edge of town and parked in the shade of a large tree. With air-conditioning running, they enjoyed their little repast. It was a comforting moment for Alan. His mind wandered to many motor trips taken as a child with his parents and older siblings.

"Why, look there," Ruby suddenly exclaimed, "There's Jack Begley!"

Alan glanced about and saw no one.

"No, right there—I remember him well as a kid."

Alan's eyes refocused on the deceased Mr. Begley's tombstone just inside the cemetery fence. Ruby continued:

"Yes, I remember the night that Jack asked to walk with Mildred and me from church in Stoutland as far as where our road turned off. When we got there, he told us girls 'good night,' mounted his horse, and rode at a full gallop over the top of Rouse Hill. We later figured out that he was afraid to travel that hill at night by himself and was looking for a little company. Remember, the Francis murder happened just about right there!"

As the sandwiches disappeared and Alan's thoughts wandered to his favorite Fig Newton cookies, Ruby persisted:

"Son, you know what I told you happened to Mildred and me, but there were all kinds of stories about strange happenings on Rouse Hill. One man said that he was coming down the hill late at night and a strange ball of light followed him almost all the way into town. Dad told me for that for years when farmers drove their cattle through there, they would start to bawl and try to stampede. Word was that one of the prominent merchants arrived at his home in town one evening, pale and shaken and at first refusing to describe what had happened. He finally stammered out that he had heard a horse overtake and pass him as he approached Rouse Hill, "clip-clop, clip-clop, clip-clop," except—there wasn't any horse. Yes, there were lots of stories and I don't know whether to believe them or not, but I sure know what happened to Sis and me.

"I will go to my grave!" said Ruby, with a firmness dismissive of any argument to the contrary, "believing that we heard Jasper Francis trying to call out for help as he lay dying."

Taking their leave of the uncommunicative Mr. Begley, the Wrights drove back through town on Route T, crossed the railroad tracks and arrived at Gene Tunney Allee's small slate-blue house just west of town.

Known by one and all as just "Tunney" (pronounced "Toony"), he was born April 22, 1927, a few months after the handsome and polished Gene Tunney knocked out the vaunted Jack Dempsey in Philadelphia, winning the heavyweight championship of the world. Tunney's older brothers idolized the boxer, and when the baby arrived, they begged that he be named Gene Tunney. And so he was.

Tunney Allee has a likeability and charisma that endears him to people. As Ruby would say, "Tunney will laugh with you or cry with you—whichever you need." Tall, handsome, and slender as a young man, but now weakened and bowed by heart trouble and a couple of car wrecks, Tunney is the first to admit that he is not the man he once was. As a 17-year-old volunteer, he served in the Navy late in WWII aboard the battleship *Maryland*, fighting off kamikaze attacks in the desperate battle for Okinawa. Suffice it to say, Uncle Tunney is a charter member of the "Greatest Generation."

After a brief chat, Tunney grabbed the telephone and rasped, "I'll call Jap and see if he's at home."

"Come right on over" was the hospitable reply.

Inhaling oxygen from a nearby tank, Tunney's fitness for travel seemed doubtful. "Nooooh, I'll go along with you and show you how to get there," he bellowed while unsnapping his oxygen supply. "I don't need this all the time."

Headed north over Rouse Hill, Tunney asked, "What kind of a durned car is this? It's sure a nice one." When told that it was a Mercedes Benz, he slapped his knee and yelled, "Hot damn, I've always wanted to ride in one of these, and I didn't think I would ever get a chance in this life!"

Seven miles and a series of turns later, the group arrived at the home of Jasper Jacob "Jap" Francis, great-nephew and namesake of the murdered man. It was obvious that Tunney and Jap had known each other for a very long time. As children, they had played on their family's neighboring farms and had gone to school together. Tunney well remembered riding "Sam," the murdered man's horse.

Jap Francis is a "salt of the earth" man with no pretenses and an earnest and sincere manner. Addressing him as "Mr. Francis" brings a quick remonstrance to "Just call me Jap." Modest about himself and his accomplishments, he is careful, to a fault, to not tell something untrue or misleading. The old saying, "He doesn't have a lying bone in his body," aptly describes this man.

Ruby and Alan quizzed Jap on a number of points, and he helpfully provided the known history of the Francis family, along with photos and copies of documents pertaining to the murder. Alan scribbled notes furiously.

Thanking him for his help, Alan asked to take Jap's picture. "That's fine," he grinned, "but if I don't put on a clean shirt, my wife will have my hide." Within minutes he reappeared sporting combed hair, a pressed shirt, and a prized rodeo belt buckle, prominently displayed. "My son says these buckles are collectibles, but I don't know—I just like it," mused Jap as he posed for posterity.

The afternoon was growing long as Ruby, Tunney, and Alan took their leave. As they headed east toward Stoutland, tall thunderheads were forming ahead signifying a thunderstorm, not uncommon on hot summer days in the Ozarks.

"Looks like maybe we'll get some rain—we sure need it," opined Tunney, as they approached Rouse Hill. Ruby asked, "Tunney, will you show us about where Jasper Francis was killed?" The car slowed to a crawl as it reached the summit.

"To the best of my knowledge, it was just about right here," Tunney replied from the backseat, pointing to the left side of the road where the woods have been cleared for the construction of an electrical substation. "Yeah, I think he was killed right by the road and dragged down in the woods a-piece. They found his horse tied to a blackjack oak down in a draw way back thatta way," motioning over his left shoulder.

"Alan, you stop here where the Fulbright Road comes in," ordered Ruby. "I want to show you where our old mailbox stood."

Always dutiful, Alan made a right, turned around, and parked in a wide part of the shoulder. A bright green street sign, ill at ease in the rural setting, now labels the "Fulbright" road of Ruby's youth "Keepsake" road.

Cracking the door open before the car had completely stopped, Ruby announced, "I want to stand just where our old mailbox was. I haven't been here in 70 years."

"Fine, let me get a picture of you," said Alan, as he grabbed for his ancient Nikon F camera, "But let's not dawdle; it looks like the storm is coming this way."

Ruby moved with surprising spryness for an 84-year-old whose worn heart had recently been re-plumbed with newfangled stents.

Alan had barely finished fiddling with the F-stops and opened the car door when an old pickup truck with stake railings, suggesting it might be used to move cattle, braked to a halt on the opposite side of Keepsake Road. A slightly built man in his mid-forties with blue eyes, a hooked nose, and thin sandy hair shouted, a little too loudly, "Can I help you!"

Tone and inflection are everything in expressing attitude and intentions. The man's greeting was rude and abrupt, conveying the message: "You're strangers. I don't know what you're doing here. I don't like the looks of it and I wish you would leave."

The man had an odd mannerism of pursing his lips, as if to whistle. Thinking that a little information might clear the air and improve the fellow's disposition, Alan replied, "Oh, no thanks; my mother lived around here many years ago, and I'm just taking her picture where their old mailbox stood."

As Alan maneuvered into a good shooting position, the man spat out the window of his truck and continued ominously, "Mister, I can show you a lot better places to take pictures than right here."

A little irritated, Alan spoke over his shoulder, "No, this will be just fine." After a few moments, the pickup sped off in a hail of flying gravel.

A puff of cool wind kicked dust in Alan's eyes as he knelt and waved his mother closer to a stop sign where the family mailbox had once stood. With blue sky and sun behind him and a roiling black cloud visible overhead, Alan fumbled with the focus and speed settings of the aged camera.

"Mom, on three now, 1-2-3," *click.* "Let's get one more now, just to be—"

The request was shattered by the crackle and ground-shaking boom of a close lightning strike in the woods across the road on Rouse Hill.

"Forget it, Mom; let's get in the car; it's going to rain!" shouted Alan as he slipped the lens cover on the camera and waited with nervous apprehension.

Ruby moved with a casual deliberateness common to those of advanced age. Without explanation, she stopped, turned, and while gazing across the main road, called out, "Son, look at that—I've never seen anything like it!"

Wishing for the safety of the car, Alan reluctantly looked in the indicated direction and noticed the trees on Rouse Hill bent low under what appeared to be a high wind. Only a slight breeze stirred the weeds where Ruby and Alan stood watching this strange line of weather demarcation. Large drops of rain spattered Route T's blacktop surface, instantly vaporizing and creating a rising fog. Then, another thunderous crash of lightning struck a little further up Rouse Hill, and the washing sounds of a hard rain could be heard in the distant trees.

"Mom, let's get out of here—do you want to be killed?" exclaimed Alan, with survival instincts in full alarm.

"Look there! Look at that hail falling across the road over in the woods," spoke an amazingly calm Ruby. "There's not one hail stone falling over here."

It was indeed perfectly dry where they stood, but Alan's patience was at an end. "Mom, get in the car!" yelled Alan.

Startled to the reality of their precarious situation, Ruby acquiesced. "Yes, let's go—Tunney is probably tired of waiting."

Safely settled in the Mercedes, Alan turned and spoke, "Uncle Tunney, did you know that guy in the pickup?"

A blank expression appeared on Tunney's face as he replied, "Noooh, Alan, I didn't notice anybody."

"Why sure, he pulled up right over there and wanted to know what we were doing. Mom, didn't you see that fellow in the pickup truck?"

"No, I didn't see a soul," Ruby responded. "I must have had my back turned."

Shaking his head in disbelief, Alan pulled the car onto Route T, cranked the air conditioner, and headed down the hill toward Stoutland. The rumble of thunder could be heard behind them.

As they turned right to deliver Tunney back to his house, Ruby suddenly shuddered and said, "Son, I believe I'm taking a chill. I think it's time to go home."

Appendix

The Killing of Merritt Fulbright, June 16, 1889

Saturday, June 16, 1889, an Agricultural Wheel meeting at the Turner School, five miles west of Stoutland, was punctuated by gunfire resulting in the immediate death of a local farmer, Merritt Fulbright. Ironically, the "Wheel" was a national organization set up to promote the interests of farmers and help settle disputes.

Fulbright alleged that one Thomas Bohannon had lied about him in saying that Fulbright routinely trespassed himself and his cattle across Bohannon's fields. In the absence of a dated complaint and at the request of several Wheel members, Bohannon agreed to a suggestion that the two make friends and drop the matter. Fulbright refused, saying that he would not give up his complaint and make friends "as long as God let him live," which as it turned out, wasn't very long. Fulbright shouted that Bohannon had lied on him, swearing such lies in open court. Bohannon then said, "You're a liar, Merritt," after which Fulbright advanced, unarmed, upon Bohannon. After warning him three times to stop, Bohannon produced a pistol and fired point-blank, dispatching Fulbright.

Charged with first-degree murder, Bohannon spent a week in jail and was released on bond. He was finally tried on a reduced charge of second-degree manslaughter and was acquitted. The judge strongly suggested that Mr. Bohannon consider relocation from the neighborhood.

The Killing of James O. Manes, November 1, 1889

James O. Manes, the constable of Laclede County's Mayfield Township, was shot in the forehead and killed by Thomas Hendricks at a dance being held at the home of Noah Light, some 2½ miles due east of Stoutland in Laclede County. In his later years, Noah "Node" Light was a well-known "character" in Stoutland. Although this social event was classified as a "dance," any young ladies present must have left early because none were ever asked to testify—perhaps to preserve their excellent reputations.

Manes was apparently not at the dance in an official capacity. Manes and Hendricks knew each other, and witnesses differed as to whether there had ever been any hard feelings between them. Most said the two appeared friendly up to the moment of the shooting. The only thing known for certain was that strong drink was present, either consumed straight or "weakened" with water and sugar.

According to eye witnesses, Hendricks, who had arrived earlier with friend Herman Laquey (pronounced "Lakeway"), walked over to Manes who was outside the building "on the ground at the end of the porch." He exclaimed, "This is the Carterville style!" at which time he pointed his pistol at Manes's forehead and pulled the trigger. Constable Manes was instantly killed. Carterville is a small town on the outskirts of Joplin, some 120 miles southwest of Stoutland. As far as anyone could determine, Carterville had no reputation for such a lethal style of gun-flourishing. Although one witness said Hendricks was not drunk, inebriates are notoriously poor judges of sobriety. Upon inquiring whether he had killed Manes and receiving the unanimous affirmation of those present, Hendricks, who claimed that he did not know the gun was loaded, quickly left the scene—and the state.

S.J. Manes, father of James Manes, offered a reward for the arrest of Hendricks. The Sheriff of adjoining Pulaski County, Thomas Imboden, who had a reputation as a bounty hunter, collected the reward by locating Hendricks in Woodville, Texas, and bringing him back to Missouri. On the lam for more than three years, Hendricks had occupied his time getting married and fathering a child.

Granted a change of venue to Phelps County, Hendricks languished in jail at Rolla and began a hunger strike. His condition having weakened "alarmingly," Hendricks asked for some kind of stimulant at which time he was administered a large "slug" of whiskey. Apparently the alcohol unleashed a ravenous appetite and the hunger strike was ended.

When finally placed on trial, the jury believed Hendricks's story that the shooting was an accident and convicted him only of fourth-degree manslaughter. The judge duly sentenced him to two years in prison. Having escaped the gallows, the wily Mr. Hendricks, unsatisfied with his light sentence, attempted a jailbreak. He was discovered and removed from the jail-yard fence at the point of the jailer's drawn revolver. The charge of attempting to escape added substantially to his sentence.

The Killings of Charles DeBerry and James Osborne in 1894

Friday night, January 19, 1894, 18-year-old James Osborne followed 24-year-old Charles DeBerry, who was in the company of a young lady by the name of Hammer, away from a church box-supper some 4 miles north and west of Stoutland. All were on horseback. Emboldened with hard liquor and jealous of Miss Hammer's attention to DeBerry, young Osborne was said to have repeatedly taunted and "abused" DeBerry. DeBerry then dismounted and "went for Osborne" who stabbed him in the throat with a pocketknife, severing the carotid artery. Osborne lashed his horse and hastily left the scene. Miss Hammer's frantic screams quickly summoned help, but DeBerry expired within a few minutes.

"This murder is one more added to the long list to be laid at the door of whiskey" sermonized the *Linn Creek Reveille*. "From all reports, young Osborne was ordinarily peaceful and lacked what is commonly called 'nerve.' On Monday night, it is stated, he had been drinking liquor, which as in all cases, stirred up his resentment and the brutal side of his nature and gave him the 'courage' to resent a fancied wrong. A man can't drink and be anything but a depraved brute."

A search by Charles DeBerry's father, Henry DeBerry, accompanied by law-enforcement officers from Camden County, failed to find Osborne in the Bolivar, Missouri, area where he was thought to have relatives. On or about February 9, 1894, Osborne, apparently homesick, gave himself up to a constable at Strafford, Missouri, near Springfield. He said he "was not afraid of the law" and "was sorry he left home for Indian Territory [later the state of Oklahoma]."

Osborne was given immediate bail by Judge Calkin. The *Linn Creek Reveille* said bail was given without notice to the State or even notice to the Sheriff. "We are at a loss to understand these proceedings," protested Camden County's journalistic pride. The unstated implication was that Calkin, a native of Stoutland and perhaps a friend of the DeBerry family, might have been a little too anxious to release Osborne.

Judge Calkin certainly did young Osborne no favors. As it turned out, the lad should have stayed on the lam in Indian Territory or been confined within the protective walls of the Camden County jail at Linn Creek. Charged with second-degree murder, James Osborne was free on bail when found shot dead on the road near his home close to the village of Wet Glaize. On or about August 16, 1894, he had been ambushed by someone hiding in the brush and shot with a double-barreled shotgun. Fifteen large buckshot were found lodged in his lifeless body. Although the DeBerry family was strongly suspected of the crime, no leads were ever developed, even though Missouri Governor William Stone offered a $100 reward for the "arrest and conviction" of Osborne's killer(s).

Neighbors who "set up" with Henry DeBerry as the old man lay on his deathbed reported that he never confessed to the crime nor implicated others.

James Osborne's tombstone at the Campground Cemetery near Wet Glaize reads: "Gone to his death by an unknown hand, but vengeance saith the Lord, I will repay."

The Killings of William and Daniel Price in 1896

In early February of 1896, a long-standing feud between the Price and Partlow families resulted in a gun battle between representatives of the two families at a location between Montreal and Decaturville, a few miles northwest of Stoutland. At issue was the straying of pigs onto each other's property and other minor disagreements. The consequences of the shootout were anything but minor. William Price dyed on the spot and Daniel Price expired later that evening. Two Partlows were seriously wounded but recovered. Robert Partlow was arrested by Constable James Brown and charged with the murder of the Prices. It took two years, several trial delays, the summoning of a hundred witnesses, and the convening of a special term of the circuit court at Linn Creek in 1898, for the prosecutor to conclude that *nolle prosequi* (no prosecution) should be the disposition of this double-murder case. Partlow was let go, a free man.

The Killing of James Begley in 1917

On or about November 10, 1917, "Little Joe" Esther of Stoutland was milking his Jersey cow at a "milk gap" in a pasture on the back side of Stoutland, just east of where today's Route T heads up and over Rouse Hill. His hands occupied with the cow's udder, Esther was approached on horseback by another Stoutlander, one James "Jimmy" Begley. Upon dismounting, it became clear that Begley was in no mood for neighborly small talk. Esther had bought some hogs from Begley a few days earlier and may well have already shipped them to market in St. Louis. Begley claimed that payment for the swine had not been received and demanded immediate satisfaction of the debt. Esther heatedly replied that he had already made payment and that Begley would not receive another cent.

With no independent witnesses, we can only rely upon Esther's account of what happened next. Esther claimed that Begley advanced upon him with a club made from a "scantling" (a small piece of lumber) on which a handhold had been cut. Esther claimed to have retreated to "avoid trouble" but after several warnings, produced a gun (presumably a revolver) and shot Begley three times, with all shots "taking effect, one ranging near the heart." The club and an unopened pocketknife were found near the body. The questions of whether Begley had truly been paid for the hogs, whether Esther routinely armed himself when doing the evening milking, and why Esther felt compelled to "plug" Begley three times, when the first shot should have settled the matter, were never addressed. The burning question: "Did Little Joe finish milking

'Bossy' before summoning the town constable?" remains forever unanswered.

The Stoutland "Items," published in the *Linn Creek Reveille*, proclaimed, "Both men had many friends and the tragedy is deeply deplored by the entire community."

After an overnight stay in the county jail at Linn Creek, Esther was freed on a $10,000 bond and never again confined. Claiming self-defense, Esther was tried twice for murder with the first trial ending in a hung jury. At a second trial in August of 1918, the jury, after "long and mature deliveration [sic]," found Esther not guilty. "Little Joe" truly had been been "delivered" from the hands of the Law.

Fascinatingly, Joe Esther was the husband of Lora Thompson, first cousin of Charles Blackburn. Blackburn was the convicted murderer of Jasper Jacob "Jap" Francis only two years earlier, in 1915. At the time of the Begley murder, Blackburn was serving a life sentence in the Missouri State Penitentiary pending an appeal to the Missouri Supreme Court for a new trial. The cases have remarkable similarities. Both involved allegations that livestock had not been paid for, the killing of the complaining party, a complete dearth of eyewitnesses, at least one hung jury, and the accused being set free.

Chapter Notes

Introduction

1. Stoutland Mayor Della Sage, Personal letter, 30 May 2003.
2. Nelle Moulder, "Vignette of Stoutland," 1969; and "Stoutland," A five-page history: 3, 4 (courtesy Camden County Historical Society).
3. Frances Shepherd Metzger, *A Stout Land: A History of Stoutland, Missouri—1869–1969* (Lebanon, MO: Lebanon Publishing Co.) 3–7, 23–28.
4. "Stoutland," 3.
5. Metzger, 15.
6. "Corporate History: St Louis-San Francisco Railway Company," <http://tacnet.org/history/railroads/ch_slsf.html>.
7. "Frank Farris," *St. Louis Post-Dispatch*, 3 Sept. 1926.

Prelude

1. "Six Persons Killed In Frisco Wreck," *Springfield Leader*, 22 July 1922.
2. Ruby (Allee) Wright, Personal interview, 2 July 2000.

Chapter 1

1. Jasper J. Francis, Personal interview, 2 July 2000; and other interviews through Dec. 31, 2006.
2. Laclede County, MO, "Marriage Records," License issued 14 Sept. 1896, Book F, 370.
3. "Information Wanted Notice," *Linn Creek Reveille*, 19 Nov. 1915.
4. Missouri State Archives, "Missouri Penitentiary Receiving Log," Chas. Blackburn, Prisoner No. 18591: 4 July 1916; and Donna (Bloomer) Crim, Personal letter and portrait, 5 Mar. 2003.
5. Charles Winfrey, Supreme Court of Missouri, Div. 2, October Term, 1917, State of Missouri, *Respondent v. Charles Blackburn*, Appellant, No. 20332, Respondent's Statement, Abstract of the Record, Brief and Argument, Appeal from the Circuit Court of Camden County, Missouri, Hon. C.H. Skinker, Judge, Missouri State Archives, (Hereinafter: Respondent) 10.
6. Simpson Francis, Supreme Court of Missouri, Div. 2, October Term, 1917, State of Missouri, *Respondent v. Charles Blackburn*, Appellant, No. 20332, Appellant's Statement, Abstract and Brief, Appeal from the Circuit Court of Camden County, Missouri, Hon. C.H. Skinker, Judge, Missouri State Archives, (Hereinafter: Appellant) 13–14.

Chapter 2

1. Ray Blackburn and Minnie Blackburn, Respondent, 21.
2. Charles Blackburn, Respondent, 31.
3. Judy Varner, "Descendants of Charles R. Blackburn," 2002.
4. Robert L. Blackburn, Personal interview, 1 Oct. 2002.
5. Ernestine F. Chapin, Personal letter to Ben T. Blackburn Jr., 27 Sept. 2001.

Chapter 3

1. "Stoutland Items," *Linn Creek Reveille*, 26 Nov. 1915.
2. Ray Blackburn, Appellant, 58.
3. Metzger, 37.
4. "Louisiana Purchase Exposition/St. Louis Worlds Fair, 1904/The Heart of the Fair" <http://bitwise.net/~ken-bill/fairhart.htm>.

Chapter 4

1. Charles Winfrey, Appellant, 19.

Chapter 5

1. Midwestern Regional Climate Center, Lebanon, MO, Station ID 234825 (Hereinafter: MRCC).
2. Missouri Agricultural Statistics Service, "Table 18, Beef Cattle . . . 1909–59."
3. Missouri State Archives, Supreme Court of Missouri, Div. 2, October Term, 1917, State of Missouri, *Respondent v. Charles Blackburn*, Appellant, No. 20332, Opinion, Reversed and Remanded (Hereinafter: Opinion), 1.
4. Official Manuals, State of Missouri, 1891–92; 1893–94.
5. David Donnelly, Personal interview, 2002.
6. Ibid.
7. St. John's Hospital–Lebanon, Missouri, "Historical Plaque."
8. Ibid.
9. J. Mel. Hickerson, *Ernie Breech: The Story of His Remarkable Career at General Motors, Ford, and TWA* (New York, NY: Meredith Press, 1968).
10. Robert L. Blackburn, Personal interview, 1 Oct. 2002.

Chapter 6

1. Missouri Division of Finance, "People's Bank of Stoutland Certificate of Incorporation. No. 1347," 15 Mar 1905.
2. William A. Settle Jr., *Jesse James Was His Name* (Lincoln, NE: University of Nebraska Press, 1977) 34.
3. Ruby (Allee) Wright's sung rendition, "The Ballad of Jesse James," Lyrics and composer unknown.
4. Rolla Smith, Appellant, 29.
5. Ibid.
6. Harold Bell Wright, *The Shepherd of the Hills*, (New York: Grosset & Dunlap, 1907) 183.
7. Bob Barr, Personal interviews, 2001–2003.
8. Ibid.
9. MRCC.
10. John Frey, Appellant, 22.
11. MRCC.
12. Fred Jacobs, Appellant, 61.

Chapter 7

1. Frisco Resource Center, "List of Stations and Mile Posts" <http://frisco.org>.
2. Rube Winfrey, Respondent, 14.
3. Charles Blackburn, Appellant, 69.

Chapter 8

1. MRCC.
2. Charles Winfrey, Appellant, 19.
3. Ibid.
4. Ibid.
5. Ibid.
6. Simpson Francis, Respondent, 3.
7. Ruby Allee Wright, *Twelve Corners* (Nashville, TN: Self Published, 1996); and mention of "Twelve Corner Church," *Linn Creek Reveille*, 13 July 1917 and 3 Aug. 1917.
8. U.S. Census (Pulaski County, Missouri, 1900).
9. Bob Barr, Jasper Francis, Gene Tunney Allee, Personal interviews, 2000–2003.
10. Ibid.
11. Ibid.
12. Bob Barr, Personal letter, 11 Mar. 2003.
13. Bob Barr, Personal interviews, 2000–2003.
14. Virgil Evans, Appellant, 45.
15. Charles Winfrey, Appellant, 19.
16. Virgil Evans, Appellant, 45.
17. Ibid.
18. Virgil Evans, Appellant, 50.

Chapter 9

1. John Frey, Appellant, 24
2. Charles Winfrey, Respondent, 10
3. Ibid.
4. Ibid.
5. Mary J. Craddock, Respondent, 23.
6. Minnie Blackburn, Appellant, 59.
7. Virgil Evans, Appellant, 50.
8. John Frey, Appellant, 22.
9. Ibid.
10. Ibid.
11. John Frey, Appellant, 23.
12. John Frey, Appellant, 24.
13. Rolla Smith, Appellant, 27.
14. Virgil Evans, Appellant, 50.
15. Virgil Evans, Appellant, 51.
16. Virgil Evans, Respondent, 17.

Chapter 10

1. Rube Winfrey, Respondent, 13.
2. Rube Winfrey, Appellant, 31.
3. Ibid.
4. Missouri Division of Finance, Bank of Stoutland File, "Affidavit of Dissolution," 2 Feb 1914.
5. Rube Winfrey, Respondent, 14.
6. Ibid.
7. James Marshall, Appellant, 36.
8. MRCC.
9. James Marshall, Appellant, 36.
10. Jack Burke, Appellant, 37.
11. John "Happy Jack" Jackson, Appellant, 37–38.
12. Arthur Miller, *Death of a Salesman* (Penguin Plays, 28 Oct. 1976).
13. John "Happy Jack" Jackson, Respondent, 14.

Chapter 11

1. Minnie Blackburn, Appellant, 60.
2. Mary Jane Craddock, Respondent, 23–24.
3. U.S. Naval Observatory, "Civil Twilight Chart for Stoutland, Missouri" 9 Nov. 1915.
4. Advertisement for "City Restaurant," Stoutland, Missouri, *Camden County Herald*, 7 July 1910.

Chapter 12

1. Jeannie Vaughn, "The Poor Man's Walking Horse?" (Foxfire Farm :1997), Reprinted by permission, *Missouri Foxtrotter News* <http://members.aol.com/oldcowb476/ASBMFThs.htm>.
2. Ibid.
3. Kimberly R. Riley, "Tom Bass, 1859–1934," Kansas City Public Library—Special Collections <http://kclibrary.org/localhistory/media.cfm?mediaID=34953>.
4. Ibid.

Chapter 13

1. Laura Hillenbrand, *Seabiscuit: An American Legend* (New York, NY: Ballantine Books, 2002).
2. U.S. Naval Observatory, "Moon Illumination Chart for Stoutland, Missouri: 9 Nov. 1915."
3. Fred Huff, Appellant, 55.
4. U.S Naval Observatory, "Civil Twilight Chart for Stoutland, Missouri: 10 Nov. 1915."

Chapter 14

1. Edna Kissinger, Appellant, 38.
2. Ibid.

3. Matthew 5:45, Holy Bible, King James Version.
4. Simpson Francis, Respondent, 4.
5. Ibid.

Chapter 15

1. MRCC.
2. Simpson Francis, Appellant, 5.
3. Simpson Francis, Appellant, 7.

Chapter 16

1. Mary Jane Craddock, Appellant, 61.
2. Ellen Castile, Appellant, 39.
3. Claude Castile, Appellant, 40.
4. Joe Piercy, Appellant, 55.
5. Minnie Blackburn, Respondent, 21–22.
6. Ibid.
7. Ray Blackburn, Appellant, 58.
8. Marvin Calkin, Respondent, 18–19.
9. Fred Huff, Appellant, 54–55.
10. L.D. Franklin, Appellant, 55.
11. Sylvan Mooney, Personal interview with Bob Barr, 19 August 1998.

Chapter 17

1. MRCC.
2. Major John McCrae, "In Flanders Fields," 1915.
3. Wes Scrivner, Respondent, 15.
4. Rolla Smith, Appellant, 29.
5. Charles Blackburn, Appellant, 68–69.
6. Rolla Smith, Appellant, 29.
7. Ibid.
8. E.A. Ellis, "Personal Statement," *Linn Creek Reveille*, 4 Aug. 1916.
9. Virgil Evans, Respondent, 17.
10. Rolla Smith, Appellant, 30.
11. Opinion, 5.
12. Wes Scrivner, Appellant, 39.
13. Ibid.
14. Ibid.
15. Frank Lumm, Respondent, 16.
16. U.S. Census (Laclede County, Missouri, 1870, 1880, 1910 and 1920).
17. U.S. Census (Laclede County, Missouri, 1910) and Tombstone inscriptions, W.I. and Louise Wallace, Lebanon, Missouri Cemetery.
18. "Copy of original check" provided to the author by Jasper J. Francis.
19. Charles Blackburn, Respondent, 29.
20. Betty Ann Butts (certified graphoanalyst), Letter analysis, 28 Jan. 2003.
21. Jim Sullivan, Appellant, 74.

Chapter 18

1. MRCC.
2. Simpson Francis, Respondent, 2.
3. Simpson Francis, Respondent, 5.
4. Simpson Francis, Appellant, 6.
5. Simpson Francis, Respondent, 7.
6. Ibid.
7. Ibid.
8. "Newspaper Clipping" (copy in possession of Jasper J. Francis).
9. *Stoutland News*, 26 Nov. 1915.
10. Simpson Francis, Respondent, 4.
11. Simpson Francis, Respondent, 7–8.
12. Wm. Frederick and Ray Eddington, Appellant, 52–53.

Chapter 19

1. Simpson Francis, Respondent, 8.
2. Ibid.
3. Charles Blackburn, Appellant, 69–70.
4. Simpson Francis, Respondent, 8.
5. Opinion, 7.
6. Minnie Blackburn, Respondent, 22.

Chapter 20

1. Simpson Francis, Respondent, 32.
2. "Stoutland Items," *Linn Creek Reveille*, 23 Nov. 1915.
3. MRCC.
4. Wes Scrivner, Respondent, 15.
5. Ibid.
6. Ibid.
7. Ibid.

Chapter 21

1. "Legal Services Contract," 28 Nov. 1915" (copy in possession of Jasper J. Francis).
2. Henry Ford, "Quotation" <http://www.brainyquote.com/quotes/authors/h/henry_ford.html>.
3. "1912 Ford Model T C-Cab Delivery" <http://conceptcarz.com/vehicle/z11881/default.aspx>.
4. MRCC.

Chapter 22

1. Simpson Francis, Appellant, 7.
2. Missouri Department of Conservation, "Mountain Lions In Missouri—Fact or Fiction?" <mdc4.mdc.mo.gov/Documents/10649.pdf>

Chapter 23

1. Charles Blackburn, Appellant, 69.
2. Harold Bell Wright Obituary, *New York Times*, 14 May 1944.
3. "03/01/2005 Branson Story Starters," <http://branson.com/branson-news17.html>.
4. Ben McShane, Appellant, 17.

Chapter 24

1. Ernest Carlton, Personal interview, 3 Nov. 2004.
2. Simpson Francis, Respondent, 4.
3. Ibid.
4. Ibid.

Chapter 25

1. *Linn Creek Reveille*, 3 Dec. 1915.
2. Dave McClure, Appellant, 14.
3. Simpson Francis, Appellant, 7.
4. Simpson Francis, Respondent, 5.
5. Dr. W.O. Pool, Appellant, 15.
6. Ray Blackburn, Respondent, 21.
7. U.S. Census (Camden County, Missouri, 1920).
8. Mary Jane Craddock, Respondent, 24.
9. *Linn Creek Reveille*, 3 Dec. 1915.
10. Simpson Francis, Appellant, 7.
11. Simpson Francis, Respondent, 5.
12. Ibid.
13. Dr. C.E. Carlton, Appellant, 16.
14. Dr. W.O. Pool, Respondent, 6 and Appellant, 15.
15. Dr. C.E. Carlton, Appellant, 15.
16. Simpson Francis and T.B. Francis, "1st Semi-Annual Estate Settlement Sheet, J.J. Francis Deceased."
17. *Linn Creek Reveille*, 3 Dec. 1915.
18. W.W. Cox, Appellant, 16–17.
19. W.W. Cox, Respondent, 6.
20. W.W. Cox, Appellant, 16.
21. *Springfield Republican*, 25 Nov. 1915.
22. Lucille (Alexander) Gregory, Personal interview, 2003.
23. Marc Markway, DVM, "Notes for your book," 3 Mar. 2004.
24. Janet Esther, "Sam—Witness to Murder," *MFTHBA Journal*, Mar. 1985: 9.
25. Ed Turner, "Final Tribute for Those Who Served," *The Washington Times*, <http://washingtontimes.com/weekend/20031105-102342-6201r.htm>.

Chapter 26

1. Clyde Wiseman, Personal interview, circa 1975.
2. *Springfield Republican*, 25 Nov. 1915.
3. Ibid.

4. R.E. Houston, "Ford Production Department Statistics," 3 Aug. 1927.
5. *Springfield Republican*, 25 Nov. 1915.

Chapter 27

1. *Camden County History* (Orig. Goodspeed Publishing Co, 1888) (Later: 2003 Ed., Higginsville, MO: Hearthstone Legacy Publications).
2. Ibid.
3. Judy Varner and Carole Roach, Personal letters, 2004.
4. Official Manual, State of Missouri, 1923–24.
5. Jackson K. Roach II, Personal letter, 8 May 2001.
6. Bob Barr, Personal interview, 2004.
7. *Linn Creek Reveille*, 31 Dec. 1915.
8. *Linn Creek Reveille*, 3 Dec. 1915.
9. *State of Missouri, Plaintiff vs. Charles Blackburn, Defendant*, Camden and Webster Counties, Missouri, 18th Judicial Circuit, Transcript of Proceedings (Hereinafter: Transcript).
10. *Linn Creek Reveille*, 3 Dec. 1915.
11. Dr. W.O. Pool, Appellant, 15.
12. Dr. C.E. Carlton, Appellant, 15.
13. Simpson Francis, Respondent, 8.
14. Ibid.

Chapter 28

1. "Brief," Appellant, 92.
2. MRCC.
3. U.S. Naval Observatory, "Moon illumination chart for Stoutland, Missouri: 23 Nov. 1915."
4. Minnie Blackburn, Respondent, 23.
5. Simpson Francis, Respondent, 4.
6. Ibid.
7. Esther, 8.
8. Edna Kissinger, Appellant, 38.
9. Virgil Evans, Respondent, 16–17.
10. Ibid.
11. Ibid.
12. Rube Winfrey, Respondent, 13.
13. Opinion, 6.
14. Charles Blackburn, Respondent, 26–30.
15. Charles Blackburn, Appellant, 73–74.
16. Simpson Francis, Respondent, 9.
17. Ibid.
18. Ibid.
19. Charlie Blackburn, Respondent, 31.
20. "The Miranda Warning," U.S. Constitution Online <http://usconstitution.net/miranda.html>.

21. Charles Blackburn, Respondent, 31.
22. Simpson Francis, Appellant, 10.

Chapter 29

1. "Full Moon," Phases of the Moon: Zoom Astronomy <http://www.enchantedlearning.com/subjects/astronomy/moon/Phases.html>.
2. Ruby Allee Wright, *Twelve Corners* (Nashville, TN: Self Published, 1996).
3. Jasper J. Francis, Personal interview, 2 July 2000.
4. Ibid.
5. Donna (Bloomer) Crim, Personal letter, 2003.

Chapter 30

1. Charles Blackburn, Appellant, 64–68.
2. Ibid.
3. Ibid.
4. Ibid.
5. Ibid.
6. Minnie Blackburn, Appellant, 60.
7. Minnie Blackburn, Appellant, 59.
8. Mary Jane Craddock, Appellant, 60–61.

Chapter 31

1. MRCC.
2. M.V.P., R. Fauset, "Funeral Ceremony . . . of the Grand United Order of Odd Fellows in America" (Philadelphia, PA: *Odd Fellows Journal* Print, 1902):10.
3. "The Story of Dwight L. Moody," <http://www. kmhm.net/moodypage.htm>.
4. Will L. Thompson, "Softly and Tenderly," <http://hymnsite.com/lection/980621.htm>.
5. Jeremiah E. Rankin, "God Be With You Till We Meet Again" <www.cyberhymnal.org.htm/g/b/gbewiyou.htm>.

Chapter 32

1. "Legal Services Contract," 28 Nov. 1915 (copy in possession of Jasper J. Francis).
2. "Application for Letters of Administration," 1 Dec. 1915 (copy in possession of Jasper J. Francis).
3. "Attachment Petition," 1 Dec. 1915 (copy in possession of Jasper J. Francis).
4. "Attachment Writ," 1 Dec. 1915 (copy in possession of Jasper J. Francis).
5. "Circuit Court Summons," 2 Dec. 1915 (copy in possession of Jasper J. Francis).
6. "Statement," Appellant, 98.
7. Simpson Francis, Appellant, 8.

Chapter 33

1. *Springfield Republican*, 24 Dec. 1915.
2. Ibid.
3. "Complaint for State Warrant," Transcript, 10 Dec. 1915.
4. *Springfield Republican*, 24 Dec. 1915.
5. Ibid.
6. "Prosecuting Attorney Information," Transcript, 27 Jan. 1916.
7. Ibid.
8. "State Warrant, A.J. Estes, J.P.," Transcript, 11 Feb 1916.
9. *Linn Creek Reveille*, 17 Dec. 1915.
10. Official Manual, State of Missouri, 1917–18.
11. Wanda Kovazovich, "Missouri Blackburn History," (undated).

Chapter 34

1. Gene Mayfield, Personal letter, 4 Sept. 2002.
2. Marsh Clark, *St. Louis Globe-Democrat*, 9 Sept. 1961.
3. "Phil M. Donnelly Biographical Sketch," *St. Louis Post-Dispatch*, 13 July 1944.
4. Ibid.
5. Jack Flach, *St. Louis Globe-Democrat*, 15 Sept. 1961,
6. David Donnelly, Personal letter, 31 Jan 2004.
7. John F. Bradbury Jr. & Lynn Morrow, "Honorable Frank Farris: 'Making a Bad Idea Look Good and a Good One Better,'" Newsletter of the Phelps County Historical Society, Oct. 2004.
8. Official Manuals, State of Missouri, 1899–00, 1925–26; and "Missouri State Legislators 1820–2000" <http://sos.mo.gov/archives/hisory/historicallistings/molegf.asp>.
9. Official Manual, State of Missouri, 1903–04.
10. Senator Phil M. Donnelly, "A Eulogy on Senator Frank H. Farris," 16 Feb. 1927.
11. Official Manual, State of Missouri, 1903–04.
12. Kenneth H. Winn, Official Manual, State of Missouri, 1999–00: 32–33.
13. Ibid.
14. *Kansas City Journal*, 12 Oct. 1903 (Courtesy: Western Historical Manuscript Collection-Columbia, hereinafter, "WHMC-C").
15. *St. Louis Post-Dispatch*, 22 Apr. 1903 (Courtesy: WHMC-C).
16. *St. Louis Post-Dispatch*, 23 Apr. 1903 (Courtesy: WHMC-C).
17. *St. Louis Republic*, 19 Apr. 1903 (Courtesy: WHMC-C).
18. Ibid.
19. *Kansas City Times*, 16 Apr. 1903 (Courtesy: WHMC-C).
20. *Kansas City Times*, 14 Apr. 1903 (Courtesy: WHMC-C).
21. *St. Louis Republic*, 19 Apr. 1903 (Courtesy: WHMC-C).
22. *Kansas City Journal*, 11 Apr. 1903 (Courtesy: WHMC-C).
23. *Kansas City Star*, 11 Apr. 1903 (Courtesy: WHMC-C).
24. *St. Louis Globe-Democrat*, 2 Sept. 1926.
25. *St. Louis Globe-Democrat*, 20 Mar. 1976.

26. Judge Michael A. Wolff, "How We Choose Missouri Judges," *St. Louis Daily Record* and *St. Louis Countian*, 27 Nov. 2005.
27. Official Manual, State of Missouri, 1915–16.

Chapter 35

1. H. Dwight Weaver, *Lake of the Ozarks—The Early Years*, (Chicago, IL: Arcadia Publishing, 2001) 75.
2. Weaver, 4.
3. Bagnell Dam History, <http://odd.net/ozarks/baghist.htm>.
4. Weaver, 14–15.
5. Weaver, 4.
6. Weaver, 82.
7. Weaver, 86.
8. Weaver, 83.
9. *Linn Creek Reveille*, 24 Dec. 1915.
10. *Springfield Republican*, 24 Dec. 1915.
11. Senator Phil M. Donnelly, "A Eulogy on Senator Frank H. Farris," 16 Feb. 1927.

Chapter 36

1. "Recognizance of the Defendant," Transcript, 26 Aug. 1916.
2. U.S. Bureau of Labor Statistics, "CPI Inflation Calculator" <http://data.bls.gov/cgi-bin/cpicalc.pl>.
3. *Linn Creek Reveille*, 31 Dec. 1915.
4. *The Lebanon Rustic*, 10 Feb. 1916.
5. "Circuit Court Record," Transcript, 21 Feb. 1916.

Chapter 37

1. "Circuit Court Record," Transcript, 29 June 1916.
2. "Circuit Court Record," Transcript, 26 June 1916.
3. *Springfield Republican*, 2 July 1916.
4. "Circuit Court Record," Transcript, 26 June 1916.
5. *Springfield Republican*, 29 June 1916.
6. Obituary—Cornelius H. Skinker, "The Busy Scissors of Cliquot, Missouri," Polk County Genealogical Society, Inc. 2002.

Chapter 38

1. Ben T. Blackburn Jr., "Blackburn Family Genealogy," 2002.
2. Robert Bloomer, "Mack Blackburn Family History Videotape," circa 1990.
3. Donna (Bloomer) Crim, Personal letter, 2004.
4. Simpson Francis, Respondent, 22.
5. Simpson Francis, Appellant, 8.
6. Simpson Francis, Appellant, 9.
7. Simpson Francis, Appellant, 10.
8. Frank Farris, Appellant, 10.

9. Sidney C. Roach, Appellant, 11.
10. Judge Skinker, Appellant, 12.
11. Frank Farris, Appellant, 12.
12. Sidney C. Roach, Appellant, 12.
13. Simpson Francis, Appellant, 13.

Chapter 39

1. Dr. W.O. Pool, Appellant, 15.
2. Ben McShane, Appellant, 17.
3. Frank Farris, "Brief, Point IV," Appellant, 93.
4. Ibid.
5. Judge Skinker, Appellant, 17.
6. Ben McShane, Appellant, 17.
7. Charles Winfrey, Appellant, 18.
8. Frank H. Farris, Appellant, 19.
9. "Q to R," *Duhaime's Law Dictionary*, <http://duhaime.org>.
10. Judge Todd M. Thornhill, "Declarations of the Dead: Hearsay's Residual Exception Comes to Missouri," <http://mobar.org/journal/2000/janfeb/thornhill.htm>.
11. Ibid.
12. "Q to R," *Duhaime's Law Dictionary*, <http://duhaime.org>.
13. "V. The Evidence, (a) (b) (c)," Respondent, 48–50.
14. Ibid.
15. Ibid.
16. Ibid.
17. "Brief, Point 1," Appellant, 91.
18. "Argument, The Evidence," Respondent, 68.
19. Charles Winfrey, Respondent, 10.
20. Respondent, 18–36.

Chapter 40

1. MRCC.
2. J.M. Vincent, Appellant, 42–43.
3. Gould's St. Louis Directory—1918.
4. Gus Mechin, Respondent, 16.
5. Gus Mechin, Appellant, 41.
6. Frank H. Farris, Appellant, 42.
7. Claude and Ellen Castile, Respondent, 14–15.
8. Wes Scrivner, Respondent, 8.
9. Minnie Blackburn, Respondent, 22.
10. Ernie Carlton, "House Sketch and Description," 11 Mar. 04.
11. Wes Scrivner, Respondent, 15.
12. Frank H. Farris, "Demurrer," Appellant, 43.

Chapter 41

1. MRCC.
2. H.L. Mencken, "'The Monkey Trial': A Reporter's Account," UMKC School of Law <http://www.law.umkc.edu/faculty/projects/ftrials/scopes/menk.htm>.
3. "United States Extreme Record Temperatures & Ranges," <http://ggweather.com/climate/extremes_us.htm>.
4. Virgil Evans, Appellant, 47.
5. Virgil Evans, Appellant, 50–51.
6. Harry Taylor, Appellant, 52.
7. Frank H. Farris, "Argument," Appellant, 107.
8. James Marshall, Appellant, 36.
9. Marvin Calkin, Appellant, 53–54.
10. Joe Piercy, Appellant, 55.
11. Fred Jacobs, Appellant, 61.
12. U.S. Census (Laclede County, Missouri, 1910).
13. Weaver, 7.
14. Guy Stanton, Appellant, 56–57.
15. Guy Stanton, Respondent, 20.
16. Guy Stanton, Respondent, 20, 32.
17. "*State of Missouri, Plaintiff v. Guy R. Stanton*, Defendant," Information, Circuit Court of Webster County, Missouri, 18th Judicial Circuit, Sept. 1921.
18. U.S. Census (Kansas City, Missouri, 1930).
19. Ray Blackburn, Appellant, 57–58.
20. Ibid.
21. Minnie Blackburn, Respondent, 22–23.
22. Minnie Blackburn, Appellant, 60.
23. Mary Jane Craddock, Respondent, 24.
24. Ibid.

Chapter 42

1. Charles Blackburn, Appellant, 70.
2. Charles Blackburn, Appellant, 65–66.
3. Charles Blackburn, Appellant, 66.
4. Charles Blackburn, Appellant, 67.
5. Ibid.
6. MRCC.
7. Charles Blackburn and Sidney C. "Sid" Roach, Appellant, 73–74.
8. Judge Skinker, Appellant, 74.
9. Frank H. Farris, "Argument," Appellant, 103.
10. Charles Blackburn and Sidney C. "Sid" Roach, Appellant, 73.
11. Appellant, 54, 62–63.
12. L.C. "Claude" Mayfield, Appellant, 75.
13. Ibid.
14. Phil M. Donnelly, Appellant, 75.

15. Judge Skinker and Dave McClure, Appellant, 75.
16. Dave McClure, Appellant, 75.
17. Ben McShane and Leroy Fulbright, Appellant, 76–78.
18. MRCC.

Chapter 43

1. U.S. Naval Observatory, "Sunrise/Sunset Table for Stoutland, Missouri: 9 Nov. 1915."
2. *St. Louis Times*, 3 Sept. 1926.
3. Frank H. Farris, "The League of Nations," oratorical address, 1–28.
4. Frank H. Farris, "The Ozarks," oratorical address, 5.
5. Frank H. Farris, "The Ozarks," oratorical address, 2.
6. Frank H. Farris, "I Don't Know Where I'm Going But I'm On My Way," oratorical address, 5.
7. Missouri State Archives, "Why Is Missouri Called the "Show-Me State?" <http://sos.mo.gov/archives/history/slogan.asp>.
8. Frank H. Farris, "Brief, Point V," Appellant, 94.
9. Frank H. Farris, "Statement" and "Argument," Appellant, 95–108.
10. Frank H. Farris, "Argument," Appellant, 105.
11. Ibid.
12. Frank H. Farris, "Argument," Appellant, 107.
13. Ibid.
14. Ibid.

Chapter 44

1. Judge Skinker, "Jury Instructions," Respondent, 37–42.
2. Ibid.
3. Jury Foreman G.M. Eldred, Respondent, 36.
4. Respondent, 42
5. Respondent, 44.
6. Judge Skinker, "Pronouncement of Sentence," Transcript, 2 July 2016.
7. Appellant, 87.

Chapter 45

1. Homer C. Wright, Personal letter, 13 June 1983; and "From the Diary of C.B. Wright," Miller County Autogram, circa 1970s.
2. Missouri State Archives, "State Penitentiary Receiving Register," 4 July 1916: 283.
3. Missouri State Archives, "State Penitentiary Discharge Register," 16 Feb. 1918: 335.
4. Opinion, 11.
5. Opinion, 8–11.
6. Opinion, 11.
7. Opinion, 7.
8. Dr. J.L. Benage, "Trial Continuance Motion," Transcript, 21 Nov. 1918.

9. Dr. Abel L. Gregory, "Trial Continuance Motion," Transcript, 12 May 1920.
10. "Motion to Dismiss," Transcript, Jan. 1921.
11. Judge Skinker, "Jury Instructions," Transcript, 14 June 1919.
12. "Motion to Dismiss," Transcript, Jan. 1921.
13. Official Manual, State of Missouri, 1923–24.
14. "Witness Subpoena for Mrs. Charles Blackburn," Transcript, 6 May 1920.
15. "Motion to Dismiss," Transcript, Jan. 1921.
16. Judge Skinker, "Circuit Court Record," May term, 1921.
17. "Alias Capias Warrant for Charley [sic] Blackburn," Transcript, 10 May 1921.
18. "Motion to Abate the Cause of Action and Strike from the Docket," Transcript, 7 Nov. 1921.
19. Sidney C. Roach, "Sworn Affidavit," Transcript, 7 Nov. 1921.
20. Grace Walk Recovery Ministry, <http://freedomfromaddiction.org/mtest.htm>.
21. Judge Skinker, "Circuit Court Record," 12 Nov. 1921.

Epilogue

1. Los Angeles County Health Dept., "Charley [sic] Blackburn—Certificate of Death," 9 Nov. 1964.
2. Robert L. Blackburn, Personal interview, 1 Oct. 2002.
3. Judy Armstrong, Museum of Western Colorado, Personal interviews, 2004–2005.
4. Donna (Bloomer) Crim, Personal letter #1, 2003.
5. Ibid.
6. Donna (Bloomer) Crim, Personal letter #2, 2003.
7. Donna (Bloomer) Crim, Personal letter #1, 2003.
8. Donna (Bloomer) Crim, Personal letter #2, 2003.
9. Ibid.
10. Ibid.
11. Robert L. Blackburn, Personal interviews, 2002–2003.
12. Ibid.
13. Ibid.
14. Ibid.
15. Donna (Bloomer) Crim, Personal letter #5, 2003.
16. Betty Ann Butts, Personal interview, Jan. 2003.
17. Betty Ann Butts.
18. Ibid.
19. Ibid.
20. Ibid.
21. Donna (Bloomer) Crim, E-mail #1, 27 Feb. 2003.
22. U.S. Census (Jackson County, Missouri, 1930).
23. Robert L. Blackburn, Personal interviews, 2002–2003.
24. Donna (Bloomer) Crim, attributed to "Uncle Bob Bloomer," E-mail #1, 27 Feb. 2003.

25. *St. Louis Post-Dispatch*, 30 June 1934.
26. U.S. Census (City of St. Louis and St. Louis County, 1920 and 1930).
27. *St. Louis Post-Dispatch*, 2 Sept. 1926.
28. *St. Louis Globe-Democrat*, 2 Sept. 1926.
29. *West Plains Missouri Journal*, 9 Sept. 1926.
30. Bradbury & Morrow, 9.
31. *New York Times*, 2 Sept. 1926.
32. Don Moore, "The 1924 Radio Election," <http://members.tripod.com/donmoore/genbroad/elec1924.html>.
33. Ted Widmer, "Rosy View of the Happy Warrior Who Shaped Modern New York," < http://www.observer.com/node/43982>.
34. *West Plains Missouri Journal*, 9 Sept. 1926.
35. Walter B. Stevens, *Missouri The Center State: 1821-1915* (Chicago, IL and St. Louis, MO: S.J. Clark, 1915), 352.
36. *St. Louis Globe-Democrat*, 2 Sept. 1926.
37. Mary Susan (Farris) Goodwin-Tubbesing, Personal interview, July 2002.
38. *St. Louis Globe-Democrat*, 2 Sept. 1926.
39. Ibid.
40. "Editorial," *St. Louis Globe-Democrat*, 2 Sept. 1926.
41. *West Plains Missouri Journal*, 9 Sept. 1926.
42. *St. Louis Post-Dispatch*, 2 Sept. 1926.
43. Senator Phil M. Donnelly.
44. Marsh Clark, *St. Louis Globe-Democrat*, 14 Sept. 1961.
45. *St. Louis Globe-Democrat*, 14 Jan. 1957.
46. Official Manual, State of Missouri, 1953–54.
47. *St Louis Globe-Democrat*, 14 Jan. 1957.
48. "Judge Theodore McMillian, 1919–2006," SLU Newslink <http://www.slu.edu/readstory/newslink/6444>.
49. Marion R. Lynes, *St. Louis Globe-Democrat*, 23 Sept. 1954.
50. "History of the Patrol," <mshp.dps.missouri.gov/MSHPWeb/AboutThePatrol/History/documents/History50s.pdf>.
51. Missouri Highway Patrol Officers, Personal interviews, MASTERS Banquet, circa 2000.
52. *St. Louis Globe-Democrat*, 24 Sept. 1954.
53. Marion R. Lynes, *St. Louis Globe-Democrat*, 24 Sept. 1954.
54. Ibid.
55. Circuit Judge James F. McHenry, Personal interview, Feb. 2000.
56. Marion R. Lynes, *St. Louis Globe-Democrat*, 24 Sept. 1954.
57. Ibid.
58. J.J Mahoney, "In The Wake of a Riot," *Crime Magazine*, <http://crimemagazine.com/stidham.htm>.
59. *St. Louis Globe-Democrat*, 14 Jan. 1957.
60. Marsh Clark, *St. Louis Globe-Democrat*, 14 Sept. 1961.
61. Gene Mayfield, Personal interview, 12 June 2002.

62. “Understanding the Age of Your Horse” < http://cariswanson.com/word-press/understanding-the-age-of-your-horse/>.
63. Esther, 9.
64. Ibid.
65. Jasper J. Francis, Personal interview, 2 July 2000; and other interviews through Dec. 31, 2006.